THE LOGIC OF
MODERN SCIENCE

THE LOGIC OF
MODERN SCIENCE

J. R. Kantor

THE PRINCIPIA PRESS, INC.

Chicago, Illinois   *Granville, Ohio*

THE PRINCIPIA PRESS, INC.

5743 S. Kimbark Avenue   *Denison University*
Chicago, Illinois   *Granville, Ohio*

Lithographed in U.S.A. by

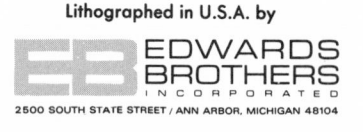

EDWARDS
BROTHERS
INCORPORATED

2500 SOUTH STATE STREET / ANN ARBOR, MICHIGAN 48104

PREFACE

Is it a unique situation or only the wheel of thought again come full circle—this intense current interest in methodological problems, the zeal with which so many workers study the logic and philosophy of science?

Change, upheaval, and reconstruction are, of course, inherent in the scientific enterprise. Intellectual inventions and the discovery of novel events periodically disturb the foundations of knowledge. Thus history records a Copernican, a Galilean, a Cartesian, a Lobatchevskian, a Newtonian and a Darwinian revolution.

But from our present vantage point it does appear that the discoveries and contrivances of the 20th century have upset scientific thinking more strikingly than ever before. Surely the unprecedented expansion of current technology (radio, radar, electronics) and of modern physics and chemistry (radioactivity, quantum mechanics, relativity) demand an unusual reformulation of basic scientific principles.

Furthermore, science being essentially cumulative, the paradox becomes intensified that the wider the vista opening before the investigator and the greater his conquests, the more fragile and vulnerable his knowledge system becomes. The record is plain. The postulational process in mathematics and experimental science has led to scepticism concerning scientific rigor. Knowledge of atomic structure, its disintegration and transformation, has precipitated the question whether any stable substance, such as classical matter, exists. Relativity principles have wrenched loose the solid framework of classical space and time. Increasing recognition of the discontinuity of energy and radiation has engendered doubts about causality, precision of observation, and the validity of laws.

Who can overlook the great need for an adequate logic of science? Scientific systematics so far has certainly failed to keep pace with developments in research techniques and with factual discovery. While the scientist has been probing deeper and deeper into things and events, increasing the range of data, he has lagged noticeably in his understanding of scientific foundations.

The trouble is easily diagnosed: instead of deriving his definitions and postulates directly from investigations the logician of science borrows them from historical solipsism, positivism, and realism. As a consequence, he substitutes metaphysics for scientific systems. Even physicists, who presumably work in the most exact area, perplex themselves with mystical questions—indeterminacy, pure chance, and, alas, free will. Is there greater proof that tradition is still powerful enough to outweigh the findings of experimental investigation!

Cultural beliefs kept alive by conventional philosophy impose upon the scientist the spiritistic doctrine that known things consist of "psychic processes" called "sensations," also that things and events are intuited or created by transcendent egos or minds. Again, "It is fashionable today to regard physics as the product of pure reason."[1] Finally, eminent scientists argue that they cannot accept a statistical theory of physics because it does not take into account such phantasms as "sense qualities."

Implied here is a definite shift of the scientist's task from the investigation of events to the correlation of "experiences." When Planck declares: "The ideal aim before the mind of the physicist is to understand the external world of reality"[2] he is concerned with metaphysics, not with scientific problems. Once the scientist frees himself from the domination of our spiritistic culture, such problems as the nature of reality and its relation to the act of knowing will no longer trouble him.

A basic theorem of this book is that the primary service of the logic of science is to separate science completely from all historical ontologies and epistemologies. How can this be accomplished? The psychological revolution of the last few decades provides an answer.

The objective psychologist makes a fresh start when investigating human behavior. He eschews completely all historical or current dogmas about "minds" and "bodies." Unencumbered he studies the interbehavior of individuals in contact with stimulus objects under specific circumstances. By investigating the scientist at work in the field or laboratory and while he constructs his descriptions, theories, and laws, the observer can easily determine

---

[1] Born, Natural Philosophy of Cause and Chance, p. 86.
[2] Where is Science Going? p. 84.

how much of a scientific system is derived from contact with things and how much from cultural sources. Only interbehavioral materials can be incorporated into valid systems. Culturally derived propositions, by contrast, lead to metasystems unassimilable to valid scientific structures.

Metasystems constitute organizations of basic assumptions concerning the nature, role, and limits of scientific work. Scientific systems properly comprise the structuring of: (1) a single, specific research task, (2) general principles of a scientific department, and (3) the processes of the entire scientific enterprise in an order of increasing generality. Now, it is clear that a scientific system of whatever generality must be backed by a metasystem whose propositions are not purely verbal creations.

Another fundamental theorem is that the full exploitation of the findings of current objective psychology helps to clarify the nature of logic itself. Since every form of absolutistic or universalistic principle is rejected, logic becomes the theory and practice of system building. Valid scientific systems (and their metasystems), it follows, are built from materials derived from scientific work and its products. Because scientific systems are produced on the basis of (1) different things and events encountered, (2) kind of work done, instruments used, and (3) laws and theories established, they vary enormously in detail, ranging from the formalized structures of mathematics to the organizations of propositions concerning the concrete events of biology, psychology, and anthropology. Wherever scientific work can be carried on the logician of science can structure a system of pertinent factors. In no case need he discriminate against any events because of cultural traditions.

Students of scientific systemology can choose between two expository methods: they can either set up formalized systems which emphasize final products or they can delineate scientific work as it proceeds most favorably toward valid systems. I have chosen the second. First I examine the general scientific enterprise (chap. 1), then offer a full analysis of scientific systems (chap. 2). Following a survey of the cultural background and interbehavioral development of the sciences (chaps. 3–5) I describe the methods and techniques of science (6–8).

The main body of the book (chaps. 9–14) is devoted to the

study of how scientific systems evolve from contacts of individuals with things and events. This is carried through not only for the physiochemical, biological, and psychological sciences, but also for the social and humanistic disciplines. Naturally the study pattern differs for each of these four divisions, but the interbehavioral principle remains paramount.

Scientific systems constitute one of the types of items making up the large cultural complex called civilization. In the final chapter I consider how scientific systems fit into this larger system; in particular I raise the question how much and in what way science contributes to the general advancement of civilization.

Attention is directed to some stylistic details. Citations to literature are only indicated in footnotes; full references are found in the bibliography. The dates of scientists are not included in the text, but when available are placed in the name index.

Once again it is my pleasure to acknowledge the constant collaboration of H. R. Kantor throughout the entire writing of this book.

To Dean Cleland and the Graduate School of Indiana University College of Arts and Sciences my thanks for providing library and typing assistance.

To Dr. A. E. Kanter my profound appreciation for his help in facilitating publication.

October 1952   J. R. K.

CONTENTS

II

The Cultural Aspects of Science

III

The Methods and Techniques of Science

V
Science and Civilization

I

THE DOMAIN OF SCIENCE

1

SCIENCE: NATURE AND GOAL

What is Science?

MUCH of the difficulty in answering this question can be obviated if we adopt an observational procedure—that is, investigate scientists at work, in the field and in their laboratories. This means examining specific situations, analyzing the scientific problem, the original events that suggested it, the method and instruments for solving it. Bringing essential features to the surface enables us to define science accurately.[1]

Interbehaving with scientific investigations helps to avoid the error that science seeks and finds universal and absolute laws. As a result the scientist is not endowed with powers he obviously does not possess, nor does science itself become a fetish. No scientist actually works on the basis of universal principles; were he to do so he would sail the same uncharted sea as the cosmos-searching philosophers. Even Mach, who yearned for a monistic view of the world, stopped short:

> Physical science does not pretend to be a *complete* view of the world; it simply claims that it is working toward such a complete view in the future.[2]

Objection to the universalistic view of science is not based on the impotence of men to achieve such a goal, nor on the necessity to pause before a verbally created universe, but on the fact that science, after all, is a definite task.

How can a scientist hope to satisfy a universalistic aim? One answer is faith in the power of numbers to achieve infinitude:

> Our ideal in natural science is to build up a working model of the universe out of the sort of ideas that all people carry about with them

---

[1] By definition, of course, we do not mean a summarizing verbal formula, but a description of observed happenings derived from marking out an area in the total field of human events (cf., Kantor, Psychology and Logic, Vol. 1, ch. 14).

[2] Science of Mechanics, p. 464.

everywhere "in their heads," as we say, and to which ideas we appeal
when we try to teach mathematics. These ideas are those of *number*,
order, the numerical measures of *times* and *distances*, and so on.[3]

The limitless scope and finality suggested here are surely not
within the range of any actual scientific enterprise. Scientists
seeking basic foundations draw from the bottomless well of traditional philosophy a mysterious power, variously called Reason,
Mind, Transcendental Unity. This entity they endow with faculties for penetrating to the heart of its counterpart *Ultimate Reality*.

A more modest characterization of science we find in Einstein's
statement:

> Science is the attempt to make the chaotic diversity of our sense
> experience correspond to a logically uniform system of thought.[4]

But we must interpret "sense experience" as actual interbehavior
with events. And unfortunately this interpretation is hardly in
line with Einstein's ideas concerning sensing and thinking, ideas
which favor systems of universalistic dimensions.

At the opposite pole from the universalists are those who
would sum up the whole of science as nothing but a method (p.
104). Such professed empiricists stand on the ground of procedure
rather than final results. But they generalize one feature of the
scientific enterprise so far that scientific method becomes abstract
and absolute. Certainly they do not stipulate that there is an
immense variety of methods for attacking specific problems.

We conclude, then, that the term *science* refers to much more
particular and limited situations than conventional descriptions
afford. What science is can only be determined on the basis of the
unique activities involved in determining (a) the existence or nonexistence of certain things and events and (b) the characteristics
of such things when they do exist. Any difficulty in defining science
arises from the multiplicity and diversity of problems and situations and from the numerous techniques scientists are required
to develop. Science, then, turns out to be an enormous accumulation of specific jobs.

---

[3] Jourdain, The Nature of Mathematics, p. 54.
[4] Considerations concerning the fundaments of theoretical physics, p. 487.

Not Science but Sciences

Every term designating scientific enterprises, like all names for human activity, should be used in a plural form. There are many sorts of sciences, just as there are many kinds of laws, arts, religions, and morals. There is, then, no single science, only series or families of sciences. The fact that scientific enterprises are more definite and deliberate in their organization and operation than ordinary pursuits, consequently more easily distinguishable, should not mask the fact that they vary in greater or lesser detail. The conventional terms *exact sciences, mathematical sciences, social sciences, humanistic sciences* suggest such differences.

Sciences in Relation

To grant that the sciences are unique and specific does not bypass the fact that in many ways they are all interrelated. This is not only true for the investigations concerned with similar types of events—for example, chemical reactions (organic, inorganic, physical)—but in some form for all scientific work. Indeed, there is some justification for the idea that a unity exists among all sciences: that, after all, they are one. The unity idea, however, has merit only when considered from the standpoint of actual problems and not from the lofty heights of a metaphysical universe.

There are various angles from which to view the interrelationship of sciences. Consider first the essential coupling of events. Even though each scientific endeavor represents a specialization and selection of data, events have a way of asserting their interconnections. This fact is recognized in the hyphenation of sciences: astrophysics, biochemistry, geophysics, and so on.

Sciences are interrelated, too, by the parallelity of investigative methods and techniques. For example, wherever possible, experimental techniques are in order. Similarly, mathematical and statistical techniques are applicable in most scientific situations.

Again, there are common cultural factors such as similarities in basic presuppositions and problems. Cultural unities influence the loci of scientific work, provide a basis for the common elements and rigidity of schools, and make room for fashions in science, though they also allow for variations.

Another powerful unifying feature is the cooperative effort among scientists themselves. The physicist's particular specilization enables him to provide instruments required by the astronomer, chemist, biologist, and psychologist. For example:

> The astronomer has borrowed almost all his tools from the physicist; the prism, the grating, the photoelectric cell, the interferometer, the photographic plate, even the telescope itself, were all used in the laboratory before they were applied to the sky.[5]

Indeed, so far reaching are the uses of electronic instruments that they seem to support the erroneous view that some sciences are basic to others. But this idea overlooks both the large number of features in any one scientific situation and the coordinate relations of the sciences with each other, with technology, as well as with social and economic circumstances.

Specifications of Scientific Enterprises

Scientific enterprises constitute a special type of industry—if we use the word *industry* in its recent generalized sense. Scientific work differs only in detail from other types of activity. What then are the characteristics which mark off scientific from nonscientific knowledge enterprises? We suggest the following specifications.

Seriousness. Scientific work is serious work. This specification can be illustrated by mathematics which has two branches: a serious and a trivial one. Hardy[6] has pointed out that mathematical operations may become decidedly trifling, as in the development of various games. As a matter of fact, a current mathematical school describes mathematics as the manipulation of senseless counters. Were the purely formal branch the only one, mathematics would be a sport, not a consequential enterprise. When we consider the so-called content sciences, in which the problems center about the nature and relations of things and events, the criterion of seriousness becomes clearer. In general, the rules of operation lead to an orientation toward things.

Originality. Scientific enterprises compared with nonscientific ones involve a factor of novelty. Problems are attacked in a new way, such that the results provide additional orientation and power concerning the things investigated. The fact that science

---

[5] Schlesinger, Astronomy, in *The Development of the Sciences*, p. 166.
[6] A Mathematician's Apology.

involves discovery is a recognition of this originality specification. If the scientific enterprise is successful, something new emerges, something, moreover, frequently incompatible with previous conditions.[7]

Originality differs in degree, of course, with particular pursuits—in fact, with the various problems in any one scientific department. In its most extreme form, originality of hypothesis and conclusion appears revolutionary and consequently provokes powerful opposition by representatives of the social order or of particular scientific schools.[8] Scientific literature is replete with instances of papers rejected by journal editors and referees of learned societies because of upsetting the *status quo*. Classic examples of the disharmony between scientific discovery and orthodoxy are suggested by the persecutions of Bruno, Galileo, and many others.[9]

Originality is favored by freedom from cultural restraint, from professional specialization and narrow and prescribed training. It is for this reason that so many major scientific advances have been made by amateurs—interlopers Darlington calls them. He writes:

> It is no accident that bacteria were first seen under the microscope by a draper, that stratigraphy was first understood by a canal engineer, that oxygen was first isolated by a Unitarian minister, that the theory of infection was first established by a chemist, the theory of evolution by a man who was unfitted to be a university instructor in either botany or zoology.[10]

Originality complements versatility. Goethe, poet and statesman, was no inconsiderable scientist.[11] Think how Fermat the magistrate became the Prince of Amateurs[12] because of his contributions to mathematics. Then there was Leibniz, master of all trades, historian and statesman. He, no less than Newton, the mathematical-physicist, helped to develop the calculus.

---

[7] See George, The Scientist in Action.

[8] An excellent description of the conflict of science and society has been given by Darlington in his Conway Memorial Lecture, The Conflict of Science and Society.

[9] We handle this problem more fully in ch. 3.

[10] The Conflict of Science and Society, p. 5.

[11] Cf., Kantor, Goethe's Place in Modern Science, pp. 61–82.

[12] Bell, Men of Mathematics.

Again, Bernard,[13] the famous physiologist, has remarked upon the value of ignorance for discovery. He was thinking, of course, in terms of medical science but what he meant is illustrated by Lalande's failure to find Neptune, even though he had evidence of its presence:

> He knew so well that there was no planet there that he could not discover it.[14]

Beveridge quotes the case of Mules, a sheepman, who discovered a means of preventing blowfly attack in Australian sheep, whereas many scientists had failed. Also Bessemer, the discoverer of the important steelmaking technique named for him, vividly describes his freedom from technological conventions.

> I had an immense advantage over many others dealing with the problem inasmuch as I had no fixed ideas derived from long established practice to control and bias my mind, and did not suffer from the general belief that whatever is, is right.[15]

And finally, Einstein and Infeld bear witness to the potency of nonprofessionalism in advancing physics:

> It is a strange coincidence that nearly all the fundamental work concerned with the nature of heat was done by non-professional physicists who regarded physics merely as their great hobby. There was the versatile Scotsman Black, the German physician Mayer, and the great American adventurer Count Rumford, who afterwards lived in Europe, and among other activities, became Minister of War for Bavaria. There was also the English brewer Joule who, in his spare time, performed some most important experiments concerning the conservation of energy.[16]

Analysis of Scientific Enterprises

Scientific enterprises can be analyzed only by studying the records of how individual workers attack their problems. From these records we shall attempt to gain information concerning the following features:

(1) The scientific worker.
(2) The work of science.

---

[13] An Introduction to the Study of Experimental Medicine, p. 37f.
[14] Darlington, The Conflict of Science and Society, p. 4.
[15] Beveridge, The Art of Scientific Investigation, p. 2.
[16] The Evolution of Physics, p. 51.

(3) Things worked with.
(4) Tools and instruments.
(5) Auspices under which enterprises are conducted.
(6) Products of the work done.

1. THE SCIENTIFIC WORKER

For centuries the attitude has prevailed that the study of science automatically includes the nature of the scientist. The basis for this view has been the apothegm that to know something it is advisable to know the instrument or means whereby knowledge is obtained. It is argued that since science involves knowledge it is important to know the nature of knowledge. Thus epistemology has been fostered as an important aspect of scientific work.

Here, unfortunately, an apparently good principle miscarries in application. Much depends upon our view of the scientist, the knower. It is characteristic of our culture to treat him, at least partially, as a mystic entity. Thereby all sorts of spurious problems have insinuated themselves into the discussion concerning the scientist and scientific knowledge, problems stemming from historical metaphysics, not from the records of actual knowing.

The primary objection to the metaphysical viewpoint is that it regards the scientist as a conglomerate of mind and body. By means of innumerable verbal formulae the psychic phase, always taken as opposite in character from the bodily, is connected with the latter. The mental component provokes many problems:

> How can mind know what is not mental? In what way can the internal and external worlds be bridged? What is mental is unique and private; hence: (a) knowledge must be precarious, unshared, and unverifiable; (b) things are only inferred and never really known.

This manner of thinking, so easily traced to the misadventures of cultural history, has evolved under theological auspices and in no way is based on the observation of how knowledge actually develops.

What room has modern science for the dichotomy of man or of any other natural object? There is no mind, and, indeed, no body considered as an adjunct of mind.[17] As an organism the scientific worker is an observable object in interrelation with other things.

---

[17] See, Kantor, Problems of Physiological Psychology.

His existence, his operations, are as public and as stable as anything else in nature.

Furthermore, modern scientific findings blot out the verbal tradition that any part of the organism—say, the brain—serves as an alembic of knowledge or as the creator of any quality or property of things. The dark chapter of scientific culture which has successively made the brain into (1) the seat of the soul, (2) the basis of mind, and (3) the source of various powers cannot be regarded as anything but folklore.

Still, the tradition flourishes that the brain and other parts of the nervous system are the seat of "material events which are bound up with our conscious activity."[18] The following quotation from one of the most recent attempts to solve the problem of how the brain mediates the mysterious processes of "thought" signalizes in a striking manner the continuation of the theologically founded mind-body (soul-flesh) dichotomy:

> If we are lost at night and look up at the sky we may notice the pattern of stars called Charles's Wain or the Plough. The sequence of material changes is that an arrangement of bright points is focused on the retina, impulses travel up the optic nerve from the nerve-fibres which lead from the illuminated points, and in the occipital lobe of the brain a pattern of excitation is set up corresponding more or less to the pattern of the stars. Then comes a whole series of events in which the mind seems to intervene. We recognize the familiar grouping, we remember that a line through two of the points will lead to the pole star, we shift our eyes to that knowing that it is in the north, and having located the points of the compass we lose our anxiety and find our way home. To achieve this result the brain must carry out various executive acts by signalling to the muscles of the eyes and then of the neck and limbs. The signals and the muscular movements can be expressed in physiological terms just like the signals from the retina which started the train of events, but in between them comes the recognition of the pattern, the memories aroused by it, the decision to look at the pole star, the inference as to the right way to go, and the satisfaction at finding it. How are these mental activities related to the excitation of nerve-cells in the occipital cortex and to the subsequent changes in the brain?[19]

The underlying presupposition of this statement stands out with

---

[18] Adrian, The Physical Background of Perception.

[19] Op. cit., p. 2–3. Adrian's difficulties have been minimized by his wise choice of a pattern illustration. He thus avoids the infinitely more troublesome problem of color and other sensory qualities.

silhouette sharpness. The duality of mind and body is simply presupposed, as well as the mystical character of mind; hence the mediating brain must operate in a mystifying way. No wonder the author concludes:

> Perhaps the chief impression which will be left by this account is of the complete inability of contemporary science to give a satisfactory picture of any kind of mental activity.[20]

Why, we ask, should contemporary science attempt to solve problems about things imagined by ancient theologians? The actual interbehavior of individuals in perceiving and thinking situations can be satisfactorily described and explained as observed events. Modern psychology does not need to anthropomorphize the brain as a homunculus sending and receiving messages. Or worse, regard the brain as a container for a ghost. Nor is it necessary to misinterpret the brain, which is a bodily organ, as a link between the body and the mind. This false notion assumes two functions for the brain: (1) conducting processes for the organism's unified action and (2) mystical processes for serving the soul. Why sacrifice on the altar of ancient priests all our recent information concerning the conducting processes of neural fibres—data, moreover, gained with arduous labor and by utilizing the most advanced technological products: electronic instruments!

Although the interbehavioral story of the misuse of the brain is easily traced, the dualistic tradition still influences scientists to make use of the brain to explain matters in a way as impossible as it is unnecessary. Perhaps there is one merit in such employment of brain "explanations"—namely, a realization that the "mind" should be replaced by something tangible.

Witness the lengths to which scientists are forced to go in order to transform the brain as a conducting mechanism—the only known brain—into a substitute for mind or consciousness. A good example is provided by Craik[21] who undertakes to explain thought. He proceeds on the sophisticated basis that he is constructing a model to represent or parallel thought. This model is not intended to be a picture of what it represents but only a verbal analogy. Since all concrete interbehavior is to be abandoned, the

---

[20] Op. cit., p. 1.
[21] The Nature of Explanation.

brain as a model is presumed to utilize mechanisms similar to those of calculating machines. And since thinking becomes imitation the brain parallels the world, as a calculating machine parallels the development of strains in a bridge.

The work of making this model involves, besides substituting the brain for the man and certain products of description and calculation for the world, a number of other arbitrary constructions: (a) thought and explanation are reduced to symbolization; (b) symbolization is reduced to the ability of processes to parallel or imitate each other. The basis for the latter is "that there are recurrent patterns in reality."[22]

In this employment of the brain model it is intended to make the brain do what the "mind" is supposed to do—think, reason, and predict. So a materialistic or mechanistic view is adopted. But what we need to do is to discover what thinking, reasoning, and predicting events are like. Our descriptions certainly do not necessitate the arbitrary creation of brain properties and activities nor the futile reductions of complex events to static structures which can be pronounced similar.

As Craik's exposition amply shows, it is men, not brains, who reason. He indicates three processes that reasoning entails: (1) "Translation" of external processes into words, numbers, or other symbols, (2) Arrival at other symbols by deduction or inference, and (3) "Retranslation" of symbols into external processes (as in building a bridge to a design). At this point Craik has been thinking interbehaviorally; his quoting of processes like translation and retranslation symptomizes a faint realization that the work done by an engineer in designing a bridge, calculating stresses, strains, costs, appearance, etc., is not simply recording data by movements of toothed wheels.

Does Craik the model maker overlook his own work in making this model? It has been asserted that his work stems from his philosophical training, from his evolution as a constructer of mechanical contrivances.[23] If this be true we see at once that his thinking and model making constitute far different events from the sheer imitation by his brain of such past and present processes.

The scientific worker operates only through his contact with events. He takes note of things, their characteristics, motions,

[22] Craik, p. 59.
[23] Cf., Adrian, op. cit., p. 93.

and interrelationships. Then he records the results of his contacts, describing them partially on the basis of (1) immediate observation, (2) his past encounters, and (3) traditional description and sheer assertion. Such records, along with other evaluations of things, accumulate to constitute the treasures of science.

Wherever there is a scientist there is an interbehavioral history—namely, a detailed basis for his development, his problems and techniques, and the interpretations of what he observes. Examining this interbehavioral story we discover how the individual acquires and justifies his scientific interest, how he adjusts himself to traditional ways of thinking, or, quite otherwise, sometimes initiates, at least suggests, a revolution in conventional practice.

For the focal point of science and its detailed operations it is tremendously important to consider the relative influences upon the worker of events and environing intellectual institutions. Historical, geographical, and socio-political circumstances may have telling effects upon the kind of problems attacked, the hypotheses set up, the sort of apparatus available, even the conclusions reached.

Consider a few of these striking effects of human circumstances. Continentals are continuists; British scientists are atomistically inclined. Continentals favor so-called rational and mathematical ways of thinking; British physicists tend toward mechanical models (p. 187). Among biologists we find strong leanings toward physiological or vitalistic ways of thinking, depending upon school situations. This constant interplay of influences, as between events and traditions, constitutes the cross currents within which all scientists work.

Motivating factors are another consideration. Some of these are extrinsic, such as the conditions accounting for some individual being a scientist rather than a banker, an artisan, or for his working at one type of problem instead of another within the same field or in a neighboring department. Intrinsic factors are those circumstances affecting his particular ways of thinking in any given situation.

2. SCIENTIFIC WORK

The basic work of science consists of so interbehaving with things and events as to increase our knowledge of them. Only by examining and manipulating things and events do we obtain knowledge and control. Knowledge, differentiated from belief or assumption, consists of new orientation; it is not a transcendent act of producing things *de novo*. Here we must not confuse metaphysical creation with the manipulative processes of analytically reducing compounds to their elements or synthetically constructing and reconstructing complex things from simpler constituents.

A large proportion of scientific investigation constitutes the observation and manipulation of evolved and constructed products. The range of scientific work is broad enough to include the results of organic and inorganic combinations and recombinations of simpler things, as well as all sorts of human artifacts. Much scientific work is consequently devoted to recovering the processes whereby present things and events have become what they are, in addition to investigating their immediate changes. Not only is the scientist interested in the evolution of galactic systems in general, our solar system, the earth, and the evolution of all living things including man, but also in the changes taking place in chemical transformations, organic mutation, and in the growth and elimination of institutions and societies.

All scientific contacts with things have one primary goal—the ascertainment of their nature: their constitution and organization. The organization of a thing includes its interrelations with other things resulting in various changes and transformations. From such manipulative contacts scientists proceed to describe and explain things. They are then prepared for the further interbehavior of prediction and control. Prediction, unfortunately, often involves aims subsidiary to the basic scientific effort to understand things and events.

It is in no sense a paradox that scientific interbehavior can occur when the objects of study are not immediately present. In that case the objects are substituted for by other things. A chemical reaction is evidence that certain substances have been treated though they are now no longer present. Even when scientists talk about imponderable masses, heat substances, electrical fluids, genetic determiners, forces, instincts, native intelligence, they are operating with things and events but at the same time misinterpreting them. Whether the scientist regards himself as studying a heat substance or an undeveloped mental power, he begins and ends respectively with combustion processes or ways in which individuals answer questions. In each instance some actual thing or event gives rise to the belief that things exist which really do not (heat substances, instinctive knowledge).

Take Blondlot and his French colleagues as examples: they reported the presence of N-rays when light from a Nernst filament was analyzed. In so doing they created a descriptive construct incompatible with what they were handling.[24] Similar incidents are Fresnel's announcement that he had decomposed water by current from a coil of wire in which a magnet had been placed, and Ampére's assertion that he had observed electromagnetic induction.[25]

It is regrettable that scientists devote a disproportionate amount of their work to prove that alleged characteristics of things do not exist. When investigators face difficult and complex problems improper hypotheses are bound to result. Freedom from medievalism has always signified to the scientist the departure both from the allegation (a) that observed things have mystic and nonexistent properties and (b) that nonexistent things, which are only verbally created, exist.

Scientific work as the behavior of specific individuals varies according to the scientific situation. These variations are based upon differences in types of things and events studied, upon one's interest in particular aspects, the uses new information can serve, and so on. Despite all this diversity we may set up four generalized types of scientific procedure.

(a) *Direct Observation.* Direct or immediate contacts with things may be extremely simple or they may involve the use of complicated apparatus, such as telescopes, microscopes, spectographs. Distant objects or those too large or too small can be studied only with a minimum of manipulation. It is characteristic of direct observation that regardless of whether it occurs in the field or in a laboratory the observed object is in no way transformed.

(b) *Instrumental Observation.* When the scientist uses instruments to compare things by way of ascertaining their length, weight, and other properties, he is in closer contact with the things

---

[24] See Thomson, Recollections and Reflections, p. 395f.; also Wood, The N-Rays.
[25] Taylor, Physics, p. 686f.

observed than when he uses instruments merely to observe times of transit or changes of color. Measurement is a definite form of manipulation. The application of a rule or rod brings the worker closer to things than when arranging them under a microscope field.

(c) *Transforming Contacts.* The chemist's analysis and synthesis of compounds is the best illustration of transformative operations. The production of new combinations of elements is certainly creative behavior, but even the most intense creative activity consists of forming and transforming combinations. The organic chemist is notorious for producing compounds unknown in nature, though his most active productivity consists primarily in manipulating familiar things.

(d) *Remote Observation.* The most subtle forms of scientific activity (generalizing, analogizing) are indirect and remote inferential operations. Despite the long range, however, the emphasis is on basic encounters with events. The chain connecting the worker and the thing upon which he operates may consist of many links, but it is characteristic of scientific work that the connection is rigidly maintained.

3. THINGS WORKED WITH

The things and events with which the scientist interbehaves have reached staggering proportions. Indeed it is impossible to list or classify them. But whoever attempts to survey the scientific domain must respect the claims of all types demanding inclusion. It is a fatal mistake to characterize some *selected* list as scientific data. The dense continuity of scientific and technological enterprises forbids us to typify scientific materials as exclusively mechanical, electrical, chemical, or vital. Such factless selection is responsible for inept constructs like the hierarchy of the sciences and physiochemical foundations of biology.

At one end of the vast range of scientific materials are directly visible objects studied by chemists, geologists, biologists, and psychologists. The physicist, too, is in small part concerned with such crude objects. Mostly, however, he is interested in processes, energies, and interrelationships which stand at the other extreme. Even when scientific problems arise from contact with things that are colored, shaped, solid and enduring, it may be expedient to treat those objects as colorless, formless, infirm, and changing motion or energy.

The more advanced a science is the more it is concerned with recondite and subtle aspects and relationships. Unfortunately this palpable fact has been so distorted by venerable epistemological traditions that scientists have questioned the independent existence of things and events. They have then unwittingly assumed that scientific subject matter comprises "mental" creations. Although scientists would spurn the allegation that they believe Priestley created oxygen, Cavendish hydrogen, or that Galileo invented sun spots or Saturn's rings, their epistemological theorizing presupposes precisely that type of creation.

No scientific investigation, but mentalistic epistemology, obliterates the distinction between events and constructs. It is the metaphysics of primary and secondary qualities that confounds autistic creations like "sensations" with an event such as our seeing a red apple. Sensations in the sense of isolated qualitative items are abstracted properties of things. By transforming these properties into "states of mind," tradition has dissipated things and made them into "appearances." Thus are created spurious reality problems.

Such problems however, can never arise from the study of the scientist's work, which plainly reveals that knowledge depends upon things, not things upon knowledge. To achieve knowledge and attain exact description and explanation we must improve our contacts with events. When Huygens in 1655 was able to perceive Saturn's ring more effectively than was Galileo, whose telescope made Saturn and its ring appear a bit amorphous, it was only because in the first place there was a planet there with its unique structure. The existence of that structure made it possible for Cassini in 1675 to report two rings with a space between. Similarly, the 1850 description of a faint semi-transparent crepe ring within the two bright rings was possible because there was something to be described.

The spurious problems of "reality" and the existence of an external world arise from the simple confusion of things with reactions to them. When observations are difficult, when observers are deficient (color blind), when relations between things observed and observers vary, those who are dominated by philosophic tradition conclude that observations contribute to the existence of observed things.

4. SCIENTIFIC TOOLS AND INSTRUMENTS

Because scientific apparatus must be individually suitable for particular investigations, they vary widely in pattern and function. Not only must instruments be designed from the standpoint of things and events investigated but also on the basis of the interests, ambitions, and working methods of researchers. Many different types of apparatus must be employed for (a) general probing and macro- and micro-manipulation, for (b) transforming things by cutting, grinding, macerating and centrifuging, (c) for making them appear larger and observationally available. Thus the electron microscope in the last ten years has made possible visual contact with things as small as 5 to 10 atoms.[26]

The invention and use of apparatus brings science into context with the technological aspects of culture. There is a direct correlation between the complication of society and the complexity of science. Large-scale industry, the magnified use of the sea and the air, have brought into operation new and powerful machines which further the invention of scientific instruments, in turn to be employed for industrial expansion.

How great is the distance between such simple situations as that of Cavendish who had to deal with currents by shocking himself, of Ohm who had to draw his own wire to study electrical transmission, and the evolution of technology to the point at which instruments often set the pace for research! In many ways the worker's scientific capacity is definitely dependent upon the technological level of society. Availability of instruments not only enables him to test his hypotheses: it quickens the development of ideas and theories.

Advance in instrumental design, it has been said, is the most important thing that has recently happened in science.[27] The same writer has declared:

> The reason why we are on a higher imaginative level is not because we have finer imagination, but because we have better instruments.[28]

---

[26] See Wycoff, Visualizing macromolecules and viruses; also Electron Microscope.

[27] Whitehead, Science and the Modern World, p. 167.

[28] Ibid., p. 166.

Imagination, of course, is the behavior of persons whose effectiveness is correlated with, if not determined by, the technological and general cultural level of a given historical period.

Stimulated by the more recent intensive development of complex instrumentation, Condon an authority on the subject asserts:

> It seems quite likely that the instrument scientist will in the future play a role of steadily increasing importance in the development of all the sciences.[29]

Engineering and technology at the point where they intersect science have become so elaborate that the study of instrument design and the adaptation of apparatus to scientific problems now constitute an autonomous science.[30] The interests of this new science of instruments are fostered by a number of publications in various countries,[31] and the effort is being made to enlarge its inclusion in university training.[32]

For the most part this recent development has been concerned with measurement. The enormous advances in subatomic and radiation knowledge have quickened the evolution of tools for detaching and counting electron and nuclear happenings. Pieper[33] has recently included the following list of instruments for detecting particles and quanta: ionization chambers, Geiger counters, electroscopes, electrometers, cloud chambers, electron multipliers, scintillation and crystal counters, and photographic films.

Evolutionally, instrumentation may be the offspring of metrology,[34] but it has certainly developed beyond measurement in scope and significance. Besides measuring machines, there are machines for the automatic control and treatment of data, for calculating and integrating data. The range of instruments is thus extremely broad, the simplest being tools which merely increase the individual's capacity to achieve contacts with things, to manipulate and measure them. Also comparatively simple are the machines which substitute for men because of more rapid, more

---

[29] Is there a science of instrumentation? p. 341.

[30] Condon, op. cit.

[31] In the U. S. A., *The Review of Scientific Instruments, Instruments;* in the U. K., *British Journal of Scientific Instruments;* in Germany, *Zeitschrift für Instrumentkunde, Archiv für technischen Messen;* in France, *Revue de Metrologie.*

[32] Cf., Wildhack, Instrumentation in perspective.

[33] Instrumentation for radioactivity.

[34] Wildhack, Instrumentation in perspective, p. 517.

standard, and more sustained action, as well as the elimination of danger, such as in dealing with extreme temperatures and harmful radiations. Complex instruments are devices which can replace human organisms by automatically drawing conclusions from data automatically sifted, sorted, reduced, and analyzed.

Up to this point we have been emphasizing things, or, as it is sometimes said, material instruments. Notice, however, that instruments constitute any means whereby investigation is carried on. Moreover, instrumentation covers both behavior and products. Hypotheses, laws or theories, as products of the scientist's prior contacts with things, are very often the most effective instruments for discovery and measurement. For example, the subtle processes of inference, the work of constructing concepts and propositions, help to further scientific enterprises. The scientist also develops symbols and formulae to record and embody his propositions and theories. Mathematical equations as well as verbal descriptions, are among the most serviceable research instruments.

These behavioral instruments are important precisely because they serve much more at the point of discovery, when new viewpoints are being developed, than in establishing the minute precision of an additional decimal point. It is some such reason which prompted the remark that for science it was fortunate Kepler did not receive Tycho's instruments,[35] since if he had he would have spent his time making more and more observations instead of devoting himself to such theoretical construction as led to his three laws.

Machines designed for scientific tasks have become so complex as to give rise to the view that the work itself can be practiced by machines. A new form of mechanistic philosophy has thus developed according to which the machines are regarded as models for human behavior. Machines which can solve problems in ten minutes that ordinarily would require a human calculator years to accomplish have been used to show man's lack of speed and efficiency.[36] In addition, there are machines that play games, separate true from false combinations or statements, machines with logical as well as mathematical competence.[37]

---

[35] Schlesinger, Astronomy.
[36] Berkeley, Giant Brains or Machines that Think.
[37] Berkeley, Symbolic logic and large-scale calculating machines.

This new machine philosophy attempts to identify the operation of electronic machines with that of the human nervous system. It is argued that, for control, both the organism and the instrument require a "feedback" of output into the sensing element.[38] Certainly there is some resemblance between the organization and operation of human and nonhuman machines, but the differences are far greater. The human machine obviously is the prototype, the originator of the counterpart. These differences can be summed up by referring to the colossal evolution required to develop the human organism, an evolution that includes social and technological growth in addition to biological development.

Howsoever effectively instruments facilitate contacts with things and events they do not create them. But what if the instrument appears to be a part of the observed event? For instance, do we merely improve our observation of spectral colors by the use of a prism or grating? No: without the instrument there is no spectral color. We must interpose the instrument in a light beam to have a color to observe. May it not be said, then, that the instrument creates or manufactures the color? No: admittedly, the instrument is a necessary factor, but this signifies only that spectral color is a component of an event which includes the interaction of light and a spectroscopic grating or prism. It is a fact of nature that a prism or grating mediates such periodicity in solar light as to produce spectral color. Spectroscopes, therefore, are different instruments from colorimeters, which only aid in matching colors and thus provide measures of comparison.

There are two problems of creation here: one the objective conjoining of factors that sum up to a certain event; the other the assumption that the act of observing some thing creates that thing. It may be said that by means of electrolytic apparatus the chemist produces or creates H—O—H from water. This does not mean, however, that he can create water or hydrogen and oxygen in any other way than manipulating the factors of a hydrogen-oxygen or water event. Dissociation and synthesis are creative operations, but they afford no occasion to confuse observation and investigation with creation.

That instruments are mediators, not creators, we may conclude from contrasting the effectiveness of instrument makers

---

[38] Cf., Wiener, Cybernetics.

when dealing with inorganic mechanisms instead of with physiological machines. With respect even to the comparatively local problems of the cardiovascular system a recent writer says:

> Reasonably satisfactory instrumentation is available for continuous recording of the electrocardiogram, heart rate, respiration, temperature, blood pressure, blood oxygen saturation, and other factors. Development is still lacking, however, in instruments capable of high-fidelity recording of many other variables of importance to the cardiorespiratory system . . . for example, blood oxygen and carbon-dioxide tension, the cardiac output, regional blood flow, and the gas composition of the breath during each respiratory cycle.[39]

5. SCIENTIFIC AUSPICES

Scientific work is widely distributed throughout every complex community. Particular investigations of varying degrees of expertness are carried on under many different kinds of auspices. It is fair to say, therefore, that science is wherever you find it. Furthermore, there is a mutuality of influence between scientific work and its cultural settings (chap. 3). Certain societal conditions favor its development, even encourage a broad interest in problems and techniques; other auspices restrict and even discourage research.

Modern industrial societies provide a milieu extremely favorable to all phases of science. Strong pressure is even exerted to hasten its growth. Recent industrial and military interests have forced a powerful development in the physical, chemical, and biological departments. Despite the demand for particular results, despite the interest of research promoters in financial returns the military and industrial have a salutary effect on both pure and applied science. Carrying on investigations into the nature of organic and inorganic things forces a concomitant development of all features of science. Whether the primary interest is in findings or principles the favoring of one aspect exerts a beneficial influence on the other. Even the incidental development of apparatus for a certain research may prove to be an indispensable factor for scientific progress in an altogether different situation.

We turn now to the effects of such correlated institutions as political units, churches, and scientific schools (p. 55f.). These may

---

[39] Wood, Special instrumentation problems encountered in physiological research concerning the heart and circulation in man.

favor science but usually exert an adverse influence. Records revealing the struggle of scientists to maintain their freedom to investigate things, to construct and propagate their theories, constitute a sad commentary on social man. Recall the political and religious attempts to suppress heliocentric astronomy and evolutional biology. On the whole, such historical instances of interference with freedom of thought and research as culminated in the trials of Bruno and Galileo and in the attempted prevention of anatomical investigation are celebrated more for their failure than anything else. Probably, the protective devices, such as codes, symbols, and mirror writing (Leonardo) used by scientists to conceal their heterodoxies ward off temporary and minor interference. But even such suppression of their writings as practiced by Copernicus, Kepler, Descartes, and others are obstacles, not permanent blocks, in the scientific path.

Scientific groups themselves often exert more damaging influence than nonscientific organizations. Established authoritative schools may determine, for instance, what is worth working at and how the work should be done. The sheer perpetuation of doctrines can be a serious danger to scientific innovation. Vesalius, Ohm, Mayer, and Semmelweiss were all victims of the intolerant treatment of their scientific colleagues.

Scientific auspices may be classified as individual and conventional. In many ways the ideal condition is one which allows the individual to develop his research interests without interference from any outside source. Recall Cavendish's circumstances: independent in his researches and under no pressure to publish. In his case, of course, the general scientific situation was very simple and he had ample means to indulge his inclinations. Certainly he did not lack freedom but he may have missed the facilities which only a cultural group can provide. Today, as compared with Cavendish's time, promising auspices are found in the surroundings of a university, governmental agency, or industrial organization.

Social or conventional auspices are obviously more favorable for such scientific work as leads to increase of knowledge about things, to the production of materials for industrial, medical and military needs. They are less favorable when a new principle is to be developed. The organization of novel points of view, new ways of thinking, requires the freedom and leisure which only the ivory tower can furnish. Of several mathematicians the story is told that upon finishing a piece of work they declared: "Thank God no one can make use of that."

6. SCIENTIFIC PRODUCTS

The common view that the products of scientific investigation consist of treatises and the scientific library[40] is not entirely false, but there is very little to commend it. From the standpoint of social institutions the formalized records of science are the materials of knowledge. But, at most, scientific products are only partially represented by static treatises. The more considerable part consists of methods, techniques, and apparatus which can be employed in other research beyond that in which they were originally developed.

The sciences, no less than other aspects of culture, are cumulative. The work done in research, the viewpoints achieved, the expertness developed constitute the stock of scientific products. This is true not only of descriptions and measurements but of ideas and knowledge. For instance, when Mayer attempted to account for the bright red color of venous blood in the tropics he could resort to Lavoisier's theory that animal heat is a result of combustion. The change of blood color in the capillaries as a sign of oxidation, Mayer observed, must be less in torrid than in colder regions. Oxidation, too, must be less, since to maintain the uniformity of body temperature less heat must be developed. Now, evolution of bodily heat is produced in two ways: not only by internal combustion but also by work done, by motion or friction. And so the physiological theory of combustion has become the basis for the equivalence between heat and work. This conclusion Mayer reached by considering whether the animal heat evolved was owing to combustion alone or to motion or work as well. To obtain a value for making the first calculation for the mechanical equivalent of heat Mayer was once again able to resort to a scientific product. In this case it was Regnault's inaccurate ratio of 1.421 for the specific heat of gases at constant pressure and constant temperature.[41]

---

[40] See Eddington, The Philosophy of Physical Science, p. 2. See note 3, ch. 3.
[41] Heyl, The Fundamental Concepts of Physics.

In recent years we have had the classic illustration of Einstein's resort to the mathematical developments of Minkowski, Ricci, and Levi-Civita for materials with which to build his relativity theories.[42]

Other prominent scientific products are the basic attitudes which become part of a society's heritage. The sophistication which a community imbibes concerning the age and character of the earth and solar system, concerning the evolution of animals and the character of man, is important both in itself and as a reciprocal influence, for good or evil, upon further scientific work.

Scientific laws when thoroughly verified are probably the most effective and valuable of all investigative products. These constructions sum up and describe the characteristics of things and events. When conditions allow, scientific laws induce considerable confidence in the value of the investigational enterprise, a confidence increasingly warranted by the satisfactory outcome of prediction, by ability to use the law in deducing the existence of additional properties of things related to those already discovered.

Because scientific enterprises are concerned with widely diverging things and events their law products vary. Some are more precise than others; they may be qualitative or quantitative; again they differ in degree of verification.

Scientific Investigation and the Philosophy of Science

Inherent in the evolutionary processes of science are the genes of a science of science. Inevitably, scientific enterprises and situations become the materials of investigation. We have already indicated (Preface) how the upheavals occasioned by relativity and quantum mechanics prompted investigation of scientific foundations. We have seen, too, that similar circumstances have prevailed in earlier eras of scientific history. Science is perennially in a formative stage.

Now, when scientists take account of the adequacy and significance of their results, system problems are bound to arise. Such problems form the basis of the science of science, the topic of our next chapter.

---

[42] Cf., Frank, Einstein, His Life and Times, pp. 20, 103.

2

SCIENCE AND THE LOGIC OF SCIENCE

Science a Five-Factor System

LOGIC is the science of systems.[1] To represent scientific situations effectively the logician of science organizes a five-factor system. Three of the central factors correspond to the three major phases of a scientific situation: (1) crude data, (2) operations, (3) products. The two flanking factors comprise (4) the thing and event matrix and (5) the cultural sources. These various components are indicated in the accompanying diagram.

When the logician of science analyzes a scientific situation he is himself engaging in a scientific enterprise. His work therefore mirrors the pattern of scientific endeavor as outlined in the preceding chapter. His essential subject matter, corresponding to the crude data of the original investigator, is the work of the latter under the exact conditions in which it is carried on.

The logic of science is primarily critical. The logician is concerned with the integration of the scientific enterprise. He asks: How consistent with scientific rules are the scientist's operations? How do the hypotheses correspond with the data? How effective are hypotheses in producing results? How carefully have the data been checked with relevant statistics? How closely do the interpretations comport with the findings?

Now, as a rule, things and events themselves serve as criteria to correct errors and lead to valid systems. Scientists, however, operate in a middle ground between two constraining borders: on one side the immense domain of things, processes, and events, including the scientist; on the other the cultural institutions which influence his ways of thinking and his operational techniques. The logician's task is to estimate the relative proportion of findings the scientist derives from cultural and from event sources (chap. 3).

---

[1] See Kantor, Psychology and Logic.

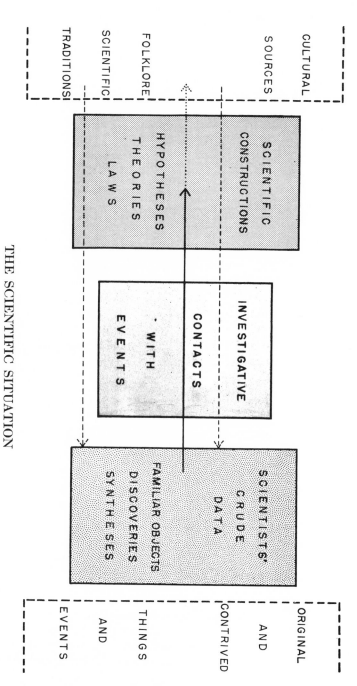

THE SCIENTIFIC SITUATION

Diagram Showing the Different Sources of Scientific Constructions

If the ratio favors cultural influences it is clear that the worker is misinterpreting his data.

Systems and Metasystems in Science

Scientific work always involves a set of underlying presuppositions. When organized these assumptions constitute a metasystem. Whether the original investigator is or is not aware of them they nevertheless influence his scientific system. It is therefore exceedingly important that the scientist include the metasystem when he examines any systemic structure. The following schema indicates the minimal design for an ideal scientific system:

I. Metasystems
    A. Criteria
        (Philosophical presuppositions)
    B. Protopostulates
        (System Assumptions)
II. Scientific Systems
    A. Definitions
        (Isolation and location of domain)
    B. Postulates
        (Relevant Assumptions)
    C. Data, Variables, Units
        (Event selection)
    D. Investigating Operations
        (Observation, Mensuration, Calculation)
    E. Product Construction
        (Laws, Theories, Equations, Explanations)

I. SCIENTIFIC METASYSTEMS

A. Criteria. These concern the scientist's general philosophical presuppositions, including his motivations. They reach back to his attitude toward the comprehensiveness, function, and goal of research. We have questioned, for instance, the attitudes of universalism, absolutism, and finality. Criteria also affect a scientist's attitudes toward such questions as causality and the autonomous vs. the representative character of symbolic structures. Does he regard mathematical equations as models of reality or merely as constructs summing up discoveries?

B. Protopostulates. These represent more definite assumptions. They indicate an awareness of background issues. In systemizing Euclidean geometry, for example, the protopostulates imply that the axioms and postulates are *different* from non-Euclidean systems.

Bridgman's logic exemplifies most effectively the nature of protopostulates. This physicist has distinguished himself by proposing the operational viewpoint to structurize the scientific chaos brought about by relativity and quantum mechanics. For one thing, the operational approach constitutes an admonition to be on guard; the physicist, for instance, must be certain how he derives his equations, how he applies them. It was Bridgman who alerted physicists to the operations which gave meaning to the concepts used. Furthermore, he indicated what sort of protopostulates to reject:

> The idea that thought is the measure of all things, that there is such a thing as utter logical rigor, that conclusions can be drawn endowed with an inescapable necessity, that mathematics has an absolute validity and controls experience—[2]

These excellent principles, however, become completely vitiated by the protopostulates that Bridgman himself adopts. He assumes that there is a mind fitted with psychic powers:

> ... direct experience embraces only the things in my consciousness—sense impressions of various sorts and various sorts of cerebrations—and naught else.[3]

Thus he accepts a solipsistic protopostulate. For him tables, clouds, and stars are mental constructions somehow projected to constitute external things. The objectivity of external things is guaranteed by the agreement generated when one solipsistic mind reacts in a similar way to the internal and purely private states of another.[4]

Can a satisfactory system of physics be erected on such a metasystem as a foundation? Bridgman himself is sceptical and relies upon "the most obvious observation"—namely, "thinking is an activity of the human nervous system."[5] Actually, his "observation" is a presupposition of spiritistic philosophy.

---

[2] The Nature of Physical Theory, p. 135.
[3] Ibid., p. 13.
[4] Ibid., p. 13f.
[5] Ibid., p. 6.

Bridgman's solipsistic protopostulate about "reacting minds" can only be integrated with a valid system by transforming it into the construction: All scientific work consists of the operations of specific individuals upon objects or events. But this means uprooting all dualistic assumptions. Tables, chairs, and clouds are not "mental" creations but everyday objects which supply the basis for constructing descriptions of their natures, constitutions, and relations.

Quis custodiet ipsos custodes? Apparently one task of the logician of science is to prevent the use of a faulty metasystem. But obviously he himself is subject to presuppositions derived from *his* particular cultural background. Does this mean we are left without systemizing criteria? Not at all, if only we abjure absolute standards. From investigations and their critical analysis valid scientific systems are derived.

II. SCIENTIFIC SYSTEMS

The basic divisions of a system we are now to consider provide a model of a typical scientific job.

A. Definitions. Scientific definitions are constructs developed for the purpose of isolating and locating a domain of work. They serve to clarify the character of scientific enterprises, whether a single research or a class of investigations.

Depending upon type of metasystem, definitions refer either to things and events or to concepts and terms. Obviously we would stress things and events, since they are what the systemizer is basically concerned with. Concepts and terms, however, must take their place within the definitional division of a scientific system.

Is a virus an organism? This question suggests how important it may be for a researcher to define the objects he investigates. Clearly, it is not a matter of how to use terms, not a matter of what attitude (concept) to adopt toward a substance progressively covering a leaf, for instance, but rather whether exclusively chemical or biological operations must be performed. Another example: To ask whether light is corpuscular, as well as radiant, is primarily a problem of light, not of terms or ways of thinking about light.

B. Postulates. Systemic postulates in mathematics are among the clearest examples because the materials are formal and relational. It is obvious, however, that all scientific work implies postulates, even though they are not formally set out. In the content sciences, postulates are frequently merged with the protopostulates of the metasystem, such as the rejection of Newton's absolute or unjoined space and time, in favor of Minkowski-Einstein speculations.

C. *Data, Variables, Units.* Data problems are crucial for systematics. How a logician treats "what is given" at once reveals his metasystem. There is a striking contrast between those who build on the conventional protopostulates of "sensations," "sense data" or "experience" and those who regard scientific data as the things and events which set problems.

The objective logician, however, differentiates between pristine and transformed things. Pristine data are best illustrated by accidentally discovered things: cosmic rays, inert gases, the function of the pancreas in insulin secretion. Transformed data are the numerous synthetic compounds the chemist produces from simpler compounds and elements. A striking instance of a *discovered* transformation datum is the artificial radioactivity first detected by the Joliot-Curies when they subjected an aluminum window to the rays of Polonium.[6]

The theorist who begins with things and events frees himself completely from the situation indicated in the following statement:

> In physical science one constructs the fundamental concepts of the things, character and processes revealed by sensation.[7]

This statement perverts the fact that scientific constructs refine and clarify the characteristics of things discovered by interbehaving with them. Rejecting spiritistic metasystems the logician looks upon variables as factors abstracted from data or from operations upon them. Again, whatever he establishes as units are similarly derived.

D. *Investigative Operations.* Fortunately logicians of science differ very little, if at all, in their description of what happens in the field or the laboratory. This agreement is owing to the fact that technical operations closely resemble the manipulative behavior of everyday life and technological procedure. Furthermore,

---

[6] Soddy, F. The Story of Atomic Energy, p. 103.
[7] Lenzen, Nature of Physical Theory, p. 1.

because of the extensive use of apparatus the operations have to conform to standards set by economic and industrial contingencies (p. 105).

Theoretical scientists, however, fail to do justice to the inter-behavioral principle. Much scientific operation is thus interpreted as processes going on within the person; this is especially true of subtle action like thinking and reasoning, which, as we have seen, are misinterpreted as spiritistic acts. But if one does not impose noncontact descriptions upon investigative operations there is no difficulty at all in treating the acts of constructing data and making hypotheses and inferences as definite contacts with things.

The most palpable type of data construction is the selection and isolation of things from their ordinary background in order to facilitate observation. More elaborate operations of this order are putting things in a vacuum, separating them into parts by dividing, splitting, or dissecting them, attaching things to others in a new way as in transplanting tissues, dissolving things, electrically dissociating, freezing and burning them.

Somewhat more remote operations require treatment by analogies and models. Such things as wind tunnels, wires which analogically conduct neural impulses, *in vitro* growings, and nerve-muscle preparations are imaginative and imitative constructions for furthering interbehavioral operations. In this manner projectiles may be treated as though they were points in motion without color, mass, size or shape.

But what about hypotheses which are conventionally thought of as preceding manipulations? The obvious answer is that no hypothesis can be constructed except by prior contact with events. Newton emphasized this point when he set down his famous exclamation: *hypotheses non fingo*.[8] He distinguished between propositions which were and were not deduced or inferred from the events studied.

It is hardly necessary to mention the inevitable manipulations required in making and reporting records. But the implication such manipulations have for a naturalistic description of scientific work is not always acknowledged. How draw and photograph things and processes unless they are available for contact? Nor is the manipulative contact to be minimized when things are

---

[8] General Scholium.

represented or merely referred to by graphs or verbal description instead of mirrored by reproductive techniques.

E. *Theory and Law Construction.* The scientific system is rounded out by the creation of formulae, equations or principles. It is legitimate to say that the goal of the entire enterprise is to attain these products.

Equations and principles are universally regarded as constituting or representing laws, theories, interpretations, explanations. Now, depending upon the protopostulates of a given system, laws and explanations are differently evaluated. In the extreme, they are taken as (a) free creations of mind or reason or (b) invariant relations independently existing in the "universe" (p. 38f.). The former view is excellently illustrated in the following:

> Physical concepts are free creations of the human mind, and are not, however it may seem, uniquely determined by the external world.[9]

Jourdain stands for the second view:

> Mathematics is independent of us personally and of the world outside, and we can feel that our own discoveries and views do not affect the Truth itself, but only the extent to which we or others see it.[10]

Interbehavioral protopostulates, contrariwise, lead to the view that scientific equations and formulae, though abstract, even abstruse, are always derived from the worker's direct or indirect contacts with events, and must therefore be verifiable in terms of the latter. Event-bound constructs (p. 59 f.) are illustrated by the physical law of freely falling bodies, the law of gravitation, and by gas laws. Scientific laws, in other words, are simply generalizations formulated from direct observation.[11] Even if a long chain of connected interpretations intervenes between original events and the final construction, the theory or law still functions as a description of events.

Description and Explanation. It has long been the tradition to differentiate sharply between descriptive and explanatory propositions and laws. The crux of this distinction is that explanation somehow transcends events, provides certain and *a priori* knowl-

---

[9] Einstein-Infeld, Evolution of Physics, p. 33.
[10] Nature of Mathematics, p. 88.
[11] Campbell, Physics: The Elements, chs. 5–6.

edge concerning their nature. Obviously, principles of metaphysical reality are at the bottom of this. Mach, Kirchoff, and Pearson, following the lead of Comte in limiting scientific laws to elaborate description, base their argument upon an epistemological doctrine of phenomenalism or positivism (p. 41).

No ultimate division between description (observation) and explanation (law) is justifiable from the standpoint of actual investigation. A scientific situation reveals only events on the one hand, activities of the scientist on the other. As we have seen, the first confrontation with events, when referred to or recorded, involves constructions. Isolating an event in a laboratory setup constitutes constructional behavior. All descriptions and propositions are constructions. Any differentiation, then, between description and explanation can only be made on the basis of convenience. As a rule, explanations constitute elaborate descriptions, typically those relating some event to one or many others.

Empirical and Rational Laws. Empirical laws have been regarded as descriptions derived from observation; rational laws as partaking of *a priori* or deductive principles. When taken in an absolute sense the distinction is worthless. Science harbors no *a priori* principles. Relatively speaking, however, some laws are more remote than others from immediate observation or measurement. Through an interval of time, law products become established and later serve as criteria and rules of system making. Laws of conservation of energy and mass, for instance, must be taken in this sense of established hypotheses. Generally, empirical laws, in contrast to rational ones, imply readily available contacts with things; it is therefore easier to verify hypotheses. In place of the above distinction we specify three types of general laws: (a) observational, (b) experimental, and (c) rational.

(a) *Observational Laws.* Kepler's laws of planetary motion are excellent examples of this type. The following three propositions he set up are definitely founded on such observations as can be made on nonmanipulable things:

> (1) Every planet moves in an ellipse of which the sun occupies one focus.
> (2) The radius vector drawn from the sun to the planet sweeps out equal areas in equal times.
> (3) The squares of two periodic times of two planets are to one another as the cubes of their mean distances from the sun.

(b) *Experimental Laws.* Experimental laws are propositions based on the direct manipulation of things. Such are Galileo's laws of freely falling bodies: $s = .5gt^2$; Hooke's law: $P = EA(l' - l)/l$; Boyle's law: $PV = C$; and Snell's law: Sin α/Sin $\beta = \mu = v_1/v_2$.

(c) *Rational Laws.* Newton's three laws of motion exemplify the rational type and constitute excellent instruments for scientific orientation, but are not close to manipulative situations. They neglect such a fundamental factor as friction, and in general bespeak more contact with mathematical relations than with experimental observation. It is the rational laws, such as Newton's axioms or laws of motion, which invoke the question how mathematical formulae can be applied to actual events.

(1) Every body continues in its state of rest, or of uniform motion in a right line, unless it is compelled to change that state by forces impressed upon it.

(2) The change of motion is proportional to the motive force impressed; and is made in the right line in which that force is impressed.

(3) To every action there is always opposed an equal reaction: or the mutual actions of two bodies upon each other are always equal and directed to contrary parts.

The relation of the three types of laws is excellently illustrated by Maxwell's famous electromagnetic equations:

$$\oint E_s \, ds = - \iint \mu \, \partial H_n/\partial t \, dA$$

$$\oint H_s \, ds = \iint (J_n + \varepsilon \, \partial E_n/\partial t) \, dA$$

where E_s = electric field along any closed path; H_s = magnetic flux along any closed path; ds = element of length; μ = permeability of vacuum; $\delta E_n/\delta t$ = rate of change in the strength of an electric field; $\delta H_n/\delta t$ = rate of change in strength of magnetic fields; J_n = density of convection current perpendicular to a surface bounded by the path; ϵ = dielectric constant of vacuum; dA = element of area.[12] Based on Faraday's concrete manipulations Maxwell's equations first appeared in the form of rational analogies, but through Hertz's experimentation became descriptions of observable happenings.

---

[12] In presenting these equations and defining their terms I have followed Pierce, Microwaves (with the courtesy of the *Scientific American*).

We have taken our examples from physics, but there are comparable laws in each of the sciences. In some, of course, the observational or experimental type is the most prominent. Actually the three types are not altogether different, nor concerned with mutually exclusive events.

Nor have we differentiated between theories and laws, though this is frequently done. For example, Campbell[13] regards theories as derivations from laws and as concerned with hypothetical entities and relations more or less imposed upon events. Other writers reverse this order and look upon laws as well established, verified hypotheses or theories.

The Role of Systems in Research

Scientific systematics is not only continuous with specific researches but plays an important investigative role. Briefly we consider the relations between focalized research and the science of science.

Like the original investigator the logician, too, is concerned with the properties of already known things and with the discovery of new events. In addition he is interested in the original scientist's interbehavior with these events, and thus plays a double role in the scientific situation. Naturally the logician is more interested in the theoretical and systematic outcome of research. For him, primary descriptions, experimental findings, and results of measurement are raw materials. The researcher by comparison is generally in more intimate contact with original events. He also keeps close to techniques and methods of dealing with things, whereas the logician focuses upon the results of employing those techniques for the purposes of general orientation and interpretation.

The logician of science obviously stands at some distance from the investigator's first trial-and-error efforts, though he is not always excluded from the satisfaction of locating new fields of work. On the whole, too, the logic of science is more formal. Even more than the original researcher the logician smooths and coordinates crude findings, organizes the materials according to accepted rules. Of course, original materials, to begin with, are

---

[13] Physics: The Elements.

channelized and standardized, but the logician introduces *still* more system.

The science of science is comparative and historical. The critic ranges over time and thus traces variations and similarities in the premises employed for setting problems at different periods and places, as well as in the techniques for implementing such premises. He is also able to cut across specific enterprises in order to compare research methods.

The primary function of systemization in research is to sensitize the worker to the implications and consequences of investigation. Compare the work of such superlative geometers as Newton and Huygens, who were severely bounded by Euclidean postulation, with the achievements of Gauss, Riemann, Klein, and Hilbert who, aided by time and circumstance, could look upon geometry as a vast operational field, in which geometric systems could be compared and new ones established simply by controlling the postulational process.

A similar comparison can be made between those physicists who refine their measurements within the limits of Newtonian mechanics and those who work with subnuclear and quantum radiation. The latter not only gather data, fit curves, but plunge as well into problems of basic relations and the final significance of their investigational results.

The practical advantage of systemological orientation over research lies in avoiding routine method and procedure. Too often scientific enterprises are fixed in a groove of specified findings. The goal being set, the worker may make hundreds of measurements, analyze hundreds of substances, all goal directed. The greater the worker's training and skill, the easier the end is achieved. Quite otherwise when investigation requires freedom of wide perspective. Was it not the advantage of broader knowledge and training than was the lot of the ordinary scientist that gave Pasteur, Metchnikoff, and Galvani their investigative impetus?[14]

Undoubtedly the science of science is the most serviceable at the creative point of setting up postulates, establishing viewpoints, formulating premises, constructing new frames of reference. Einstein, it is said, has been able to make his momentous

---

[14] Beveridge, The Art of Scientific Investigation, p. 2.

contributions because he spurned axioms; in other words, he was willing to discard established systems and replace them by newer ones.

The logic of science has its dangers as well as its merits. There is considerable hazard in systemological procedures because of extrapolating from specific findings. However, this merely reinforces the view that sophisticated scientific work is an adventurous enterprise.

Logic of Science and Historical Philosophy

Scientists agree that the work of constructing concepts, laws, principles, and hypotheses are activities of the scientist. They do not agree, however, concerning the nature of these constructional processes, chiefly because of their entanglement with historical philosophy and its fallacious ideas of mind. This is true whether they adopt what they call a realistic, idealistic or materialistic standpoint.

Our conviction that individuals formulate theories or laws on the basis of past and present contacts with things does away with the futile speculation of how knowledge can be correlated with an external world. And constructs based upon historical ideas of mind are no longer regarded as an acceptable underlying philosophy, as Jordan assumes:

> The new physics is not conceivable without the influence of the positivist perception theory; conversely, positivism was first stabilized and rendered precise with the replacement of thinking in objective processes by the new thought form of complementarity.[15]

Just how, in our interbehavioral system, perceiving and knowing lose their immaterial and transpatial quality, and knowledge its precarious nature, we consider fully in the chapter on Psychology, but some preliminary orientation is necessary at this point.

We make a direct approach to perceptual events, which consist of contacts with objects during which the organism builds up response functions corresponding to the objects' stimulus functions. Depending upon numerous factors, such as setting and stimulational media, interbehavioral (psychological) *fields* are developed, fields which may be described as differentiating inter-

---

[15] Physics of the 20th Century, p. 159.

behavior. In other words, the organism performs a number of different responses to the same object, and each response is specialized on the basis of the setting in which the contact occurs. For any one individual every object or event usually has a very large number of stimulus functions. The individual in turn develops many corresponding response functions. Notice that modern science cannot tolerate the view that physiological impulses are transformed into psychic experience. With this brief preparation of the ground let us consider the relation of science to various traditional philosophies.

Science and Realism. Though realistic scientists may admit that they really construct principles and laws, they still regard the constructional work as merely formulational and, as we have seen, believe the formulae represent independent existents discovered by scientists.

Realistic philosophy has two aspects: the ontological and epistemological. The ontological constitutes a belief in the autonomous existence of a world entirely independent of the scientist; in this world are placed entities and forces looked upon as Platonic reals. So when the scientist sets up mathematical equations they are not simply conventional symbols or linguistic forms, but signs for invariable relations in nature.

On the epistemological side, realistic scientists refuse to admit that mental states or sense data constitute the objects studied; they are but evidences of things-in-themselves. These things-in-themselves are not unknown entities which only stir up knowledge in the mind: they are more or less completely known. Atoms and their parts, genes, the various forces and processes the scientist works with are existences partially or completely discovered, not simply mental projections.

Realistic philosophy is based upon the rationalistic view of mind. To discover the independently existing principles and relations a powerful cognitive agent is required. To illustrate the operations of "reason" emphasis is placed upon such processes as selection, abstraction, and integration.

For some scientists the inclination toward realism is coupled with definite theological attitudes. Such is obviously the case with Planck.[16] But even those writers who do not directly align them-

---

[16] *Scientific Autobiography and Other Papers.*

selves with a religious way of thinking do so indirectly by espousing some form of traditional philosophy which draws from theological sources.

Science and Idealism. Idealistic scientists are the extreme creationists. Knowledge for them frankly consists of ideas or concepts—in short, states of mind, whether or not corresponding to external things. Historically, the idealists trade upon the commonsense fact that knowledge is different from things known; thus they emphasize the relativity, the incompleteness, the possible uncertainty of scientific principles

Inevitably these scientific idealists lapse into solipsistic doctrines. Beginning with an emphasis on experience they soon stress the individuality of experience and, because they are psychists or spiritualists, they land squarely in the predicament of mental privacy. Eddington's position is pertinent here:

> The (logical) starting point of physical science is knowledge of the group-structure of a set of *sensations* in a consciousness.[17]

Some idealists, attempting to extricate themselves from this difficulty by operationism, stress the fact that by various manipulative techniques the utter privacy of both the contents and the acts of observing can be made public.

Whether an idealist accepts or rejects *a priori* principles depends upon his detailed notions of the mind's structure. He may adopt the view that the mind is a stable and enduring entity capable of sustaining powers or antedating specific knowledge and giving it its character. Such is the view of the Kantians, Hegelians, and other rational idealists. On the other hand, experience may be thought of as atomic and ephemeral mental states, as Humeans hold. For them all laws and principles are presumed to be derived from diaphanous experiences, by creative powers based on nothing more than *ad hoc* assertions.

Modern objective psychology completely undermines these idealistic constructions. When concepts and ideas are taken to be specific responses to things and events, or the products of such responses, a "knowing" which creates the things known has no place in scientific theory.

Science and Positivism. The positivists' primary thesis is that

---

[17] Philosophy of Physical Science, p. 148.

principles and laws are direct correlates of things studied. The basis for their thesis, of course, is that the things dealt with in science are themselves constructed from elementary processes called sensations (psychic elements). Mach represents this view. He assumes that both physical and mental things are constructed from neutral entities. These neutral entities are "colors, sounds, temperatures, pressures, spaces, times, feelings, volitions," etc. The avowed intention of the positivist is to begin with common-sense events, then to show how the principles of science are constructed from them; in other words, how an external world is created by organizing internal sensations or sense data.

In this creational hypothesis the process of developing descriptions of things (names, concepts, laws) is transformed into the creation of things. Abandon Berkeleyan spiritualism, the primary factor in this type of misconstruction, straightway the dilemma vanishes.

Logical empiricists who have become dissatisfied with the role of psychic states in the scientific domain have adopted two notable means of deleting them. One is verbal exorcism, the simple declaration that the universe is monistic and material. The other is to resort to a dialectic procedure as follows: first, science is reduced to statements or propositions; next linguistic entities are claimed to be free from blemish—incorruptible. Finally it is declared that since every statement about psychic entities can be equated with statements about material ones, the psychic and the material (nonpsychic) are equivalent.[18] These are dubious ways of making spiritualistic psychology acceptable.

Science and Conceptualism. The conceptualist is to be commended for not emphasizing absolute truth or autonomous essences. Following the constructional procedures of mathematics he stresses concepts or terms. Thus scientific laws and descriptions become conventional symbols for representing things. In this manner he hopes to mediate between spiritistic ephemeralities and substantial realistic essences, but unfortunately, the conceptualist's formulation remains superficial since he clings to spiritistic metaphysics.

Although he avoids both the extremes of absolute truth and

---

[18] See, for example, Feigl, The mind-body problem, and other items in his appended bibliography.

Platonic essences, he still misrepresents the scientific enterprise, even its mathematical aspects. He overlooks the fact that the scientist works with definite materials. Who can deny that when relations constitute scientific data, there is greater constructional freedom than in the case of things? But relations are facts, too, even when they are freely selected and deliberately set up. Hence the constructive procedure cannot be independent of the items interbehaved with. The scientist is not a spiritistic entity arbitrarily creating statements or laws out of his own substance. He is an individual reared in a certain culture, acting on the basis of his background and contacts. This cultural background we consider in the following chapter.

II

THE CULTURAL ASPECTS OF SCIENCE

CHAPTER

3

SCIENTIFIC ENTERPRISES AS CULTURAL INSTITUTIONS

The Cultural Matrices of the Sciences

WE HAVE already seen that the sciences are set in particular cultural matrices which influence their origin, problems, techniques, and the use made of their results. Science is thus a phase of culture, along with such enterprises as making and using tools and weapons; producing, preparing, distributing food; manufacturing clothing, pottery, sledges; fashioning and furnishing dwellings; evolving rites and ceremonials.

Culture consists of the civilization of a group of persons united on the basis of societal, political, historical or geographical criteria. It may be separated into two aspects: behavior and behavior products.

Cultural *behavior* constitutes every variety of interaction with things, persons, and events. Though these interactions are all rooted in the biological process of self, family, and group maintenance they take on certain characteristics depending upon environmental circumstances, the degree of group development, and relations with other groups.

Cultural *products* consist of institutions—namely, civilizational furnishings. These comprise (a) behavior patterns (rites, techniques, customs, manners, ceremonials) and (b) objects (tools, records, fetishes, symbols, social organizations of persons functioning in the domains of art, law, language, religion, politics, and domestic life).

Institutional objects arise, of course, as products of the coordinated behavior of human individuals. Churches, libraries, industrial techniques, customs, manners, forms of intercommunication all evolve through the cumulative actions of persons acting alone or in concert. Because the origin and preservation of cultural things involves human behavior mentalistic writers have

45

fostered the erroneous view that institutions consist of "phases of the public mind."[1]

Science as a Cultural Institution

Scientific behavior and its products are continuous with the behavior and products of other cultural divisions. Scientific origins are rooted in the everyday life of individuals, regardless of how far back we go to the primitive stages of anthropic evolution.[2] Moreover, no matter how highly evolved scientific enterprises become they carry with them their basic cultural characteristics. The most abstruse and technical disciplines bear the impress of technology, philosophical and religious speculation, social organization, and folklore. Science, therefore, as a specialized cultural institution has been established along with art, industry, religion, law, and economic organization. This coordination of science and other cultural institutions is excellently described by James and the letter he quotes:

> The aspiration to be "scientific" is such an idol of the tribe to the present generation, is so sucked in with his mother's milk by every one of us, that we find it hard to conceive of a creature who should not feel it, and harder still to treat it freely as the altogether peculiar and one-sided subjective interest which it is. But as a matter of fact, few even of the cultivated members of the race have shared it; it was invented but a generation or two ago. In the middle ages it meant only impious magic; and the way in which it even now strikes orientals is charmingly shown in the letter of a Turkish cadi to an English traveller asking him for statistical information, which Sir A. Layard prints at the end of his "Nineveh and Babylon." The document is too full of edification not to be given in full. It runs thus:
>
> "My Illustrious Friend, and Joy of my Liver!
>
> "The thing you ask of me is both difficult and useless. Although I have passed all my days in this place, I have neither counted the houses nor inquired into the number of the inhabitants; and as to what one person loads on his mules and the other stows away in the bottom of his ship, that is no business of mine. But, above all, as to the previous history of this city, God only knows the amount of dirt and confusion that the infidels may have eaten before the coming of the sword of Islam. It were unprofitable for us to inquire into it.
>
> "O my soul! O my lamb! seek not after the things which con-

---

[1] Cooley, Social Organization, p. 313.

[2] Tylor, Anthropology, p. 309.

cern thee not. Thou camest unto us and we welcomed thee: go in peace.

"Of a truth thou hast spoken many words; and there is no harm done. For the speaker is one and the listener is another. After the fashion of thy people thou hast wandered from one place to another, until thou art happy and content in none. We (praise be to God) were born here, and never desire to quit it. Is it possible, then, that the idea of a general intercourse between mankind should make any impression on our understandings? God forbid!

"Listen, O my son! There is no wisdom equal unto the belief in God! He created the world, and shall we liken ourselves unto Him in seeking to penetrate into the mysteries of His creation? Shall we say, Behold this star spinneth round that star, and this other star with a tail goeth and cometh in so many years! Let it go! He from whose hand it came will guide and direct it.

"But thou wilt say unto me, Stand aside, O man, for I am more learned than thou art, and have seen more things. If thou thinkest that thou art in this respect better than I am, thou art welcome. I praise God that I seek not that which I require not. Thou art learned in the things I care not for; and as for that which thou hast seen, I spit upon it. Will much knowledge create thee a double belly, or wilt thou seek Paradise with thine eyes?

"O my friend! if thou wilt be happy, say, There is no God but God! Do no evil, and thus wilt thou fear neither man nor death; for surely thine hour will come!

The meek in spirit (El Fakir)
Imaum Ali Zadi."[3]

The inevitable specialization constantly developing in well populated societies is immediately reflected in the proliferation of scientific institutions. The range is wide, including such diverse items as personalities, techniques, apparatus, doctrines, and laws. Of especial interest are general scientific institutions, those expansive cosmological and philosophical systems (realism, idealism, positivism) we have already discussed (chap. 2) and which purport to specify the nature and purpose of science. Specialized institutions concern the nature of theories, hypotheses, instruments, and procedures—in short, the factors of investigation.

The most pointed scientific institutions consist of technique systems intimately integrated with the scientist's particular researches. Examples are the different conventions of making chemical analyses, the variations in research designs developed by communal or national scientific schools. The elaboration of scientific

---

[3] James, Principles of Psychology, Vol. 2, pp. 640–641.

techniques is a concomitant not only of societal complexity but also, and more particularly, of coordinated industrial efforts. Naturally, we can observe the development and operation of scientific institutions most advantageously at those complex stages where accumulations of problems, techniques, and results have become so great as to provide palpable materials and evidential documents.[4]

To study the sciences as cultural institutions promotes a factual description of them in contrast to treating them as (a) formal and deductive or (b) ultra inductive entities, which reduces science to rationalistic and verbal description. There are many who criticize the impersonal and autonomous description and wish to avoid identifying descriptive abstractions with concrete investigations. In their turn, however, they offer an equally restrictive formula. For example, they assert that "Science is a system of behavior by which man acquires mastery of his environment."[5] This description reflects a socialistic attitude toward human society; the abstractive description an aristocratic view.

Both of these attitudes hark back to traditional ideas concerning the motivation of scientists. If Aristotle and other Greeks were wrong in making science the abstractive product of wonder and leisure, they pointed nevertheless to actual components of scientific situations. Their theory was wrong mostly because it hypostatized one feature and excluded or minimized others. The proponents of the human-need theory similarly hypostatize the factors of work, economic conditions, application, and service. Since many factors contribute to the making of science, both attitudes may be incorporated in a proper description.

The Science-Culture Spiral

Once we grant that scientific enterprises arise out of societal and political conditions, we must note that this is not a one-way process. Scientific institutions once evolved become cultural items potent enough to influence other cultural phases. Science, it is

---

[4] Relevant here is Eddington's remark that physical knowledge might be identified with certain encyclopaedic works such as the *Handbuch der Physik* (The Philosophy of Physical Science, p. 2). More pertinent is Hertz's assertion that Maxwell's electromagnetic theory is simply his equations (Electric Waves, p. 21).

[5] Crowther, Social Relations of Science.

declared, modifies all other aspects of human living. Now obviously the intricate circumstances of human events do not transpire on a single level. The constant changes taking place can be likened to an upward-moving spiral, in that the reciprocal influences of science and social events produce their effects at progressively different stages.

Culture Affects Science. Before any organized science can evolve human individuals and groups must reach a stage of life favorable to scientific growth. For this reason elaborate scientific enterprises are comparatively late developments in social evolution. As far as individuals are concerned, scientific work is favored by their satisfactory adjustment within their societal habitats. For ethnic and national groups this is only partially true. Wars and conquests create on the one hand paralyzing and destructive group relations, but on the other contribute greatly to the expansion of scientific enterprise.

The mere fact that science has originated and flourished in certain societies and not in others is evidence enough of cultural influence. For example, historians look to Egypt for outstanding developments in geometry and medicine, including surgery; to Mesopotamia for astronomy and mathematics.[6]

Historians vie with each other in celebrating the marvellous flowering of science in Greece. It is still a strongly established institution to localize the origin of the sciences in various specific Hellenic centers, especially Ionian Greece, though it is becoming more and more evident how much the Greeks were indebted to their neighbors near and far.[7] Those historians who grant Greece the palm do not agree upon the circumstances that made science flourish there nor upon the criterion that establishes the original claim. Some regard the "miracle" of Greek science as the result of the rigid deductional principles the Greeks developed. Reymond says:

> Here the human mind for the first time conceived of the possibility of establishing a limited number of principles, and of deducing from these a number of truths which are their rigorous consequence.[8]

---

[6] The question of preservation and transmission which may be involved here adds unique and important items to the cultural picture.

[7] Cf., Neugebauer, The Exact Sciences in Antiquity.

[8] Reymond, Science in Greco-Roman Antiquity, quoted from Farrington, Greek Science, p. 13.

Notice the culturally influenced presupposition. The writer evidently values what has become valuable in his *own* culture; he overlooks the particular social facts, such as borrowing and the local human circumstances which have made deductive forms of thinking feasible both in the milieu of the admirer and that of the admired. All scientific "miracles" resolve themselves, upon closer analysis, into a profusion of cultural details.

Science Affects Culture. Granting that institutionalized science evolved somewhat later than social organization or even technology, we must also admit that as soon as science reached even modest growth it impinged upon social conditions. So intense is the impact that it stimulates the exaggerated belief that science is an independent entity which brings about changes in industry, economic conditions, health, and longevity. A favorite theme is that science is or is not responsible for unemployment, for the development of destructive instruments and techniques (armaments, bombs, biological warfare, etc.). The peak of such assumptions is the advocacy of a vacation for science, a period when the worker abandons his laboratory, stops making atomic bombs, in other words.

The science-culture spiral operates in both a linear and areal fashion. In the former it advances or retrogresses along a space-time line; in the latter there is contraction and expansion according to various spatiotemporal dimensions.

Effects of Scientific Institutionalization

Solidification of so highly fluid an event as scientific interbehavior upsets the proper balance between the worker and his materials. For example, institutionalization may affect (A) the relative weight of fact and tradition in investigation and theory and (B) the proportion of derived and imposed constructs in scientific interpretation.

(A) If the worker and his cultural background predominate, events inevitably are made to conform to various ideological (mathematical, statistical models) or procedural traditions (experimentalism, utilitarianism, or just plain expediency, in the sense of dealing only with easily handled materials). Emphasis on events, on the other hand, ordinarily obviates such influences. Recall those striking situations in which scientists have been forced to behave in a unique and unorthodox way in the presence of certain objects: Perkin confronting the murky mass in his test tube when he attempted to synthesize quinine; Ramsay and Rayleigh perturbed in the face of the recalcitrance of their nitrogen which turned out to be argon.

Again, in the interpretation of his work the scientist may be swayed so much by traditional formulations that he neglects his actual findings. Equally competent scientists take such opposing views as (1) that laws are arbitrary constructions imposed upon events or (2) that laws constitute Platonic entities independent of the scientist.

(B) The theory of least action as developed by Maupertuis is an excellent example of *imposed* constructions. As Whewell says:

> Maupertuis conceived that he could establish *a priori* by theological arguments that all mechanical changes must take place in the world so as to occasion the least possible quantity of action.[9]

Obviously such impositions are purely verbal and coincidental; consequently more of the nature of private speculation than the result of investigation. The construct of least action can be used because it really refers to an operation upon things—namely, the measurement of action as the product of energy and time. For this reason alone it was possible for Kelvin to assert that the theorem of least action:

> ... was magnificently developed by Lagrange and Hamilton, and by them demonstrated to be not only true throughout the whole material world, but also a sufficient foundation for the whole of dynamical science.[10]

Explanation in science is based upon coincidence and analogy. Recent cosmologists, such as Eddington and Milne, not only set up theories underived from contact with events, but argue strongly for axiomatic and deductive procedures.[11] Cognate rationalistic theories formulated to support indeterminacy, free will, and the

---

[9] History of the Inductive Sciences, Vol. 2, p. 94.

[10] Popular Lectures and Addresses, Vol. 2, p. 588.

[11] Cf., Milne, Relativity, Gravitation, and World Structure; also Kinetic Relativity; Munitz (Scientific Method in Cosmology) attacks such cosmological theories.

mathematical contrivance of a geometrizing god are sheer traves-
ies on the scientist and the things with which he works.[12]

Derived constructs stem from operations upon events and
from prior constructs based directly or remotely upon interbehavioral situations. Scientific laws, for example, refer to unit
events and are therefore founded upon data constructs (descriptions). When propositions interrelate various unit events we have
essentially theoretical or abstract constructs—explanatory laws.

Scientific Canons as Cultural Institutions

Institutionalization of the scientific enterprise does not stop
with reification and standardization of assumptions, procedures,
and interpretations: it extends to canons and rules. When scientific canons, which originally arise from specific procedures of
analyzing, synthesizing, comparing, and evaluating things and
events, become fixated they thereafter exert both beneficial and
harmful influences.

Outstanding beneficial canons are the standards of precision
which regulate hypotheses and procedures and govern the measurements made in solving specific problems. Although efforts to
increase precision in measuring the velocity of light have almost
reached the proportions of autonomous ends, the balance between
the new precision tradition and the worker's interest in the event
is maintained. But this is not the case when canons and their
application are separated from apparatus and instruments—in
other words, from concrete working conditions.

For this reason such general cultural developments as the
evolution of technology offset any bad effects from the standardization of scientific procedures. Not only have scientists derived
great powers from the evolution of an adequate vacuum pump
and radio tube, but these technological products prevent the stultification of scientific research. And so instruments designed to
study electrical discharges through rarified gases help to attain
x-rays and electrons.

Disserviceable canons are illustrated by (1) the impact upon
ancient mathematicians of the Greek horror of the infinite and
(2) the influence of Greek finitude upon the canons of fixity in the

---

[12] See Born's sharp attack (Experiment and Theory in Physics) on Eddington and Milne.

treatment of biological species. In more recent times improperly conceived causal canons have blocked scientific advances. But the irrepressible force of events is inducing such shiftings in institutions as to allow the development of a new canon of causation; 20th century science is now able to eliminate internal forces in favor of *event fields*. Instead of pondering over creative causes, the scientist constructs patterns—systems dealing with things and events in interrelationship.

The Dualistic Institution and Its Issues

The dichotomy principle (pp. 9, 62) is without doubt the most influential and harmful of all scientific institutions: influential because of its pervasion of every cultural department; harmful because it has engendered offshoot institutions which hamper many phases of science. Since Kepler, Galileo, and Newton, among other natural philosophers, introduced into science the theological belief in spiritual and material substance, physicists without exception have assumed that they study an external reality sharply differentiated from what exists in the mind. Throughout the many variations of this general dualistic principle scientists have agreed that colors, sounds, tastes, warmth, cold, etc., are merely phantasms which are not as real as particles in motion.

Mach, Einstein, and Poincaré, looking upon science as a process of ordering sense data by means of conceptual construction, remain squarely in the bifurcation tradition. Behind their views stand the Kantian analytics and synthetics. Other scientists, Eddington, for instance, hark back to an earlier form such as Berkeley represented.

From the large dualistic principle arise the following specialized dualistic institutions. These produce even more potent effects since they impinge more directly upon the scientific worker's interpretations.

Subject and Object. The simple fact that science is the work of persons who construct descriptions and formulae about the things and events with which they interbehave has been transformed into the mystery: How can a knowing mind interact with things known? On one side it is asserted that the knower and the known are absolutely different and incompatible entities. Hence science is packed with such verbal formulae as the unknowable source of the known (things-in-themselves), absolute probability, eternal ignorance (ignorabimus, postulates of impotence). On the other, subject and object are regarded as verbal correlates from a single homogeneous (psychic) source. Notice how a description concerning the knowing interactor is created which bypasses the factors of the event presumably described. The description's ingredients are wholly derived from traditional sources. The original event serves merely as a cue for the creational effort.

Inner and Outer Worlds. A specialized form of world-dichotomization is the institution that sets inner psychic processes over against the external world of reality. The knower is reduced to states of consciousness or endowed with a mind consisting of such states. Problems are then raised whether the inner states mirror independent outer conditions or whether the outer world comprises projections of the inner state. Consider the following remarks of Einstein:

> The belief in an external world independent of the percipient subject is the foundation of all science. But since our sense-perceptions inform us only indirectly of this external world, or Physical Reality, it is only by speculation that it can become comprehensible to us. From this it follows that our conceptions of Physical Reality can never be definitive; we must always be ready to alter them, to alter, that is, the axiomatic basis of physics, in order to take account of the facts of perception with the greatest possible logical completeness.[13]

Einstein accepts without question traditional psychological assumptions concerning mental states. To erect an axiom system for physics on this basis is to turn away from original events, to indulge in what Whewell once charged the Greeks with doing—namely, examining words and the thoughts which they call up, instead of attending to facts and things.[14]

Appearance and Reality. The mind-matter and inner-outer dichotomies lead to the appearance-reality institution designed to differentiate between phenomena and the ultimate reality existing beyond them and giving them their basis and validity. Phenomena are presumed to be what is in the mind or what the mind mediates.

---

[13] Maxwell's Influence on the Development of the Conception of Physical Reality. In *James Clerk Maxwell:* A Commemoration Volume, 1831–1891, p. 66.

[14] History of the Inductive Sciences, Vol. I, p. 27.

What is behind the mental processes may or may not be known. A specialized form of the appearance-reality dichotomy separates ultimate principles from proximate events, laws from facts. Laws are often regarded as Platonic forms hovering over concrete and contingential happenings.

The appearance-reality institution is also responsible for the spurious differentiation between sciences regarded as basic and those superimposed upon them. The invention of a scientific hierarchy simply reflects a preference unrelated to events. The notion of degrees of reality and the idea of essential ways of attaining them are extrascientific dogmas.

Existence and Value. Scientists justifiably object to intermixing personal judgments and evaluations with the observation and measurement of things. This is equivalent to the proper refusal to confuse things with descriptions of them. Paradoxically, however, this laudable injunction conserves traditional presuppositions. Personal judgments are not merely regarded as selective, perhaps arbitrary, attitudes. No: they are looked upon as psychic factors, therefore unreal. Realities by contrast are presumed to be ultimates beyond the reach of a person's actions. Overlooked entirely is the fact that evaluations are genuine events made on the basis of interbehaving with things (p. 324 f.). Values, of course, may be personal, but they may also be authentic evaluations of essential properties of things and of the way events operate.

The Practical Role of Scientific Institutions

Established institutions take on various roles through their sponsorship by particular individuals, schools, parties, and other groups. When techniques become standards and practices become mores they form authoritative institutions which block the discovery of the nature and operation of things. Classical examples are the long-lasting reigns of Aristotle, Galen, and Euclid.

Historians of the physical sciences repeatedly point out how Newton's corpuscular theory retarded the development of the physics of light. Each instance of scientific authoritarianism demonstrates the opposition between events and favored constructions. Though Newton came close to a wave interpretation of the color in his Rings the particle theory was too well established to be touched. Moreover, Young's notion that Huygen's undulatory theory provided a better interpretation of Newton's Rings could make no headway against the institutional power of the particle theory. Neither could the facts of Young's light interference have any immediate effect upon it.

Later the thoroughly established wave institution in turn offered stout resistance to a particle or discrete-unit theory in the subdomain of light. This fact comports with the recent incident in physics when Planck struggled to make his constant h—the elementary quantum of action—fit in with the established institutions of classical physics. Many physicists regarded the obduracy of the constant, with its threat to the continuity institution, as a tragedy of science.[15] One is reminded here of the notorious power of the caloric heat doctrine and of the phlogistic doctrine of combustion.

Every subdomain of science offers a similar story. Biologists must be perennially vigilant to ward off the insalutary results of institutionalized vitalistic theories. In one guise or another teleological and other extrafactual constructs interfere with research or interpretation. And we have already observed how institutionalized theories concerning psychic powers and the nervous system as the seat of mental states have dominated and retarded not only psychology but other sciences as well.

Institutions also compete and clash. In geological history Neptunists have been pitted against Plutonists; Catastrophists against Evolutionists. The historian of biology tells us of the conflict between Preformationists and Epigeneticists, while Special Creationists seem only yesterday to have battled against Evolutionists. In the subdomain of psychology Mentalists and Behaviorists attack each other.

Since institutions can only conflict through the agency of the individuals who invent and foster them the entire drama is played out in the enmities and suppressions of school leaders and their disciples when dealing with opponents. The various acts of this drama come to life in a glance at the following list of refusals to publish what later came to be acceptable, even authoritative, institutions.

---

[15] Planck, Scientific Autobiography and Other Papers.

Royal Society Transactions refused to publish Franklin's electrical experiments.[16] Poggendorf's *Annalen* rejected both Mayer's paper on energy conservation in 1843 and Helmholtz's in 1847.[17] The editor of the Royal Society's *Philosophical Transactions* not only refused to publish Marshall Hall's 1837 paper on reflex action, but the Society made that journal inaccessible to him as an avenue of publication.[18] The *Journal of Hellenic Studies* rejected the paper of Ridgeway.[19]

Murray has collected many such incidents; though he aims to show the fallibility of science in the interest of religion he throws light on the problem of scientific institutions.[20]

A striking clash of institutions has developed in connection with quantum mechanics. On one side those who believe that science is rational and constructional insist that statistical formulations constitute the total laws of the field. On the other hand are the realists who cannot accept the principle that chance and risk, rather than solid reality, is the basis of physics. Proponents of the first view, Bohr, Born, and others, look upon the intransigency of their opponents—for example, Einstein and Planck—as clinging to an outworn classic stage of science.

When the scientist is an aggressive young biologist like Huxley, intent on making his scientific career in a comparatively local situation as in the England of his time, all the essentials of scientific competition and conflict are vividly illustrated, as in the following letter:

> I told you I was very busy, and I must tell you what I am about and you will believe me. I have just finished a Memoir for the Royal Society, which has taken me a world of time, thought, and reading, and is, perhaps, the best thing I have done yet. It will not be read till May, and I do not know whether they will print it or not afterwards; that will require care and a little manoeuvering on my part. You have no notion of the intrigues that go on in this blessed world of science. Science is, I fear, no purer than any other region of human activity; though it should be. Merit alone is very little good; it must be backed by tact and knowledge of the world to do very much.

[16] Pupin, Law, description and hypothesis in the electrical science.
[17] Cajori, History of Physics, p. 222.
[18] Fulton, Selected Readings in the History of Physiology, p. 271.
[19] See Macurdy's review of Ridgeway, The Early Age of Greece.
[20] Murray, Science and Scientists of the 19th Century.

For instance, I know that the paper I have just sent in is very original and of some importance, and I am equally sure that if it is referred to the judgment of my "particular friend"——————that it will not be published. He won't be able to say a word against it, but he will pooh-pooh it to a dead certainty.

You will ask me with some wonderment, Why? Because for the last twenty years —————— has been regarded as the great authority on these matters, and has had no one to tread on his heels, until at last, I think, he has come to look upon the Natural World as his special preserve, and no "poachers allowed." So I must manoeuvre a little to get my poor memoir kept out of his hands.[21]

---

[21] Quoted from Huxley, L. Life and Letters of Thomas H. Huxley, Vol 1, p. 109f.

CHAPTER

4

SCIENTIFIC SYSTEMS AS CULTURAL INSTITUTIONS

From Scientific Enterprise to System Institution

As soon as scientific enterprises reach the stage of theory and law construction generalizations begin to multiply. This is accounted for by the vast number and variety of things interbehaved with, and the necessary differences in scientific methods. Questions then arise concerning the effectiveness and coherence of laws; this leads at once to the institution of systems. These institutions, we saw in Chapter 3, change with shifts in the matrices of historical and cultural circumstances. Thus the scientific goal has been differently pursued by successive generations of workers.

In the early period of our scientific history the search for principles appeared primitive, but nevertheless admirably facilitated the prediction of events, the explanation of the existence and operation of things, and the formulation of significant rules of work. When we compare Western European science with its Hellenic antecedents we observe the enormous transformations brought about by the change from Pagan to Christian civilization. This shifting may be described as turning away from event-bound to autonomous (event-free) constructs. In the former, descriptions and explanations are drawn from one's interbehavior with things and events; in the latter, descriptions derived from some other than a scientific source are imposed upon events.

Historical Evolution of Scientific Systems

Current scientific institutions have grown from roots in the culture of ancient Greece. Historians easily trace back the development of science to the period when the Greeks assimilated and formulated the wisdom of their time.

A. PERIOD OF EVENT-BOUND SYSTEMS

Early Greek science provides excellent examples of building event-bound constructs. From Thales on there was a feverish scramble to discover the basic principles of things. In a primitive way the Greeks sought vigorously for some formula of reality. The significant fact, however, is that they kept close to visible materials as a basis. Thus, Thales made water the fundamental principle of *physis* or nature because of its nourishing properties, its influence on existence and growth.

Now we may look upon the various selections of everyday elements, such as the air of Anaximines, the fire of Heracleitus, the limited of Anaximander, in two ways: either as merely primitive principles of reality or—and we prefer the latter interpretation—as an objective starting point in the search for satisfactory theories. Certainly the early cosmologists were direct and practical. And so Empedocles thought it wise to combine air, water, fire, and earth; in addition he found something more fundamental in the love and hate or strife and attraction principles which brought the elements together. His science, therefore, involved a more complex set of factors than those of his predecessors.

The theories of Leucippus and Democritus constitute giant upswings in the cultural spiral. Taking the position that basic principles could hardly be sought in the visible and tangible characteristics of things, they reached the heights in their atomic hypothesis. Recall Democritus:

> By use of words there is color, sweet, bitter. But in truth there are only atoms and the void.[1]

This attempt to deepen the knowledge of principles departs in two ways from that of Anaxagoras. The latter invented his *nous* to account for changes in things simply on the assumption that their properties differ only in being crude or refined. Refined substances constituted the change principle. The atomists, on the other hand, developed a complex system of factors to explain observed facts.

In the period of the Sophists distinctive changes in Greek social life were correlated with a new type of principle of existence and reality. At that time the doctrine evolved that "man is the measure of all things." Science consisted of the imposition of law or name upon events. The place of the observer or theorist in the

---

[1] Diels, Die Fragmente, Vol. 2, p. 168.

development of principles therefore assumed unusual importance. Hence arose the institutions of epistemology and experience. The Pythagoreans now preempt the center of the stage. For them the essence of reality lies in numbers, ratios, proportions. The culmination of this view is the rationalistic attitude of Plato who denigrated trivial events in favor of "Ideas"—namely, fundamental patterns or formulae.

Greek culture of the fifth and fourth centuries had a powerful influence on the development of Aristotelian science. Although Aristotle vigorously criticized the Platonists for separating (a) form from matter and (b) calculation and construction from immediately perceived things, he himself lapsed into an extreme formalism. Aristotle the biologist may have checked the glorification of mathematics; nevertheless, he made rapid strides in establishing deductive logic and the general institutions of form, fixity, and permanence. As a mirror of the aristocratic-and-class-division aspects of Greek society Aristotelian deductionism is still closely tied to concrete events, but the emphasis is upon universality and totality as over against specificity and detail.

B. EMERGENCE OF AUTISTIC CONSTRUCTS

The historical shift from the Hellenic toward the Hellenistic period marks a definite stage of scientific evolution. Constructs, laws, and theories were no longer integrated with concrete happenings; instead of event-bound they were event-free, in other words, products of reflective and creative behavior. As such they gained distinct autonomy and set the stage for the production of speculative systems.

There is no better way to describe this development than to point out the power achieved by symbols (numerals, mathematical formulae). As soon as persons calculate and measure relations, when they need to refer to more subtle things than crass, tangible objects, symbols are in demand. The evolution of mathematics among the Greeks, especially the Pythagoreans, had already revealed the potency of symbols. To seek for the essence of things, for the basic reality in numbers, was therefore a fashion well established in early Western European culture.

One can hardly underestimate the importance of the autonomy of constructs. By means of symbols and propositions assertions are made, doctrines stabilized, principles established which encourage distant and indirect contact with things.

The general cultural source of this autistic type of construct we find in the Hellenistic intermixture of civilizations. Following the Alexandrian conquests the ancestral institutions of Western Europe became thoroughly intermixed with ways of thinking and feeling derived from India and Iran. Emphasis is placed upon abstract values. Significance is accorded to those alleged counterparts of events which elude and transcend actual contacts. By abstractional references, by the employment of substitute symbols, reality is made into something nobler than the things and events of direct interbehavior. Supreme authority is relied upon. Ways of old, what the sages have taught, and "thus sayeth the Lord" supply new sources of evidence. In general, belief in investigation is supplanted by faith in doctrine and in the word.

Historically speaking, we have been describing the birth of "spirit," the belief in realities beyond any power of penetration by the scientist who asks how things happen and of what they are made. The basis of this enormous cultural mutation lies in the history of thought from the Neoplatonists through the Church Fathers, and in the deposit which this line of thinking has precipitated in the science of the 20th century. Beginning with the Platonic schema of form and matter the Neoplatonists made formulae, which for them became symbols or assertions, into a superior reality. The source of all things was found in the creator who is and does *everything*.

Through such hypostatizing the Church Fathers and priests finally succeeded in establishing the dichotomy of the world, both as a philosophical and scientific institution. As a result, when Renaissance scientists revived the naive atomism of the Greeks, they transformed (1) crude things into sophisticated matter and (2) knowing interbehavior into spiritual substance or process. The reality accorded to matter and motion as qualities of things was counterbalanced by assuming that all their other qualities were reducible to spiritistic gossamer. The thorough establishment of event-free constructs and their continuation in modern science is excellently illustrated by the following lengthy quotation from

Galileo's *Il Saggiatore:*

> ...I want to propose some examination of that which we call
> heat, whose generally accepted notion comes very far from the truth
> if my serious doubts be correct, inasmuch as it is supposed to be a
> true accident, affection and quality really residing in the thing which
> we perceive to be heated. Nevertheless I say, that indeed I feel myself
> impelled by the necessity, as soon as I conceive a piece of matter or
> corporeal substance, of conceiving that in its own nature it is bounded
> and figured in such and such a figure, that in relation to others it is
> large or small, that it is in this or that place, in this or that time,
> that it is in motion or remains at rest, that it touches or does not
> touch another body, that it is single, few, or many; in short by no
> imagination can a body be separated from such conditions: but that
> it must be white or red, bitter or sweet, sounding or mute, of a pleasant
> or unpleasant odour, I do not perceive my mind forced to acknowledge
> it necessarily accompanied by such conditions; so if the senses were
> not the escorts, perhaps the reason or the imagination by itself would
> never have arrived at them. Hence I think that these tastes, odours,
> colours, etc., on the side of the object in which they seem to exist, are
> nothing else than mere names, but hold their residence solely in the
> sensitive body; so that if the animal were removed, every such quality
> would be abolished and annihilated. Nevertheless, as soon as we have
> imposed names on them, particular and different from those of the
> other primary and real accidents, we induce ourselves to believe that
> they also exist just as truly and really as the latter.
>
> I think that by an illustration I can explain my meaning more
> clearly. I pass a hand, first over a marble statue, then over a living
> man. Concerning all the effects which come from the hand, as regards
> the hand itself, they are the same whether on the one or on the other
> object—that is, these primary accidents, namely motion and touch
> (for we call them by no other names)—but the animate body which
> suffers that operation feels various affections according to the different
> parts touched, and if the sole of the foot, the kneecap, or the armpit
> be touched, it perceives besides the common sense of touch, another
> affection, to which we have given a particular name, calling it tickling.
> Now this affection is all ours, and does not belong to the hand at all.
> And it seems to me that they would greatly err who should say that
> the hand, besides motion and touch, possessed in itself another faculty
> different from those, namely the tickling faculty; so that tickling
> would be an accident that exists in it. A piece of paper, or a feather,
> lightly rubbed on whatever part of our body you wish, performs, as re-
> gards itself, everywhere the same operation, that is, movement and
> touch; but in us, if touched between the eyes, on the nose, and under
> the nostrils, it excites an almost intolerable tickling, though elsewhere

it can hardly be felt at all. Now this tickling is all in us, and not in the feather, and if the animate and sensitive body be removed, it is nothing more than a mere name. Of precisely a similar and not greater existence do I believe these various qualities to be possessed, which are attributed to natural bodies, such as tastes, odours, colours, and others.

But that external bodies, to excite in us these tastes, these odours, and these sounds, demand other than size, figure, number, and slow or rapid motion, I do not believe; and I judge that, if the ears, the tongue, and the nostrils were taken away, the figure, the numbers, and the motions would indeed remain, but not the odours nor the tastes nor the sounds, which, without the living animal, I do not believe are anything else than names, just as tickling is precisely nothing but a name if the armpit and the nasal membrane be removed; ... and turning to my first proposition in this place, having now seen that many affections which are reputed to be qualities residing in the external object, have truly no other existence than in us, and without us are nothing else than names; I say that I am inclined sufficiently to believe that heat is of this kind, and that the thing that produces heat in us and makes us perceive it, which we call by the general name fire, is a multitude of minute corpuscles thus and thus figured, moved with such and such a velocity; ... But that besides their figure, number, motion, penetration, and touch, there is in fire another quality, that is heat—that I do not believe otherwise than I have indicated, and I judge that it is so much due to us that, if the animate and sensitive body were removed, heat would remain nothing more than a simple word.[2]

Systems in the History of Science

Since the 17th century logicians of science, whether practical investigators or theoretical observers, have been deeply impressed with the discoordination between propositions derived from events and those stemming from cultural sources. Such writers as Descartes, Bacon, Newton, Herschel, Whewell, and Mill have made powerful attempts to develop improved systems for evaluating methods and basic postulates. A brief survey indicates to what degree these systems fostered traditional institutions or replaced them.

Descartes. At the dividing point between the medieval and modern periods of science Descartes proposed the following precepts for rightly conducting the reason and seeking for truth in the sciences:

The first of these was to accept nothing as true which I did not

---

[2] Translation quoted from Burtt, Metaphysical Foundations of Modern Science, pp. 75–76 and 78.

clearly recognize to be so; that is to say, carefully to avoid precipitation and prejudice in judgments, and to accept in them nothing more than what was presented to my mind so clearly and distinctly that I could have no occasion to doubt it.

The second was to divide up each of the difficulties which I examined into as many parts as possible, and as seemed requisite in order that it might be resolved in the best manner possible.

The third was to carry on my reflections in due order, commencing with objects that were the most simple and easy to understand, in order to rise little by little, or by degrees, to knowledge of the most complex, assuming an order, even if a fictitious one, among those which do not follow a natural sequence relatively to one another.

The last was in all cases to make enumerations so complete and reviews so general that I should be certain of having omitted nothing.[3]

These Cartesian precepts bespeak a simple scientific situation. The proposer might be primarily a mathematician, a believer in the potency of the scientist's rational powers.

Bacon. Impressed as were many men of his age by the scientific futility of medieval intuition and abstractionism—erroneously called Aristotelian deductive method—Bacon offered his "general" and "fertile" inductive principle. From particular things to universal laws (axioms) marked the path of scientific progress. The following aphorisms from Bacon's *Novum Organum* illustrate his idea of a scientific system.

I. Man, being the servant and interpreter of Nature, can do and understand so much and so much only as he has observed in fact or in thought of the course of nature: beyond this he neither knows anything nor can he do anything.

II. Neither the naked hand nor the understanding left to itself can effect much. It is by instruments and helps that the work is done, which are as much wanted for the understanding as for the hand. And as the instruments of the hand either give motion or guide it, so the instruments of the mind supply either suggestions for the understanding or cautions.

III. Human knowledge and human power meet in one; for where the cause is not known the effect cannot be produced. Nature to be commanded must be obeyed; and that which in contemplation is as the cause is in operation as the rule.

VI. It would be an unsound fancy and self-contradictory to expect that things which have never yet been done can be done except by means which have never yet been tried.

VIII. Moreover the works already known are due to chance and

---

[3] Haldane and Ross, Philosophical Works of Descartes, Vol. 1, p. 92.

experiment, rather than to sciences; for the sciences we now possess are merely systems for the nice ordering and setting forth of things already invented; not methods of invention or directions for new work.

XII. The logic now in use serves rather to fix and give stability to the errors which have their foundation in commonly received notions than to help the search after truth. So it does more harm than good.

XIX. There are and can be only two ways of searching into and discovering truth. The one flies from the senses and particulars to the most general axioms, and from these principles, the truth of which it takes for settled and immovable, proceeds to judgment and to the discovery of middle axioms. And this way is now in fashion. The other derives axioms from the senses and particulars, rising by a gradual and unbroken ascent, so that it arrives at the most general axioms last of all. This is the true way, but as yet untried.[4]

Applaud as we must these aphorisms, especially when their date is taken into account, we cannot but regard them as remote from concrete enterprises.

Newton. The rules of reasoning for natural philosophy set up by Newton reflect an advanced stage of scientific achievement. But though he speaks of experimental philosophy, the workers of this period still sought the absolute laws governing the system of the world.

Rule I. We are to admit no more causes of natural things than such as are both true and sufficient to explain their appearances.

Rule II. Therefore to the same natural effects we must, as far as possible, assign the same causes.

Rule III. The qualities of bodies, which admit neither intensification nor remission of degrees, and which are found to belong to all bodies within the reach of our experiments, are to be esteemed the universal qualities of all bodies whatsoever.

Rule IV. In experimental philosophy we are to look upon propositions inferred by general induction from phenomena as accurately or very nearly true, notwithstanding any contrary hypotheses that may be imagined, till such time as other phenomena occur, by which they may either be made more accurate, or liable to exceptions.[5]

The age of Newton still had ahead of it the full flowering of scientific method. The intense fluidity and relativity of research were yet to be discovered. Newtonian principles are impressive in their austerity and relative paucity of minute correlation with any concrete scientific job.

---

[4] Ellis and Spedding, The Philosophical Works of Bacon, pp. 259–261.

[5] Principia Mathematica, p. 398.

Metasystems in the History of Science

Traditional metasystemic presuppositions concern the nature of reality and the cognitive power of the knower. Underlying the Cartesian, Baconian, and Newtonian systems, for instance, is the assumption that science results from an impact of things upon some sort of psychic substance or process. In Descartes the dualistic opposition between extension and thought is the primary item. With Bacon and Newton the same duality reaches its focal point in differentiating between the soul and the body and the effect each has on the other.

On the whole, technical scientists, such as mathematicians and physicists, stress primarily the "psychic" factors of knowing. Things known are still allowed a modicum of neutral and objective existence, especially if they are subject to metric treatment. Such is Galileo's classic distinction between the objective, independently existing corpuscles, with shape and motion, and the heat sensed by the soul (p. 63). Again, Newton distinguishes sharply between colors, which exist only in the mind, and their external excitants, the differently refrangible rays.[6]

Though meeting with great opposition from mathematicians, it has been the tendency of the succeeding period to reduce the known to substances and to processes of knowing. The history of this procedure is worth a moment's consideration. Following closely upon Newton's trenchant development of science the British empiricists emphasized more and more the prominence of mind in the domain of knowledge and science.

Locke. By his insistence that there are no innate ideas or basic processes of knowledge independent of known things, Locke pushed the dependence of the mind, which he regarded as a *tabula rasa*, so far as to reduce things to ideas. Throughout his writings he insisted that ideas existed only as they were instituted by some outside factor. What this factor was, however, he could not say except that it excited in the mind two sorts of ideas: primary and secondary. The primary had to do with shape and extension; the secondary with the so-called sensory qualities.

The opposing mathematicians however could not regard the mind as simply a *tabula rasa*. They believed there were knowledge principles not derived from impacts of things on the mind, prin-

---

[6] Opticks, 4th ed., p. 108.

ciples that depended upon a basic harmony between invariable relations in nature and upon the power of the mind to recognize them.

Berkeley. Those thinkers who tended to absorb things known into the process of knowing raised the banner of empiricism. They argued that all knowledge is dependent on the mind. Berkeley insisted that Locke was mistaken: it was not necessary to differentiate between primary and secondary qualities; all knowledge, whether of shape, size, or impenetrability, of color or taste, originated in the mind.

Berkeley was a bishop; his whole philosophy therefore was erected upon theological foundations. Thus when the embarrassing problem arose that nothing really exists unless observed by a mind he fell back upon the ever-present and ever-sensing God. To an eminent Oxford theologian is attributed the following limerick aptly expressing this philosophy. We also quote the answer presumed to settle the problem.

> There was a young man who said, "God
> To you it must seem very odd
> That a tree as a tree simply ceases to be
> When there's no one about in the Quad.
>
> Young man, your astonishment's odd,
> I am always about in the Quad
> And that's why the tree continues to be
> As observed by, Yours faithfully, God.[7]

Hume. Modern science, through the development of the meta-systems we are tracing, has acquired a giant paradox. Science attempts nothing less than to establish the existence of the external world. In this development Hume is a pivotal figure. He not only refused to follow Berkeley in making use of God to establish the existence of external things: he also advocated the extrusion of the unified soul. What was left, then, were states of consciousness, sensations, with only the psychic principles of association to bind them together. Causation and objectivity were reduced to mental habits which themselves had no inhering substance.

---

[7] Dampier, From Aristotle to Galileo. In Needham and Pagel, *Background to Modern Science*, p. 40f.

Kant. Kant's so-called Copernican revolution was his heroic attempt to reconcile the claims of the empiricists and rationalists. With Hume and his British cohorts Kant agreed that experience is only the beginning of knowledge. But he could not tolerate Hume's dissipation of things in momentary sensations. From the rationalists he drew the principle of organization and form. Thus he built up his complex epistemology: a transcendental unity of apperception at one end; a thing unknown and unknowable at the other; in between these two the empirical mind and empirical objects.

Naturphilosophie. The Kantian epistemology proved to be an effective means of intermixing investigative and metaphysical systems. Scientific facts were employed to support metaphysics and vice versa. In the German, Romantic *Naturphilosophie* we see the consummation of the attempt to naturalize spirits by connecting them with the nervous system. What Descartes began when he made the pineal gland the mediator between the soul and extensible nature was completed by Lotze, Müller, Helmholtz, and their successors.[8]

Müller. Briefly, Johannes Müller invented the doctrine of specific nerve energies with which to account for the existence in the soul of sensation qualities when the external qualityless, even unknown, thing-in-itself acted on the end organs. When Müller proposed that afferent nerves and their brain terminals could transform indifferent energy into qualities of things he established a physiological agent for spiritistic entities. As Helmholtz asserts:

> Müller's law of specific energies was a step forward of the greatest importance for the whole theory of sense perceptions, and it has since become the scientific basis of this theory. In a certain sense, it is the empirical fulfilment of Kant's theoretical concept of the nature of human reason.[9]

Helmholtz. As eminent physicist, physiologist, and anatomist, Helmholtz not only exerted great authority, but meticulously fostered and amplified the doctrine of the biological basis of knowledge. He invented many specific energies in place of the four which Müller proposed. We may well credit Helmholtz with establishing the cerebrum and cerebral functions as central features of spiritis-

---

[8] Kantor, Problems of Physiological Psychology.
[9] Treatise on Physiological Optics, Vol. 2, p. 19f.

tic epistemology. His technique of supporting cerebral dogmas on the basis of spiritistic presuppositions constitutes a typical example of circularity. As we saw in the preceding chapter, the brain and its powers have become so integrated with scientific culture that the brain can perform the soul's functions, although originally it was presumed to be only the vehicle or seat of the soul.

Inductive Systems. In the nineteenth century an inductive type of scientific system was developed presumably to replace the old deductive metaphysics. By this time science was developing at a tremendous pace. Astronomy and physics were no longer confined to mechanics. Electricity and thermodynamics were appearing on the scene, and the biological sciences had become imposing factors of culture. In 1840 Whewell brought out his *Philosophy of the Inductive Sciences.* In this period, too, belong two famous systems of science: Herschel's *Preliminary Discourse on the Study of Natural Philosophy* and John Stuart Mill's *Inductive Logic.*[10]

On the whole, as Whewell's title indicates, the content sciences, regarded as inductive, were separated from mathematics as deductive. In his philosophy, however, Whewell followed Kant in insisting upon formal principles which the mind of the scientist contributes to events. What this presumed separation between (1) scientific systems as descriptions and rules of investigation and (2) philosophically rooted metasystems really amounted to was the relegation of the metasystem to the cultural matrix. The knowing mind and its *a priori* principles could be left unmentioned though they influenced the character of scientific systems nevertheless.

Once spiritistic epistemology became the basic presupposition of scientific metasystems it played a vigorous role. Even today problems involving *a priori* factors in knowing, intuitive powers in mathematical work, and ultimate and invariant relations in nature continue to maintain themselves. Some scientists deny the existence of any real world independent of the knower (p. 17). All data are reduced to evanescent states of consciousness; in other words, the external world becomes completely absorbed in

---

[10] See Bibliography.

"thought." Whatever exists are correlations of experience.[11] This is a modernized version of Berkeley-Hume metaphysics.

Four Stages of Scientific Systems

A summarizing glance at the history of system making reveals the successive development of four unique types of scientific logic. In some cases these various systems of ideas, beliefs, and investigational techniques operate only in historical, social, and economic situations similar to those in which they developed; in others the four types interoperate in varying patterns on a single complex level.

Thing Systems. In early stages of science, we have seen, the aim was to construct propositions concerning the nature and operation of things. To validate propositions required only such criteria as could be furnished by objects and events. Historians acclaim this fact in asserting that science was born when attributive properties were substituted for by causes—that is, factors localizable within event-fields.

Unfortunately the conventional historian's evidence is marred by an erroneous belief that prescientific attributions uniformly consisted of mystical powers. This belief is coupled with the notion that so-called primitive people were prelogical, that they lived not in the concrete world of direct contact with things but in an imaginary realm of spirits and magical powers. This view itself is highly attributive; it creates a folk endowed with speculative interests and a degree of sophistication entirely out of line with the circumstances of preliterate peoples.

All our available records clearly indicate that enterprises which fit into a scientific continuum are originally thing-centered. Even wrong descriptions and explanations, including illegitimate ascriptions, emerge from a person's effort to orient himself to the things surrounding him.

Knowledge Systems. Enterprises featuring the observer or scientific worker mark the second type of system. The central question is: What properties and conditions of things are discernible? Since at this point the worker's beliefs, attitudes, and evaluations influence his records we need to inquire what differences he intro-

---

[11] Dingle, A Century of Science, ch., 20.

duces into scientific situations by his expertness and shortcomings. The scientist in this stage is motivated by a stock of epistemic principles, as well as sheer interest in things, though in no sense can things be displaced from their central position.

Particular knowledge systems are illustrated by the Continental emphasis on Reason, the British stress of individual experience. In both types of epistemology interpretations and explanations become loosened somewhat from their close attachment to objects and events.

Operational Systems. A comparatively late stage in scientific evolution has yielded systems designed to check on the relations between the behavior of observing and the behavior of observed things. Operational institutions arise out of the complication of researches and the resulting necessity to evaluate and confirm scientific propositions. This means scrutinizing what observers do in their interbehavior with things; it means clarifying and formalizing investigative procedures. As a consequence, procedures become second-order events, in that the work of the observing scientist is added to the interbehavior of things. Operational systems are essentially methodological.

Postulational Systems. This type implies surveillance over all the features of any scientific job. Workers take special notice of background conditions, of basic assumptions and presuppositions. Then follows a careful formulation of procedures. The scientist considers the potentialities and limitations of technological and ideological currents. He balks at confusing ignorance with some ultimate principle. Since postulational principles constitute the base of current systemology they were prominently featured in our discussion of the ideal scientific system (p. 28f.).

Current Scientific Systemology

The prevalent view that science is a self correcting enterprise is certainly justified by the technical development of individual sciences. Paradoxically enough, this notion miscarries when applied to systematic aspects. Here we face the fact that there is discoordination between theory and practice, between research and logic. Whereas it should now be possible to formulate satisfactory scientific systems we find mainly hesitation, clash of viewpoint, incompatibility of system and metasystem.

The current scientific revolution is not merely an occasion of assimilating the discovery of radioactivity, the nonexistence of absolute simultaneity, and the discontinuity or quantal character of energy: it also means reorganizing the significance of the postulational character of mathematics. There is hardly a doubt that an intensified understanding of postulational methods would greatly contribute to the techniques of scientific system building.

What the postulational technique fundamentally signifies is the appreciation of the work of man in science and logic. The fact that scientific work is interbehavior with things becomes a postulate of the system. It allows for the integration of postulates and protopostulates, of system and metasystem.

On a full postulational basis the laws formulated integrate with the assumptions of the worker as he manipulates things in his biological, psychological, physiochemical, and astronomical environment. This encourages research; avoids ineptitudes of interpretation.

Since the postulational procedure as a formal principle was first effectively developed in mathematics it is interesting to trace a bit of its history. When various mathematicians—Wallis, Saccheri, Legendre, Gauss, Lobatchevsky, Bolyai—attempted to perfect the Euclidean system, they were troubled, as doubtless Euclid himself was, by the fifth postulate. But neither Euclid nor all the mathematicians from his time to the 19th century hit upon the fact that the trouble arose from the discoordination between the otherwise excellent system and its underlying metasystem. The whole matter can be briefly put: modern mathematicians discovered that Euclidean geometry represented a concealed identification of system and metasystem; they discovered that Euclidean postulates were not postulates of geometry but postulates of *Euclidean* geometry.

The shock occasioned by this revelation is now a matter of history. Non-Euclidean geometries delivered a mighty blow to absolutism. In particular, they were fatal to the Kantian epistemology based on the absolutistic theory that space and time were *a priori* intuitions of the mind. This epistemological cataclysm led to a series of divergent mathematical theories. One group asserted that mathematics is the logical activity of formulating invariable Platonic relations; another that it was constructional activity limited to specific systems; a third that mathematics is the manipulation of neutral entities according to certain rules.

Similar upsetting conditions in the content disciplines forced scientists to become aware of metasystemic problems. Developments in electromagnetism, thermodynamics, and atomic energy upset the smug systems hitherto established.

This shifting began with the development of statistical mechanics. The investigation of the kinetic energy of molecules forced upon the scientist the necessity of remote and indirect observation. Averages in thermodynamics, as against those in macrophysics, were derived not from manipulating direct measurements but from the intrinsic measurements themselves (chap. 6).

What consequences follow from the invariable preoccupation with statistics? The answer in science, as elsewhere, depends upon the interpretation placed upon the nature of calculation. If calculation is the free exercise of an autistic operator one obtains scientific anarchy, which is nonsense. But if calculation is the manipulation of data by reliable representational procedures it fits into a verifiable system. Which view one adopts depends upon the kind of psychological theory one entertains.

More upsetting than statistical mechanics has been the development of quantum mechanics. Here the experiments are concerned with events which can never be directly observed. Forever hidden from "sight" is the interatomic jump of an electron from one energy level to another. It is presumed to be a far cry from such an event to the observation of an emission line in a spectroscope.

Perhaps relativity theory has been even more disturbing:

> ... it is even being questioned whether our ordinary forms of thought are applicable in the new domain; it is often suggested, for example, that the concepts of space and time break down.[12]

In view of the fact that the disruption in the content sciences arose from laboratory problems we can only conclude that the basic difficulty lay in the disharmony between the system of descriptions (laws) and the metasystem on which the system was based. What scientists did then was to fall back to prescientific

---

[12] Bridgman, Logic of Modern Physics, p. xi.

philosophy—that spectre perpetually stalking the outer fringes of our culture. Had they not built upon a metasystem grounded on an obsolete spiritistic mind the disruption would never have occurred.

If we refuse to go beyond interbehavior with objects and events, microphysical problems do not lead to helplessness in knowledge. When a physicist says we cannot have direct experience of a certain thing, he does not really mean we cannot interact with that object: he means we do not have "mental states." A psychology freed from spiritistic constructs finds only minute differences between (1) observing something by perceiving it directly (seeing a tree) and (2) by means of a substitutive factor, such as observing heat by thermometer readings. An objective approach to psychology and other sciences is provided by the interbehavioral plan we have been proposing.

5

INTERBEHAVIORAL EVOLUTION OF THE SCIENCES

From Crude to Refined Contacts

I N THE preceding chapters we have indicated that all contemporary sciences are products of a detailed cultural evolution. The nucleus of this evolution is the interbehavior of individuals with stimulus objects. Now we trace the links connecting all the sciences, even the most intricate, with crude contacts with events.[1]

Scientific evolution is in no sense a straight-line development. There are many misses as well as hits, permanent and temporary blocks as well as regressions. But every phase is directly intertwined with the specific circumstances of persons and their social background.

In view of the complexity in the careers of scientists and their work how can we trace the evolution of the sciences? By inferring actions from products. No matter how abstruse the level reached we can infer the step-by-step averaging of results, the substitution of numbers for things measured, and the formulation of an equation to show the organization of variables or the rules for operating upon them. The inferences may be only indicative and symbolic, but they penetrate to investigative acts of recording, measuring, analogizing, synthesizing, and describing events.

The procedures of progressive elaboration and abstraction may be stratified on various levels. The resulting epistemic spectrum we illustrate by the enlargement of contacts with water. Originally water is entirely an unculturalized object. Then we have H_2O. Now water is not a fluid but a compound of two gases in a certain proportion. Then there are the ionization processes, the components of the gases electrically charged, and still further along the spectrum the electron-proton configurations. Beyond this we have new constructions centering around heavy water;

---

[1] Though technology is an important item in this evolution we need not consider it further at this point.

deuterium and triterium involve a completely fresh set of contacts and a corresponding advance in knowledge.

Priestley has aptly summarized the increased power to inter-behave with things after the chemical and electrical sciences evolved:

> Hitherto philosophy has been chiefly conversant about the more sensible properties of bodies; electricity together with chymistry and the doctrine of light and colours, seems to be giving us an inlet into their internal structure, on which all their sensible properties depend.[2]

Evolution of the Particular Sciences

To illustrate the interbehavioral development of the various sciences we sample several departments in order to trace successive contact levels.

1. ASTRONOMY

Because astronomical things and events are such obvious and compelling factors of man's environment, the evolution of astronomy is easily traced from early and simple origins. An elementary acquaintance with astronomical facts was inevitable even in the case of the most primitive people. Alternation of day and night, the transformation of the blue celestial sphere to star-studded black, could hardly fail to be connected with the sun and its movements. The appearance and disappearance of the moon, its relative motion and variation in shape, soon gave rise to allegories, myths, and folklore. Side by side with such cultural developments arose elementary knowledge of the sun and the planets, as well as of other stars and constellations.

It is of considerable theoretical importance to stress the humble beginnings of all the sciences. In astronomy, therefore, we go back to (1) the primitive observation of orbits and their shift-ings by shepherds and seamen who learned to apply their knowl-edge,[3] and (2) the astrologers who learned to exploit the ignorance of others concerning astronomical things. The accumulation of such elementary facts we may regard as the raw-material stage.

---

[2] Priestley, History of Electricity. Quoted from Taylor, Physics, The Pio-neer Science, p. 576.

[3] Cf., Pannekoek, The Origin of Astronomy.

Contacts with things are relatively passive, the motivation primarily practical.

The scientific origins of astronomy are embedded in the period of simple prediction. The embryo astronomer was concerned principally with recurring and easily observed events—for example, lunar and solar eclipses. Recall the construction by the Chaldeans of the *saros*, a description of an eighteen-year period within which eclipses repeat themselves as in a preceding interval, but with a ten-or-eleven-day lag in the succeeding year. Incidentally, this is the evolutional beginning of a procedure of time calculation connected with recurring events.[4]

Associated closely with early calculative techniques are expansive developments in geometric measurement, such as the attempts to determine the relative sizes and distances of astronomical things. Aristarchus in the third century B. C. developed the technique of measuring the angle between the sun and the moon when the disk of the latter is exactly in the first or third quarter. In the same period Eratosthenes determined by geometric methods the approximate size of the earth, the spherical nature of which had already been accepted.

For an elaborate development of astronomy the technological evolution of culture was a prime necessity. The employment of observational and research instruments always implies an advanced stage of science. For example, the development of astrolabes and their improvement by Hipparchus made possible plane and spherical determinations of celestial objects. This technological evolution, of course, had to wait for its peak until Renaissance civilization had advanced beyond medieval handicraftsmanship. In such an age Tycho Brahé, Kepler, Galileo, and others could enter upon the telescopic and observational operations which culminated in Newton's law of gravitation.

Since astronomy is an observational instead of a laboratory science its instruments facilitate an inspective rather than a manipulative contact with things. Thus the heliometer became an effective means of determining parallaxes.[5] Increasingly accurate measurements of stellar distance demanded the spectroscope.

---

[4] Concerning the saros, see Neugebauer, The Exact Sciences in Antiquity, p. 134f.

[5] The heliometer was invented by Dollond and Bouguer and improved by Frauenhofer.

Physical principles applied to the intensity of lines of stellar spectra yielded information concerning stellar distance. Absolute stellar magnitude could therefore be differentiated from relative magnitude based upon distance.

Spectroscopy as a means of interbehaving with distant astronomical objects reached its climax when Huggins, Lockyer, Pickering, and other workers developed the astrophysical and astrochemical branches of astronomy. By means of the spectroscope it became possible to penetrate into and determine the physical and chemical constitution of astronomical objects.

A culture which possesses (1) a descriptive astronomy employing such powerful tools as an observatory housing a 200-inch telescope and (2) a cosmogony which penetrates into the most distant reaches of extragalactic space, and thus is able to elaborate theories concerning the origin and movements of planetary systems and galaxies, has no occasion to conceal its struggle in achieving such riches. It is to be expected that in this complicated development folklore has crept in at many points to replace the workers' direct contact with objects.

2. GEOMETRY

Mathematicians sometimes openly display their contempt for the humble origin of geometry. In their way of thinking the fact that it originated in the crass circumstance of boundary or land measurement is not a source of pride. From the standpoint of the history of science, however, this is an improper attitude. Certainly we must admire the industry and insight of numerous generations of land measurers, surveyors, and mathematicians, through whose efforts geometry evolved from rope stretching to the subtle activities of constructing n-dimensional relationships.

Perhaps more than in other historical enterprises the historian who traces the evolution of geometry must be selective and atomistic. How else move back and forth between the lengths, shapes, and relative positions of concrete things, between the abstruse relations of multidimensional geometric constructions?

Mathematicians agree that in part geometry originated in the practical needs of the Egyptians to relocate land boundaries after the periodic inundations of the Nile. The Egyptians, too, are credited with the discovery that a triangle with sides of 3, 4, and 5 units length forms a right-angle triangle. To develop from this observational result the Pythagorean generalization that the square of the hypotenuse of the right-angle triangle equals the sum of the squares of the other sides is the typical evolutional path of geometric science. True, the interval from practical beginnings to fully developed axiomatic or postulational method is an enormously extended one, but to maintain the continuum intact is to avoid false views concerning the sources of geometrical work and products.

As it happens, the evolution of geometry affords a transparent view into the operations of both the practical and theoretical participants. Practical workers labored at problems concerned with concrete things and their relations. Early theoreticians undertook to explain the fittingness of the Euclidean system. For example, Kant, the scientist-philosopher, assumed that Euclidean postulates immediately reflected the basic rational character of the human mind.

The nonexistence of such a mind, the lack of conformity of Euclidean geometry with the "real world" became established through the early work of Saccheri (1733)[6] and later through the efforts of Lambert, Beltrami, and especially those of Gauss, Lobatchevsky and Bolyai. Saccheri only intended to clear up the imperfection of Euclid's parallel postulate, but the ground was nevertheless laid for the transformation of geometry into a postulational system. The hyperbolic system of Lobatchevsky and Bolyai and the elliptic system of Riemann constituted more positive developments.

When finally the highly abstract non-Euclidean geometry became associated with the physicist's description of nature, especially the principle of gravitation, a significant circle in geometric evolution was completed. Of greatest moment for us is the fact that complex theories concerning space and time again became integrated with descriptions of concrete things and events.

3. CHEMISTRY

To the ancient Greeks who believed there were only four "elements" *air*, *fire*, *water*, and *earth*,[7] the following modern ele-

---

[6] *Euclides ab omni naevo vindicatus.*

[7] The Chinese dealt with five elements: water, fire, wood, metal, earth. See Partington, A Short History of Chemistry, p. 32.

ments were known: gold, silver, copper, iron, mercury, sulphur, lead, tin, and carbon. Note the difference in the two "conceptions," and especially how crude contacts with the later-to-be-called *elements* could exist at a period when a technical, though erroneous, theory about elements prevailed.

Chemistry is basically concerned with the nature of elements. To understand the composition of things and their modes of interbehavior under such specified conditions as temperature, pressure, temporal and spatial contacts requires a knowledge of elements. All manipulation and control of organic and inorganic objects depend upon understanding how elements combine and recombine. To a great extent, then, the history of chemistry consists of (1) the processes of increasing the number of elements and (2) the progressive changes in interpreting them.

The evolution of chemistry admirably illustrates the continuity between contacts with things in ordinary situations and the most elaborate theoretical developments, because chemical contacts, immediate or remote, are highly apparent. As social and technological circumstances increase in complexity, new compounds and materials for tools and other objects are required. This need matches the discovery of new elements and means of combining them.

Notwithstanding the false ideas and vain pursuits of the alchemists, they employed the manipulative operations basic to scientific work. Though their elements consisted only of the four ancient ones plus the three principles *salt*, *sulphur*, and *mercury*,[8] their idea that all substances are combined from these elements, when mixed with primordial matter, promoted such activities as heating, dissolving, distilling, sublimating, condensing. Actually they performed a great many effective operations, even discovered ammonia, alcohol, oil of vitriol and the mineral acids, arsenic trioxide, and tartar emetic,[9] albeit they simultaneously uttered magic formulae and incantations. As children of their time the alchemists conformed to their culture in placing so high a value upon gold and certain concoctions they deemed desirable or necessary for healthy and prolonged life. The transmutation of metals, the search for an elixir of life, excellently demonstrate the inter-

---

[8] Salt was a fire-resisting principle of calx, sulphur a combustible principle; mercury the basis for metallic properties.

[9] See Taylor, Alchemical illustrations.

behavior with things leading to the evolution of chemistry as an investigative enterprise.

Modern chemical development continues the search for (a) the elements which combine to form things and (b) the processes and conditions of combination. Technically this development has gone side by side with the elimination of traditional beliefs in nonexistent substances—for example such imponderable items as phlogiston and caloric. By the use of the balance chemists supplanted their alchemical ancestors and established the principle that the processes of chemical composition and decomposition neither increased nor decreased the quantity of the substance involved.

Lavoisier, credited with engendering the new chemistry even beyond Boyle, who so effectively attacked the alchemists, produced the first modern list of chemical elements. Ten of the thirty-three items are not today accepted as elements; five are oxides: lime, magnesia, baryta, alumina, and silica; three are radicals: muriatic, fluoric, and boracic, while light and caloric are also included. There remain, then, the following twenty-three items contained in current lists: oxygen, nitrogen, hydrogen, sulphur, phosphorus, carbon, antimony, silver, arsenic, bismuth, cobalt, copper, tin, iron, manganese, mercury, molybdenum, nickel, gold, platinum, lead, tungsten, and zinc.

The volume, *Traité Élémentaire de Chimie*, in which Lavoisier published his list of elements, appeared in 1789. In that same year Klaproth discovered uranium. Before the end of the century three other elements were isolated: titanium (1791), chromium (1797), and tellurium (1798). To the twenty-seven elements known at the beginning of the 19th century it was possible to add large numbers because of the evolution of techniques in an expanding culture. Only thirty years were required to double the entire number.

The development of precise and effective analytical techniques is excellently typified by the successes of such chemists as Wollaston and Berzelius. Between them they added seven new metallic elements associated with platinum which was entered in the list in 1750. Wollaston isolated palladium and rhodium; Berzelius worked with cerium, selenium, zirconium, silicon, and thorium.

With the evolution of electrical science the chemist's working horizon became vastly enlarged. By his brilliant work on electrical dissociation Davy was able to bring into the table of elements the basic substances which Lavoisier had to leave out—namely, the fixed alkalis. In the single year 1807 Davy isolated potassium, sodium, borium, strontium, calcium, and boron.

Newton's discovery of the prismatic spectrum initiated a series of manipulations and observations which had a far-reaching influence upon chemical progress. Through the work of Wollaston, Herschel, Frauenhofer, and many others the technique of spectral analysis assumed crucial importance for chemical research. In 1860 Bunsen and Kirchoff used this method to discover caesium, and in the next year found rubidium. In 1861 Crookes isolated thallium; two years later Reich and Richter observed the blue spectral lines of indium. The significance of the optical technique of chemical analysis becomes obvious when considering the minute amounts of substance that can be spectroscopically detected. What Bunsen and Kirchoff could easily discern with the spectroscope as caesium and rubidium required the evaporation of 40 tons of water from the Durkheim spring in the Palatinate and 300 pounds of the mineral petalite to obtain enough material for chemical identification and investigation.

Spectroscopic methods also played a large part in the discovery of many elements which, up to the recent evolution of atomic science, had reached close to 90 in number. In 1868 Lockyer could identify helium in the solar spectrum. This and other members of the inert-gas family required the addition of a new group (VIII) in the Periodic Table of the Elements. The high point reached around the later years of the 19th century in knowledge of the constitution of things became surpassed by combining the above manipulations and instrumental methods with more subtle processes and by using theoretical tools evolved from former simpler situations. Earlier analyses and syntheses led to far-reaching transition processes.

Then came the strategic advance in chemical science when it was demonstrated that living things could also be subjected to analysis. That organic substances are compounded of hydrogen, nitrogen, carbon, oxygen, sulphur, phosphorus, and small proportions of other elements brought living things within the range

84 THE LOGIC OF MODERN SCIENCE

of manipulation and experimental observation. On such a basis the scientist could rid himself of mysterious vital forces and essences.

The classic example is Wöhler's transformation of ammonium cyanate into urea in 1828, and still better, Kolbe's authentic synthesis of acetic acid in 1844. The famous Liebig carried on elaborate investigations into the complex chemical processes of plants and animals, and thereafter biochemistry, as the study of the interaction of substances in living things, began its overwhelmingly successful career. Emboldened by such achievements, the chemists quite expectedly overemphasized their knowledge and power and soon provoked innumerable controversies. Among the most notable was the conflict between the proponents of the chemical theory of fermentation and their opponents who feared the spontaneous-generation implication.

Alcoholic fermentation of sugar solution has been known since early times. The observation that yeast plays an essential role in fermentation was also equally early. By Pasteur's time the question arose: What is yeast and how does it play its part in alcoholic fermentation?[10]

About the middle thirties of the 19th century Cagniard de la Tour made the microscopic observation that yeast consists of minute organisms responsible for alcoholic fermentation. His observations were supported by the studies of Schwann, Kützing, Turpin, and others. These workers were joined by Pasteur who, though a chemist by training, insisted upon the key place of living things in fermentation events.

A vigorous campaign soon came to be waged against the biological theory of fermentation by a powerful group of chemists —among them Berzelius, Wöhler, Liebig, and Thenard. Berzelius declared that at most yeast plays the modest role of catalyst. Liebig argued that only as lifeless chemical substances could yeast materials bring about fermentation; further, that yeast was not present in lactic and butyric fermentation, and so not necessary for alcoholic fermentation at all. All these eminent scientists took the position that chemistry could well dispense with the notion that biological factors are necessary to start and continue chemical reactions.

---

[10] Dubos gives a vivid account of this development in his book, Louis Pasteur, Free Lance of Science.

Perhaps it is not strange that chemists should appear to range themselves on the side of vitalistic principles and the theory of spontaneous generation. The chemists mentioned could incline toward an abiogenetic theory on the ground that possibly yeast could originate from grape juice. The entire fermentation controversy has had its happy and only possible end in the development of many specific findings which made a place for all the partial evidence used by both sides. In 1897 Büchner made the accidental discovery of zymase which was capable of producing alcohol from sugar without the presence of yeast cells. From this beginning many biochemical substances were developed—substances important for the understanding of things without involving traditional principles. To eliminate animal or vital principles from biology, to eradicate ultimate chemical principles from chemistry, is to do a tremendous lot in the way of seeing things as they are.

So far we have stressed the evolution of chemistry in its more palpable aspects. We have emphasized the workers' direct contacts with their materials. Now we must consider a more complicated and remote development—namely, the interpretative views concerning the nature of chemical things and events.

Invariably, chemical interpretation brings us to the development of atomic theory. Chemical elements to begin with were construed as indivisible particles. Whether the credit for first developing the atomic theory in chemistry goes to Lavoisier, Dalton, Higgins,[11] or Berzelius,[12] the theory of atoms must be traced to the traditional atomism espoused by Newton, Gassendi, and, back through history, to Lucretius, Democritus, and Leucippus.

Newton's espousal of the particle theory is indicated by the following quotation from the Opticks, Query 31.

All these things being consider'd, it seems probable to me, that God in the Beginning form'd Matter in solid, massy, hard, impenetrable, moveable Particles, of such Sizes and Figures, and with such other Properties, and in such Proportion to Space, as most conduced in the End for which he form'd them; and that these primitive Particles being Solids, are incomparably harder than any porous Bodies compounded of them; even so very hard, as never to wear or break in pieces;

[11] Soddy (The Story of Atomic Energy) insists on Higgins' claim as the real founder of atomic theory. See also the Partington and Soddy discussion in *Nature*. 1951, 167, pp. 120, 734–736.

[12] When atomic theory is separated from molecular theory Berzelius is credited with founding atomic theory. See Soddy, loc. cit. p. 18.

no ordinary Power being able to divide what God himself made one in
the first Creation.[13]

Maxwell took over this view and accordingly stands at the
transition point between ancient and modern constructions concerning particles. Today, chemistry has reached a stage of complex
analysis which does not tolerate eternal substances and absolute
particles. As in subatomic physics, atoms which were formerly
regarded as indestructible are now considered as complex organizations of electrons, protons, and neutrons which in various modifi-
able configurations constitute, in an improved form, the structures
and changes of specific substances.

4. MEDICAL SCIENCE

In a unique manner medical science illustrates the accumulation and refinement of constructs (principles, laws, theories) from
direct contact with particular things. It originated from an interest
in the unsatisfactory hygiene of particular individuals.[14] The physician's task was to induce some change in the patient. Certainly
Hippocratic medicine reached the high order of sophistication in
which medical practice consisted in understanding the construction of the organism, its variations in health and disease, and the
conditions under which it existed, satisfactory or unsatisfactory,
minimal or optimal. Depending upon the patient's condition the
physician prescribed changes in diet, adjusted him to the seasons,
the air and the winds, the qualities of water, and in general the
nature of the place in which he lived.[15]

Even though the primary conditions surrounding the origin
and evolution of medicine were practical ones, the medical field
was, after all, dominated by scientific interests. That it was "the
aim of the Hippocratics to make medicine thoroughly scientific"[16]
has been satisfactorily established. After all, it is impossible for
medical science not to keep close to the actual disease situation.
And so the evolution of medicine consists partly of bringing to
bear upon medical situations all the techniques serviceable in
changing anomalous and undesirable conditions, and partly of

13 Opticks, p. 375.
14 See Heidel, Hippocratic Medicine, ch. 6.
15 See On Ancient Medicine; and Air, Waters and Places.
16 Heidel, Hippocratic Medicine, p. 37.

developing knowledge and theory concerning the objects of organic nature.

The history of medicine traces out the step-by-step development of medical practice and theory along with the cultural evolution of technology. So far as the grosser features of technology are concerned, there are innumerable records of all sorts of instruments developed in early antiquity for medical purposes. It will be recalled that trephining is a technique practiced even by prehistoric man. Aside from instruments devised specifically for surgical use, medical science has been fostered by the application of all sorts of tools. The development of the thermometer, stethoscope, microscope, and other products of optical technology has testified to the persistent interactions of physicians with specific things. The use of drugs, the general development of empirical pharmacological procedures, likewise indicate corresponding progress in technological evolution.

Let us return for a moment to the progress of medicine through improved contacts of scientists with organic things. Whether the practical interest in organisms has been paramount or the more general scientific curiosity, medical science has evolved on the basis of improved knowledge concerning the human organism. It is probably unwise, however, to assume that the sciences of physiology and anatomy, embryology and bacteriology, with their manipulations, techniques, and final theory constructs, have all been derived from medicine as a matrix. Much as they may have been influenced by an interest in human health, their detailed evolution can just as readily be traced to other motives. Bacteriology, for example, originated from an independent interest in minute animalcules, such as Leeuwenhoek discovered under his microscope. Similar autonomous interests can be analyzed out of the complex events from which physiology, anatomy, and biochemistry emerged.

Probably the highest peak in medical science to be reached so far is centered in the relatively abstract biochemical and biophysical studies. Greek speculations concerning bodily humors have advanced to the complex experiments on the blood and its constituents, the numerous hormones, and other elaborate aminoacid compounds found in the animal organism. Not far behind these developments are the complicated biochemical processes making for hygiene and dyshygiene, susceptibility and immunity to many kinds of disease. The employment of various biotic substances in cooperation with therapeutic chemical procedures has led to the development of extensive medical-science specialization.

On the whole, this evolution constitutes a long record of discoveries and inventions connected with the problem of maintaining organisms in their environment. All the manipulations performed for the purpose of warding off and overcoming disease are correlated with the more subtle behavior of believing something about it. In other words, medical practice and research are overlaid with theory. Thus the writer of the Hippocratean treatise *On the Sacred Disease* protested against the theory that epilepsy is without natural cause:

> Men regard its nature and cause as divine from ignorance and wonder, because it is not at all like to other diseases. And this notion of its divinity is kept up by their inability to comprehend it, and the simplicity of the mode by which it is cured, for men are freed from it by purifications and incantations. But if it is reckoned divine because it is wonderful, instead of one there are many diseases which would be sacred. . . .[17]

Today, medical theories are strictly subject to at least potential validation. To be acceptable medical hypotheses must lend themselves to experimental testing. In short, only by physical, chemical, and biological operations can propositions be sustained.

5. PHYSICS

Although physics has become so abstract as to give the appearance of being mainly concerned with mathematical formulae, we still can trace out its step-by-step development from crass contacts with simple things. This is certainly true of electricity and thermodynamics. And mechanics quite obviously stems from such simple but effective operations as the development and use of levers, wheels, and water screws. Hydrostatics, too, may be traced back to elementary operations like those of Archimedes with the golden crown. Electricity has its foundations in the simple observation of amber; magnetism developed from the striking but simple actions of the lodestone.[18]

---

[17] Adams, The Genuine Works of Hippocrates, p. 347.
[18] See ch. 10.

Because of the things and events which interest the physicist, his domain, more than other scientific branches, has historically been closely articulated with technological situations. Not only do the physical sciences depend upon tools, machines, and other technical apparatus, but physics constitutes the science which studies such machines. This situation is excellently pictured by Rumford in his article on *Frictional Heat*:

> It frequently happens, that in the ordinary affairs and occupations of life, opportunities present themselves of contemplating some of the most curious operations of Nature; and very interesting philosophical experiments might often be made, almost without trouble or expense, by means of machinery contrived for the mere mechanical purposes of the arts and manufactures.
>
> I have frequently had occasion to make this observation; and am persuaded, that a habit of keeping the eyes open to every thing that is going on in the ordinary course of the business of life has oftener led, as it were by accident, or in the playful excursions of the imagination, to useful doubts, and sensible schemes for investigation and improvement, than all the more intense meditations of philosophers, in the hours expressly set apart for study.[19]

The great upheaval in physics occasioned by the introduction of statistical mechanics is a tribute to the interbehavioral principle. Physicists were considerably troubled when they had to shift from the observation of specific particles to collective events in which the results could only be formulated in terms of averages. Actually what happened was merely a slight change of position on the observation-event continuum. Instead of visible motions of things, scientists had to concern themselves with particles and movements too small to see: the changes taking place had to be calculated. Still further, the kinetic theory of gases prompted scientists to build constructs concerning ratios of energy, of entropy or probabilities.

This need for adjustment is troublesome only because it involves a shift in cultural attitude. Traditional beliefs in the visible and tangible nature of reality no longer hold. Energy once bothered scientists because it is "immaterial." There is more than a suggestion that it is traditional philosophical views which are perplexing rather than problems of the laboratory or of natural events.

---

[19] Philosophical Transactions, 1798; from Magie, Source Book in Physics, p. 151.

Physics is successful precisely because its abstract constructs are derived from manipulations. Difficulties arise only when contacts with things are separated from the final formulations summing up those contacts. For example, problems of material-immaterial stem from skipping over all the detailed operations with falling bodies, dynamos, generators, etc., then jumping to abstract constructions like matter, motion, force, energy. Relativity theory, too, illustrates the change in view when concrete objects and operations are taken into account.

All recent arguments by physicists concerning the reality or irreality of statistical constructs completely fail to differentiate (a) the original events, (b) the operations performed upon them, (c) the transformations wrought in such events by investigational operations, and (d) the final constructs built up to describe them. A statistical formula does not imply (a) that there are no definite events aside from those the investigator constructs or projects, or (b) that there is no access to them. The necessity to use tools, the fact that manipulations and calculations are different from things and events interbehaved with involves no reality problem.

Evolution Within the Sciences

As in general scientific evolution, the internal development of the sciences consists of a progressive movement toward abstract constructs. The most striking modern example is the complete reduction of substances and objects to electrical charges.

This progressive refinement of constructs marks an increased sophistication concerning the things studied as well as the general scientific enterprise. We have already discussed (p. 71f.) the four stages (thing, epistemological, operational, and postulational) through which all sciences progress. The points on this epistemic spectrum represent constructs varying in degree of descriptive effectiveness. We now illustrate this development in the physiochemical, biological, psychological, and anthropological sciences.

1. PHYSIOCHEMICAL SCIENCE

Although the physiochemical sciences have developed the most abstract constructs—for example, wave packets, phase waves, probability densities—they are still basically rooted in objects and their relations. This fact is reflected in the prominent definition of physics as the science of matter, and more so in the difficulties encountered by physicists to shift from particles to fields.

Even in the earliest *thing* stage physical scientists sought for abstruse constructs to sum up the nature and properties of objects. When physicists developed kinematics as the science of motion their interest in the relations and actions of things was fostered in terms of point masses and other types of mathematical constructs. On the whole, mechanics was developed on the basis of such numerical constructs as inertia, velocity, and force.

Similarly, energy in its kinetic and potential variations is closely connected with concrete things. Recall that early energists were interested in machines that would operate without fuel. The construct of energy and energy conservation dates not only from attempts to develop perpetual motion, but also from the time when energy was still thought of as a substance.

Early electrical constructs also were linked closely with things; first fluids, then particles. Again, in the beginning electrical field constructs were tied to media intervening between charged objects.

The physiochemical emphasis upon bodies, their impacts and general relationships, makes it inevitable that physicists should strive toward quantization and mathematical models. Physiochemical laws invariably take the form of functional equations: $y = f(x)$. Accordingly, the facility of constructing equations to represent and to organize relations assumes a towering place. Unfortunately some physicists misinterpret the part they play in the description of events and identify their descriptions with the events they describe and interpret.

The necessary physiochemical abstractness thus leads scientists away from concrete events. Physicists, we have seen (p. 3ff.), regard themselves as searching for the underlying reason and reality of all things. Achievements like the development of machines and techniques for manipulating things are looked upon as minor accomplishments.

Operationism in physics developed first from the procedure of isolating a body or system for study. The behavior and interbehavior of objects could thus be determined by a manipulatory operation. The ideal example is the isolation and determination of a gravitational field or the equilibrium of forces. Problems in thermodynamics and statistical mechanics provided a powerful impetus to the operational principle, though its peak was not reached until relativity physics evolved. Recognition of the necessity to take specific frames of reference into consideration brings to the front the place of operations in scientific work.

> In classical physics, we had one clock, one time flow, for all observers in all CS (coordinate systems). Time, and therefore such words as "simultaneously," "sooner," "later," had an absolute meaning independent of any CS. Two events happening at the same time in one CS happened necessarily simultaneously in all other CS.[20]

Now depending on the frame of reference two events can be described as simultaneous in one coordinate system, while in another they are sequential.

Postulational physics stresses not only the events and procedures of a particular research but also systemic problems. It is assumed that problems involving ambiguities and indeterminacies are to be treated freely but with a definitely acceptable system. Extrapolative hypotheses are apt to be kept within the orbit of authentic events and tolerable postulates.

We have a good example of the postulational stage of physics in the development of electrodynamics. Before Maxwell constructed the displacement current, electrodynamic events could be equally well described in terms of (a) attractive or repulsive forces acting at a distance between elementary currents, by analogy with the interaction between Newtonian particles or (b) an electromagnetic field as the carrier of energy. Of course, from an experimental standpoint, the field theory proved to be more advantageous. As an autonomous hypothesis either construct could be employed.[21]

The implications are clear. In the first place, as long as the scientist keeps close to a concrete research situation he can weave long strands of constructs. Light events may be described as photons or waves. Energy may be continuous or discontinuous. He can readily harmonize these gross and direct observations, which some events allow, with the more subtle ones demanding

---

[20] Einstein and Infeld, Evolution of Physics, p. 188.

[21] See Elsasser, Quantum mechanics, amplifying processes and living matter, p. 301.

calculative and inferential techniques. Similarly, he can coordinate his observations of unique and particular things with those requiring collective and aggregative leveling and smoothing.

In the second place, the scientist enjoys the freedom of combining two or more old systems into a new one. He can thus avoid contradictory propositions based upon exclusive and monopolizing premises.

2. BIOLOGICAL SCIENCE

The biological sciences being limited to organic things and events are narrower in range as compared with physics and chemistry, and thus have undergone a specialized evolution. Biologists emphasize (1) uniqueness and specific organization—that is, individuality of form and structure, (2) changes involved in metabolism and growth, and (3) historical continuation despite variations of successive generations and evolutionary modifications.

The *thing* stage of biology centers around natural history, with its interest in taxonomic and geographic distribution. At this point, biology finds great scope in ascertaining the morphological traits and relationships of the vast number of organisms categorized in species, genera, families, orders, classes, and phyla.

The *epistemological* stage of biology is characterized by a curious opposition of interpretation and evaluation. On the one hand, biologists build technological and vitalistic constructs which retreat from original events. Among such are spontaneous generation, immortality of germ plasm, directors, determiners, organizers, and regulators of all sorts. On the other hand, biologists incline toward the physiochemical aspect of organisms which aids research. Biophysics and biochemistry certainly encourage contact with events. They do not, however, *ipso facto* blot out cultural impositions upon organic events; nor inhibit the attempt to reduce biological organisms to physiochemical happenings.

The *operational* phase of biology pertains to the manipulative (dissection) and experimental developments. Important anatomical constructs are cell, tissue, system, and organism. Corresponding constructs of a more analytic sort stem from the innumerable embryological details of organisms. Particular experimental constructs mark the processes of infection, immunization, and the secretion of antibodies as responses to antigens.

When the biologist treats actual interbehavioral fields in which the primary happenings are the mutual interactions of organisms and environing factors he achieves an authentic *postulational* phase of construct building. The constructs here are all persistently drawn from the original biological situation.

3. PSYCHOLOGICAL SCIENCE

Unlike the physiochemical and biological sciences psychology did not evolve by the discovery of new things, since psychological happenings are obvious and paramount features of everyone's environment. To be sure, psychological science lacks the conditions for discovering things comparable to electric currents, radioactivity, quanta of energy, cosmic rays, and so on.[22] The basic problems therefore are analysis and interpretation.

The ubiquity of psychological events, their integration with biological facts, make it possible to trace back the *thing* stage of psychology to ancient medicine and biology. Psychological events constitute simply the processes and movements of the various animals. It is probably the most signal feature of European culture that the vegetative and locomotor functions of Aristotle's psychology became transformed into vitalistic processes, while the sensitive and rational functions were metamorphosed into psychistic entities.

When modern scientists returned to the view that psychological events are *activities* of biological organisms they reattached psychology securely to concrete things. This refounding of psychology, which required centuries to complete, provided data relatively free of psychic imposition.

The historical spiritistic interval between the two biological periods marks the *knowledge* stage of psychology. Psychic states were regarded as cognitive on the one hand; motivational on the other. The central cognitive construct was awareness or knowledge. Set over against things known it receded so far from things that it became glorified as intuitive contemplation or degraded to a pale cast of thought. On the motivational side, the central construct was a power that moved the organism and controlled its actions. Sometimes it was regarded as blind and unreasonable, at others thoroughly aware and calculating. This power, described as

---

[22] Cf., Köhler, Dynamics in Psychology, ch. 1.

mind or soul, was (a) immediate in action, effective without fore-seeing ends (instinctive), and (b) rational in the sense of knowing and weighing results and consequences.

Psychologists doubtless stand on solid ground when they regard their discipline as dating only from its experimental period. This view pays tribute to the *operational* and interbehavioral view of science, but applies only to the manipulative and not the inter-pretative phase of the early experimental period. Experimental investigations make possible additions to the general store of science even when performed under mystical ideological auspices. When we consider the spiritistic constructs developed by early experimenters we must regard psychology as a very old discipline indeed. Certainly their constructs can be traced back to the early days of our cultural era—in fact, as we have seen, to the ideas of the early Church Fathers (p. 62).

The *postulation* stage of psychology is achieved by adding to experimentation and mensuration, which guarantee close contact with things and events, a systemic background with postulates de-rived from events, not from extrascientific sources.

4. ANTHROPOLOGICAL SCIENCE

In anthropological science the four stages, for obvious reasons, do not stand out. Certainly the *thing* and *epistemological* stages are thoroughly intermixed. Man the scientist could not, of course, discover himself as a natural object. When anthropological science first began man was already thoroughly set in his cultural matrix. He could be an object of study only as a *zoon politicon*, an organ-ism with moral and social properties. All descriptions given him were obviously drawn for the most part from the realm of cultural values.

Circumstances of human organisms and their culture deter-mine that the *operational* stage of anthropology should be ex-tremely specialized. Modern-science constructs concerning human organisms became naturalistic only after evolutionary theories broke down the barriers connecting humans with other animals. Likenesses and differences between various groups or communities began to be stressed with respect to the behavior of men and the nature of their cultural products. Hence the generalization that while human animals vary immensely in their characteristics they are all alike in participating in cultural systems. All societies have their unique languages, religions, laws, social organizations, arts, and sciences.

Postulational anthropology is in its infancy. So far the primary advance has consisted of withholding impositions from one's own culture. Thus descriptions of particular societies taken in relative isolation or in comparative correlation are made on the basis of the actual living conditions of the communities studied. More positive interpretative and explanatory constructs will evolve as anthropologists develop distinctive anthropic systems against a background of postulational biology and psychology; and as a consequence, free their discipline from internal (instinct, urges) and external (competition, cooperation) "forces" in favor of constructs drawn from the observation of the particular group and its relation to other groups and the geographic scene.

The interbehavioral principles exhibited in the evolution of the sciences operate equally well in their prosecution, a point we develop in the next three chapters where we consider the fundamental scientific methods and techniques.

III

THE METHODS AND TECHNIQUES
OF SCIENCE

6

THE LOGIC OF SCIENTIFIC EXPERIMENTATION

Experimentation as Interbehavior

EXPERIMENTATION is the life of science. This widely accepted generalization is valid, however, only in a setting of concrete circumstances. For one thing, scientific progress occurs even when experimentation is not feasible. Furthermore, in numerous enterprises experimentation becomes available and effective only after other forms of activity are completed.

Obviously, since experimental work is technical and restrictive, to make it the ultimate scientific criterion blinds one to the scientist's actual task and motivation. Everyone agrees that experimental observations are among the most efficient and fruitful methods of science, but only because they constitute means toward given ends.

Take the most solidly established departments of science, such as physics. Who contributes more, the theorist or experimentalist? To mention the great historical figures of macroscopic physics, Kepler, Galileo, and Newton, is to enforce the point that the foundations for that science were laid before experimentation was available. It is sometimes asserted that no one before Newton, not even Galileo, was a perfect scientific man in the sense of realizing that mathematical deduction has to be confirmed by experimentation.[1] In view of Newton's *hypotheses non fingo* no one need hesitate to accept this evaluation of the great man. But consider that the circumstances of Newton's life set very narrow boundaries to the quantity and quality of his experimental activities.

Turning to the flowering period of classical physics we may well ask: Who can match Maxwell and Poincaré in furthering electrical and thermodynamical science? Still, Poincaré was at

---

[1] Cf., Sullivan, The Limitations of Science, p. 13. Also Butterfield, The Origins of Modern Science, ch. 5.

most a theoretical physicist, if not entirely a pure mathematician. Concerning Maxwell, Jeans writes:

> ... I do not think he ever felt any deep interest in experimental methods, nor showed any outstanding skill as an experimenter. When experiments were not an amusement to him, they were merely fodder for mathematical investigation.[2]

With the development of microscopic physics the theorist, mathematician or not, takes on a weighty role. Consider the debt owed to Lorentz, Einstein, Planck, Jordan, Born, von Laue, Schrödinger, and Heisenberg. It is impossible to overvalue the theorist's work of developing problems and suggesting their experimental solution. But this is not only true for physics, where manipulations and other operations are most available: it is the case in every scientific specialty.

Those who honor Harvey as the scientist who revolutionized medicine and biology by means of observation and experiment, must not spoil their encomium by (1) exaggerating the scope of his experimentation and (2) denying that his reputation rests to a great extent on his turning away from the authority and writings of Galen and his followers. To turn from the learning and teaching of anatomy, from books and the sayings of philosophers, to dissection and the fabric of nature[3] reflects a shift from a period when there were few or no experiments.

Theoretical and experimental specialization merely enhances the rule that experimentation is the essence of science. It enforces the inseverable relation between theorists and experimentalists. Howsoever the theoretician may be inclined toward mathematical relations, he constructs his equations with a close regard to experimental findings. Experimentalists, on the other hand, are not simply manipulators: they are guided closely by the hypotheses suggested by theoretical considerations. It is appropriate here to refer to Larmor's explanation of why Heinrich Hertz was able to perform the experiment establishing Maxwell's theory that electrical waves exist:

> ... as a theorist he was aware of what he was to expect and could fit an

---

[2] James Clerk Maxwell, A Commemoration Volume, 1831–1931, p. 93.

[3] An Anatomical Disquisition on the Motion of the Heat and Blood in Animals, Dedication.

interpretation to casual observation such as encouraged further pursuit.[4]

To emphasize experimentation in science is to pay a signal tribute to our constantly stressed interbehavioral principle that science proceeds on the basis of contacts with things and events. It is for this reason alone that vitalists in neurology (Magendie, Johannes Müller) and mystics in psychology (Fechner, Wundt) could, by experimentation, advance science. Scientific experimentation, then, is nothing more nor less than an evolution of ordinary trial-and-error procedures, rule-of-thumb manipulations, during which the worker develops increasingly greater expertness and precision.

Evolution of Experimentation

Experimentation being but an expert type of contact with objects and events can easily be traced throughout human culture. Especially we might hope to follow its development through the Greeks and their predecessors as the progenitors of our own science and technology.

Many historians of science criticize the Greeks on the ground that they were not experimenters—an attitude hardly to be maintained unless, of course, experiments are defined as what is being done in current laboratories. But who would expect the Greeks to compete with a worker armed with electrical equipment! One can scarcely overlook the work of Archimedes, Hero, Aristotle, even Pythagoras and Plato. And what about the Greek physicians from Hippocrates on? To criticize the Greeks because of certain lacks and failures is to regard scientific work as magic and ritual.

A definite basis for the view that the Greeks were nonexperimenters, even opposed to experimentation, is the common opinion that they spurned labor and exalted reason. The record of Greek achievement defies such an interpretation. There is a misunderstanding here of what is implied in the Greek glorification of law, formulae, and general principles. True enough, from our standpoint an enormous simplicity prevailed in Greek times. Technology was primitive: indeed the dawn was only beginning. Elaborate experimentation demands a massive accumulation of things and processes. This implies intricate contacts with things requiring intermediation—that is, the use of tools. An interbehavioral atti-

---

[4] James Clerk Maxwell, A Commemoration Volume, p. 81.

tude is helpful in dispelling the erroneous view that experimentation first began in the Renaissance. It flourished from then on, but only because the roots had slowly been developing.

To survey the span which includes Petrus Hispanus, Albert, Thomas, Roger Bacon, Peregrinus, Cusanus, Oresme among others is to realize that manipulative forms of experimentation were performed in the medieval period. Even Peter of Spain could boast that the ancients were philosophers, while his contemporaries were experimenters.[5] Scholars are beginning to see clearly, and we may say justly, that a close relationship exists between alchemical manipulations and the development of modern chemistry (p. 81).[6]

No one denies that the stirrings of populations in the Renaissance, the reception from the Far East of technological methods and products so helpful in stimulating Western European science, resulted in a decided peak of scientific development. It is therefore only a form of historical shortsightedness to overlook that experimental techniques and procedures, like language, custom, law, and art, are never full-blown creations of any particular time: they evolve within a spiral bounded by events that are nowhere discontinuous.[7] We can go back even to Peregrinus (*De Magnete*) who places considerable emphasis upon experimental skill. An investigator:

> ... must himself be very diligent in handicraft also, in order that through the operation of this stone he may know wonderful effects. For by his carefulness he will be able in a short time to correct an error which in an age he could not possibly do by means of his knowledge of nature and mathematics, if he lacked carefulness in use of hands. For in occult (i.e., scientific) operations we search out much by manual industry; and for the most part, without it we can make nothing perfect or complete.[8]

---

[5] Cf., Thorndike, History of Magic and Experimental Science during the First Thirteen Centuries of our Era, p. 979.

[6] Interesting here is Lavoisier's borrowing of the alchemist's pelican apparatus to disprove water-earth transmutation by "cohobation". Cf., McKie, Antoine Lavoisier, p. 95.

[7] Among relevant literature concerning scientific continuity may be cited the Thorndike volumes mentioned above; also by the same author Vols. 3 and 4 of A History of Magic and Experimental Science in the Fourteenth and Fifteenth Centuries. Further, Dingler, Das Experiment.

[8] Thompson (tr.), Peter Peregrine, Epistle, quoted from Taylor, Physics: The Pioneer Science, p. 585.

Observation, Manipulation, Transformation

In the continuum of scientific interbehavior there are three salient procedures—observation, manipulation, and transformation. Manipulation is localized midway between the two other processes. It is a conventional view that experimentation does not begin until manipulation is reached. Observation, however, is not something entirely different from manipulation, nor manipulation from transformation. Nor are the differences exclusively based on diversity of subject matter. These three procedures vary according to concrete conditions, such as availability of techniques and the immediate problem.

Observation. As a rule, observation is a field method. Geological studies constitute instances in which, because the events have long since ceased, one can observe only the results. In other fields, as in astronomy, events are transpiring, but there is no way of controlling them; one can only report what is happening.

Manipulation. Chemical analyses and the dispersion of light rays by means of prisms and gratings are typical of manipulatory processes. These experiments are characterized by the fact that instruments of various sorts can be employed to modify things and events.

Transformation. When the chemist develops organic compounds synthetically, he performs a type of experiment which transforms previously existing things. Notice the difference between transforming and creating. The former is an elaborate rearrangement of materials which are in no sense created by the experimenter. Another telling illustration is the nuclear physicist's elaboration of the periodic table. The addition of the transuranium elements constitutes a high-powered procedure of transforming substances and energies.

In all scientific work the observational procedure is paramount, since even the most complex transformations consist merely of intensifying the trend of events previously discovered. Although observation, manipulation, and transformation comprise a continuum of procedures it is scientifically advantageous to respect their differences. For example, we can eliminate the age-old problem of mechanism versus vitalism and similar scientific puzzles simply by not applying mechanical methods to biological events. This does not imply that biological events involve *vital* principles or essences, but only takes account of the patent organizational intricacies of organisms and the complexities of their environmental adjustments.

Experimentation and Scientific Ritual

A well established scientific convention runs: Science is a method. Frequently this is intended to counter the view that science is a type of philosophy, a generalized set of beliefs and attitudes. Both views are equally bad. By excessive insistence upon method, experimentation becomes a ritual. The spontaneity of scientific work is reduced, the task of discovering the nature of events minimized.

All three phases of the ritualistic view—namely, (1) emphasis on procedure, (2) stress of apparatus, and (3) autistic self-expression lead to a stultification of science. Science becomes restricted to situations amenable to certain kinds of contacts with events. At the same time, immense ranges of scientific enterprises, especially those not yet formalized and established, are neglected. Here is the basis for harmful orthodoxy in science and for inertia in its expansion and development.[9]

1. *Emphasis on Procedure.* To emphasize procedure is to encourage standardization, dull routine, and insensitivity to new methods. While manipulation is always a guarantee of definite contact with things—in other words, a path to laboratory work—one is never released from the obligation to fit means to ends. No scientific work consists of sheer manipulation. There must be a legitimate and worth-while problem; also a rational plan of attack, an available procedure, a workable experimental design.

Furthermore, manipulation must be adapted to the exigencies of the research situation. True as it is that more is known about manipulable things, that more applications can be made of knowledge gained through manipulation, it is nevertheless a violation of scientific principle to maximize such situations. Laboratory techniques are certainly not the exclusive methods of investigating events, and when they become prescribed forms of operations they tend to function as research-hampering traditions.

---

[9] This orthodoxy supports the attitude that if something can not be experimented upon it is *ipso facto* not a scientific datum.

The scientific liabilities inherent in rituals are exemplified by the vigorous discussion of operationism in the last three decades. On the whole the operational principle was intended to combat the view that scientific work was furthered primarily by the autistic creation of formulae. The proposition was set up that scientific concepts are coincident with the operations engendering them. What followed, then, was that operations were taken to be ritualistic procedures. The fact that direct contacts with things—the basic point of the operational principle—comprise a large series of activities, including calculation and inference, was disregarded. Research is not ritual.

2. *Stress of Apparatus*. Tools and instruments obviously facilitate work. Yet overemphasis of apparatus is likewise ritualistic. Does not the history of science indicate conclusively that tremendous developments have been brought about by the use of very simple apparatus? For example, consider the achievements of Galileo and Newton with such trifling apparatus as balls rolling down inclined planes, a glass prism placed in the path of a beam of light let in through a tiny hole in the window-shut. How momentous was Franklin's identification of electricity and lightning —demonstrated by the use of a kite and key. These researches, of course, took place at the very beginning of an extensive development. But similar evidences are available in the case of the supreme accomplishments of Priestley and of Lavoisier, whose apparatus consisted of a sensitive balance. More recently still we may cite the chemical advances which Ramsay brought about by apparatus simple enough to be suspended from the ceiling by wires and strings.[10]

No one who has followed our suggestion that research must go hand in hand with the problem and the type of event worked upon will interpret our discussion as minimizing the value of apparatus. Certainly, in nuclear physics the early stages of research have been furthered by the use of such powerful machinery as cyclotrons. There are also decided limits to research in astrophysics until a powerful 200 inch telescope is available. However, scientists frequently point out that many results achieved by the

---

[10] Here one is reminded of the assertion, current in a simpler technological age than ours, that scientific achievement is in inverse proportion to amount of equipment.

use of elaborate machinery may only be technical, occasionally trivial.

Consider, too, that difficulties arise in the use of apparatus. For one thing, apparatus is costly. To assume that investigations cannot go on without complicated instruments is a distinct deterrent to research. Again, the cost not only in money but in time needed to build up elaborate apparatus sometimes impedes scientists. Frequently, workers persist in using apparatus over too long a period and for too many problems.

3. *Autistic Self-Expression*. No matter what motivates a scientist to attack a particular problem, the attack proper must be directed by the event studied. Thus his independence and self-assertion with respect to the situation are severely limited. Einstein refers to three motives which actuate scientists in their work: (1) they cultivate science as an opportunity to exercise their particular talents: men exult in science as an athlete enjoys exercising his prowess; (2) they must earn a livelihood; (3) they are devoted to science.[11] These motives, however, must be sublimated in the worker's actual interbehavior. Naturally, because a scientific situation is complex there is room for all sorts of factors, but they must be focussed. Let the scientist be even slightly interested in pecuniary gains aside from the intimate scientific core of the situation and his research is immediately affected. Egotism has only a restricted place in science.

The scientist's spontaneity, individuality, and freedom of operation concerning the events and problems which concern him we do not count as autistic self-expression. We are at present interested in the comparison between different scientists or between the work of the same scientist with different problems. The greater facility of some particular worker, his more intense insight, his wider range of resources, all stem from increased contact with similar events and problems.

Scientific originality, at times so commanding as to appear to give science a completely new turn, is certainly individualistic, but always there is the groundwork, the slow accumulation of materials which make possible the apparently sudden expansion of the flower. It is the final outcome that is new and surprising. The changes, the mutations, are firmly embedded in numerous

---

[11] Preface to Planck's Where is Science Going?

events. The scientist's originality lies therefore in seeing at one glance the various features of the composition.

Einstein's vast originality is sometimes compared with the colossal mastery of factors which challenged Newton. The assumption is that Einstein's attack on his problems stems from a completely new way of looking at things. Our interest is not to minimize this comparison between the two scientists, but merely to call attention to the differences in their scientific situations. First, there is an enormous complexity which, indeed, is rooted in Newtonian developments. Then there is the complication in mathematics achieved in considerable isolation from physical problems. Again, the physical problems themselves have evolved through invention and discovery. The final act is impressively original, but it is a synthetic one. It is interbehavioral.

Experimentation: Method or Magic?

However reasonable the view that science is certainly in part theoretical, even speculative, experimentation remains a pronounced feature of all investigational situations. It is inseverably interrelated with occasion, with developments of technique and instrument. In many cases, too, there is a slow plodding procedure, gigantic amounts of trial and error, and oftentimes tremendous loss of effort. Millikan asserts:

> Four fifths of all the experiments which we make in our physical laboratories in the hope of developing new relations, establishing new laws, or opening up new avenues of progress, are found to be directed along wrong lines and have to be abandoned.[12]

Experimentation, then, is method, not magic.

That experimental operations follow after much reflection and sometimes pilot manipulations is gathered from Franklin's notebook, under date of Nov. 7, 1749, where he sets down a series of similarities between electricity and lightning:

> (1) Giving light; (2) colour of the light; (3) crooked direction; (4) swift motion; (5) being conducted by metals; (6) crack or noise in exploding; (7) subsisting in water or ice; (8) rending bodies it passes through; (9) destroying animals; (10) melting metals; (11) firing inflammable substances; (12) sulphurous smell.

---

[12] *Science*, 1923, 58, 297.

Then he asks the question: Will lightning be attracted and drawn off by points like the electric fluid in Leyden jars? Franklin says: "Let the experiment be made."[13]

The role of scientific experimentation in verifying or testing hypotheses offers further proof that it is method integrated with subject matter. Only after making a theoretical and practical survey of a situation do we construct an hypothesis. The assertion that the formulation of a problem is more essential than the solution implies that manipulations depend directly upon hypotheses. The solution may be merely a matter of experimental skill.[14]

The choice of experimental design depends upon particular circumstances. Take Galileo's experiment to determine the velocity of light. Placing two men with covered lanterns a mile apart to signal to each other by uncovering their lanterns seems much below Galileo's capacity as an experimenter, but it is undeniable that this method fitted his training and experience better than the later type of experiment by Fizeau—namely, to transmit light back and forth by means of mirrors.

Experiments fail. This fact must not be thought of as exceptional. It is often said that scientists report only their final success, whereas a close inspection of the complete handling of a problem indicates many failures and back-tracking. An excellent example is the work of the brilliant physicist Hertz. Hypothesizing that the development of a magnetic field would be convincing evidence that a cathode beam of rays consists of particles, he set up the experiment. It gave negative results: he could not detect a magnetic field. A few years later he set up the experiment of discharging cathode rays between a negatively charged and a positively charged plate, and made the hypothesis that if cathode rays consisted of particles they would be deflected by the charged plates. No such result occurred. The hypotheses, however, were not incorrect; the experiments were defective.[15]

With more refined techniques and better apparatus Perrin and Thomson were able to demonstrate the particle character of cathode rays, a result which had the powerful consequence of

[13] Cajori, History of Physics, p. 129.
[14] Einstein-Infeld, The Evolution of Physics, p. 96.
[15] Cf., Taylor, Physics: The Pioneer Science, p. 776.

establishing the particle character of electricity—the discovery of the electron.[16]

The ambiguous results of careful experiments argue strongly against the magical notion of experimentation. One of the most striking features of 20th century science is that with all the advancement in theory and technical competence the nature of electromagnetic rays cannot be experimentally determined. Experimental set-ups yield discordant results. The Compton effect demonstrates that electromagnetic rays act as particles. On the other hand, the experiments of Davisson and Germer conclusively indicate that light is of a wave nature.

Nor is this an isolated instance of the laboratory. Many other examples prove that discordant results are frequently obtained. Think of the disputes between individual scientists and schools. Whether the varying styles of the experiments are at the basis of these differences, whether we should look for imperfect techniques, for inadequate apparatus, the conclusion is the same: experimentation is part of a concrete situation. Interesting is the incident which Beveridge quotes:

> In Dr. Monroe Eaton's laboratory in the United States influenza virus can be made to spread from one mouse to another, but in Dr. C. H. Andrewes' laboratory in England this cannot be brought about, even though the same strains of mice and virus, the same cages and an exactly similar technique are used.[17]

In scientific circles, of course, magic never meant the use of a wand to obtain results. It merely indicated confidence in the *experimentum crucis*. In other words, it was assumed that a set of operations (demonstrations) would definitely and permanently settle scientific questions. The *experimentum crucis* is properly called a myth.[18] Actually, no important problem is ever solved by one experiment or by one type of experiment. Indeed, different sorts of operations may yield similar results, a fact which interferes violently with the notion of a crucial experiment.

---

[16] Cf., Perrin, Nouvelles propriétés des rayons cathodiques; and Thomson, Cathode Rays. These papers are partially reprinted in Magie, A Source Book in Physics, pp. 580–597.

[17] The Art of Scientific Investigation, p. 24.

[18] Campbell, Principles of Electricity, p. 62.

Experimentation is both an adventure and an arduous labor. This is demonstrated by the breakdown of the ideal of varying one variable at a time and keeping all the other variables constant. In any legitimate research no such simple formula is possible.

Experimentalism and Scientific Slogans

Both the importance and appreciation of scientific experimentation have led to an unsavory consequence: the creation of an ism—*experimentalism*. Experimentation becomes a slogan, a battle cry. No one objects to the slogan when employed to admonish regard for careful and controlled study. Nor is it objectionable when it appears in friendly arguments between theoretical and experimental workers. Nevertheless, there is considerable advantage for science as a whole when we distinguish between experimentation as an integral feature of scientific situations and as a weapon wielded in extra-scientific circumstances. For example, the experimentation argument is used to decry other men's work and to exalt one's own scientific culture by comparing it with one existing at another time.

As a rule, experimentalism is urged in the interest of fact and manipulation. The overemphasis of data leads to devaluation of the work of structuring facts to yield laws and principles. Probably because of an enthusiasm for efficiency, writers have carried into purely scientific work a disproportionate emphasis upon production. The cry is for facts and more facts. Once a technique has been perfected facts are rather easy to obtain. The assumption, however, that facts are ends in themselves pushes aside the theorist, whose work makes facts tell their story and prove their worth. We quote Krogh, the eminent Danish physiologist:

> Facts are necessary, of course, but unless fertilized by ideas, correlated with other facts, illumined by thought, I consider them as only material for science.[19]

He goes on to say:

> I am prepared to submit the thesis, revolting though it may seem, that too many experiments and observations are being made and published and too little thought is being bestowed upon them. It is a statement not too infrequently met with in physiological papers that a cer-

---

[19] The progress of physiology, p. 203.

tain experiment has been repeated on, say, 47 animals. Very often, though by no means always, such a routine procedure is sheer waste of time and animals, and at the root of the apparent diligence lies a mental inertia which carries the experimenter along the accustomed groove with a minimum exertion of the mind.[20]

The gulf between theory construction and fact production may be indicated by still another quotation:

> It is an almost invariable custom of editors of journals to reject papers which do not contain new 'facts.' It is natural to be skeptical toward reasoning not supported by facts, but it must happen in many cases and to many physiologists that their thoughts are illumined by facts which were incompletely understood by those who brought them forward, and I remember more than one occasion where published experiments could be given a much more consistent explanation than that adopted by their authors.[21]

Lord Rutherford aptly expresses the need for both theoretical and experimental activities:

> Experiment without imagination or imagination without recourse to experiment, can accomplish little, but for effective progress, a happy blend of these two powers is necessary.[22]

The insistence upon facts is not so serious as the demand for sheer manipulation to which experimentalism frequently descends. In this case the emphasis is upon mere activity no matter how vain the operations, how trivial the results. Sometimes it is but manipulation of apparatus, the use of instruments borrowed from a neighboring domain. Let it be argued that there is value in sheer manipulation. Surely an interest in apparatus itself can often be justified. Who can tell when an instrument, developed for its own sake, will serve an important and useful purpose? But this engineering enterprise achieves its value only when properly oriented.

Granted, history shows contrasting periods in our civilization, dark ages when science did not flourish and experimentation was not pursued. But this only means that science languished not merely because there was no experimentation: experimentation was not practiced because of prevailing social and political conditions.

---

[20] Ibid., p. 203.
[21] Ibid.
[22] The electrical structure of matter, p. 221.

To sharpen the difference between experimentation as (a) an effective form of scientific investigation and (b) a slogan employed in argument we discuss the following points.

Experimentation not Absolute. Experimentalism implies that instrumental studies are absolute in method and result. One overlooks that interpretation is an integral part of an experiment, moreover that results are frequently capable of varying interpretation. Experimentation is not a universal solvent. The relativity of experimentation is clearly recognized in the assertion that almost any experimental result can be reconciled with almost any theory, provided sufficient subsidiary assumptions are made. The only question is whether it is worthwhile.[23]

Rejection of Experimental Findings. Experimentation as a slogan fares badly in view of the fact that experimental results are not always accepted. New discoveries are resisted when experiments go counter to preferred theory (p. 50 f.). Scientific history provides us with dramatic tales of the gruelling wars fought in the interest of one theory or another. An excellent example is the acceptance and rejection of experimental results concerning fermentation (p. 84) by Pasteur, Cagniard de la Tour, Schwann, Kützing, and Turpin on one side, and Berzelius, Liebig, Wöhler, Helmholtz, and Berthelot on the other. The evidence was much more valued on the basis of the vitalism-physicalism polarity than on laboratory findings.

Discoordination of Results and Interpretations. The dependence of experimentation on time periods, both with respect to available apparatus and ideational system, takes experimentation completely out of the range of formalized argument. When Prout, for example, in 1815 proposed his protyle theory according to which atomic weights should be whole numbers, because atoms were aggregations of the hydrogen element, his suggestion was rejected as being out of line with current experimentation.

> The more results (the chemists) obtained the more impossible it was to express the atomic weights of all the elements as whole numbers.[24]

That Prout's hypothesis was resuscitated in new form after (a) the structure of atoms became known and the proton identified as

---

[23] Cf., Campbell, Principles of Electricity, p. 63.

[24] Aston, Mass Spectra and Isotopes, p. 2.

hydrogen and (b) Aston had discovered that isotopic masses were integral in terms of oxygen as 16 is strong enough evidence that experiments are particular investigative procedures which may sometimes completely miss important facts. Aston comments on this wide gap between the experimental findings (atomic weights) of the 19th century chemists and their consequent rejection of Prout's hypothesis.

> It is interesting to consider the reasons which led to a decision which the subsequent history of science proves to have been as wise in principle as it was wrong in fact.[25]

Experiments Impede Progress. A potent warning against treating experiments as other than tentative interbehavior we find in those situations in which experiments impede proper theories and thus become obstacles to scientific progress. Recall van Helmont's famous willow-tree experiment which is said to be "perfectly correct in both plan and execution"[26] but was made to demonstrate "that all vegetables do immediately and naturally proceed out of the element of water only."[27] Again, the history of chemistry shows an accumulation of observations and experiments covering a century, all serving to establish the phlogistic theory. Though it may be true that ultimately it was the balance that overthrew it, it has been said that the phlogiston theory:

> ... is a remarkable evidence of the fact that at this time the results of weighing and measuring were not the decisive factors in the formation of chemical doctrine.[28]

Soddy dramatizes the historical incident of scientists first rejecting and later accepting Prout's hypothesis. What Stas called an illusion, on the basis of experiments and measurements performed by himself and others (Turner, Penny, Dumas, Marignac), became "the corner stone of modern theories of the structure of atoms." Soddy regards the experiments mentioned as obstructions to scientific progress:

> There is something surely akin to if not transcending tragedy in the fate that has overtaken the life work of that distinguished galaxy

---

[25] Aston, Ibid.
[26] Nordenskiold, The History of Biology, p. 140.
[27] Quoted from McKie, Antoine Lavoisier, p. 65.
[28] Butterfield, Origins of Modern Science, p. 178f.

of nineteenth century chemists, rightly revered by their contemporaries as representing the crown and perfection of accurate scientific measurement. Their hard won results, for the moment at least, appear as of as little interest and significance as the determination of the average weight of a collection of bottles, some of them full and some of them more or less empty.[29]

Psychology, above all, supplies a classic example of how experimentation impedes progress. Psychological experimentation began as an attempt to demonstrate the mystical theory known as Fechnerian psychophysics. Fechner, trained in physics, presented subjects with various stimuli and obtained a generalization $S = K \log R$ presumed to show how psychic states vary with the variation in stimulus energy applied. Despite the fact that his manipulations were quite accurate and his experimental set-up as a whole well conceived, his work nevertheless blocked the path of psychological advancement. The reason is clear: in a scientific enterprise one cannot separate manipulations from interpretations any more than from preceding hypotheses.

Experimentation: The Core of Science

Dissect from the body of experimentation such accretions as exploitation and improper bias: what remains is the core of science. The most effective means of interbehaving precisely with objects and events is through experimentation, assuming, of course, that the situation lends itself to experimental treatment. But note that frequently experiments have to be designed to ascertain whether an alleged event exists. Manipulation in this case follows a critical examination of the allegation. Only when a high probability can be calculated for the existence of the alleged event is the experimental procedure initiated. Generally speaking, there is little difficulty in determining the presence or absence of an event. For the most part the problem shifts to detailed analysis and interpretation of its nature. Experimentation no less than science in general is an adventure in contingential situations. Experimentation is the core of science because a free manipulation of investiga-

---

[29] The Interpretation of the Atom, quoted from Needham and Pagel, Background to Modern Science, p. 107.

tional objects and a judicious handling of events under scrutiny are the best means of reaching desired results.

Experimental Goals

Each specific enterprise has its unique objective. In the following list we indicate some of these experimental goals.

Occurrence Determination. Excluding those situations in which mere tradition and repeated assertion shape the problem—for example, whether something exists or not—occurrence problems arise from the compresence of some thing in a certain situation. Take the classic illustration of phlogiston. Burning metals are observed; it is then alleged that some substance escapes to leave a residue called *corth* or *calx*. The metal is therefore presumed to be composed of calx plus phlogiston. This phlogistic substance is copiously mixed with carbon, such that the regeneration of metals is achieved by heating with carbon. The experimental goal is to demonstrate that the calx residue weighs more than the original metal. Phlogiston must be the scientifically suspected imponderable type of substance. Again, the experimenter may be bent on demonstrating that combustion involves oxygen and the formation of oxides. Then there are the manipulations for reversing the combustion process and controlling the heat-energy transformation.

The twin substance *caloric* similarly illustrates manipulation initiated to test existence or occurrence. Heat was believed to be an imponderable substance until a comparatively late date, despite contrary suggestions made earlier.[30] Here, as in the case of phlogiston, the balance, which Lavoisier made into an important experimental instrument, entered as a prominent manipulative tool. As to lack of weight of caloric, Rumford sums up his mensuration operations as follows:

> The weight of gold is neither augmented nor lessened by *one millionth part*, upon being heated from the point of *freezing water* to that of a *bright red heat*, I think we may safely conclude that all attempts to discover any effect of heat upon the apparent weights of bodies will be fruitless.[31]

---

[30] Bacon, Locke, Bernoulli, Hooke, etc., see p. 238.

[31] Philosophical Transactions of the Royal Society of London, 1799. Quoted by Taylor, Physics: The Pioneer Science, p. 267.

But Rumford also weakened the allegation that caloric exists by showing that it not only was negative in weight but in potency of presence also. Rumford's cannon-boring operations demonstrated that heat could be generated in great quantity by friction.

Presence or Absence. Another experimental goal is to determine the presence or absence of some item already established as existing. Is acetylcholine a necessary factor in neuro-muscular action? Is lactic acid the essential product discoverable in muscular fatigue?

Nature of Object or Event. Many types of experimental manipulation are designed to discover the nature of some object or event. In some instances the manipulations involve analysis and dissection—breaking up a thing to determine its component parts and their interaction. In other situations manipulations are performed to reveal the interrelation of two unreduced objects in a single reaction. The problem here is the effect of one thing upon another. Will the magnetic field deflect a beam? If so, in what direction?

Quantity or Magnitude. A specialized type of experimental goal is directed toward the ascertainment of quantity or magnitude. The discovery of complicated variables, such as rates and amounts, may require the development and application of mensurational instruments. Here experimentation and mensuration converge.[32] Goals are reached by the development of quantitative laws—for example:

$$s = .5gt^2, f = MN/r^2, T = 2\pi\sqrt{m/k}, \Delta x = \sqrt{RT\tau/3\pi\eta rn}$$

Origins and Developments. Experimentation with respect to origins and developments marks the specific manipulations of the biological sciences. By contrast, the physical sciences are primarily concerned with *status quo* problems. Experimentation in physics does not penetrate behind the presently existing properties of things.[33] The frequently quoted exceptions, such as fatigue of metals and hysteresis, by their paucity simply establish the rule.

---

[32] See p. 150.

[33] For this reason physicists favor the principle that "Explanation of a phenomenon is to be sought not in its origin but in its immanent law." Weyl, Philosophy of Mathematics and Natural Science, p. 286.

The biological sciences, featuring embryology, immunology, and genetics, are devoted primarily to genetical experiments. Even when biologists deal with *status quo* factors, as in taxonomy, morphology, and, to a certain extent, ecology, they do not depart from the genetical type of experimental goal.

Synthetic Experiments. Organic chemistry distinguishes itself by its combinatorial and synthetic experiments. Because chemistry is basically a domain of reactions—interrelations between substances—many problems concern the transformation and recombination of elements and radicals. To a great extent, manipulations may be characterized as analogical—namely, the reproduction of structures already known in other related chemical substances.

Event Relations. Because relations constitute generalized event features, our discussion has already included results of relating experiments. We want to point out, however, that there are special relational goals. Correlations and functions are required for connecting two or more different kinds of things. In psychology this is stated in the form of stimulus and response relations; in biology, stimulation and reaction (immunity, antibody, food-growth relations, etc.). The gas laws of Boyle and Gay-Lussac illustrate the kind of formulae achieved by relating variables or events.

Contacts and Constructs in Experimentation

We have seen (p. 103) that experimental contacts for the most part concern observation, manipulation, and transformation of elements and situations. By contrast, constructs concern the worker's references to events, his descriptions and interpretations of them. Contacts and constructs, however, go hand in hand. That experimental manipulation involves construction follows from the fact that experimentation always occurs in situations which exclude casual and random handling of things.

Perhaps in the first place we should put the selection of a problem and the hypotheses governing the investigative procedures for solving it. Lapicque illustrates this feature by contrasting the views of Magendie and Dastre. The former is quoted as going about the solving of problems concerning the physiological processes of the organism's interior in the following manner:

> I wander around there like a rag picker, and at each step I find
> something interesting to put in my basket.[34]

Dastre, horrified by this maxim, used to say:

> When one doesn't know what he is looking for, he doesn't know
> what he finds.[35]

Involved here, of course, is the working hypothesis. It is a guiding and selecting construction, indicating essential ignorance and search; at the same time an orientation which makes manipulations rational and results promising.

At almost every step in any complicated research one needs to devise controlling activities such as hypotheses and alternative trials. When a scientist compares experimental skill, for example, with power of observation, as Thomson does in the following:

> Crookes' success was due not only to his skill as an experimenter
> but also to his power of observation.[36]

he refers not only to his alertness in taking account of any general factor, but even more to his imaginative efficiency in relating things and contriving means of discovering something about them. Thomson indicates that Stokes commended Crookes very highly for enlarging the physicist's conception concerning the "ultimate working of matter."[37]

Why does Lavoisier, instead of Priestley or Scheele, for example, merit the honor of being the founder of modern chemistry? The following is a significant answer:

> Priestley and Scheele were far greater experimenters than Lavoisier: Lavosier as a thinker outran them both.[38]

The inevitable relationship between contacts and constructs is succinctly displayed when experimentation appears to give way

---

[34] Lapicque, L'Orientation actuelle de la Physiologie. Quoted from Moore, Mathematics and Science, p. 31.

[35] Idem.; this is an investigative principle already set forth by Tycho Brahé; cf., Butterfield, Origins of Modern Science, p. 54.

[36] Recollections and Reflections, p. 378.

[37] Ibid.

[38] McKie, Antoine Lavoisier, p. 219.

to "intuitive illumination." Soddy refers to the "pure logical reasoning" by means of which Mme. Curie concluded that alpha rays
were radiant material particles, and Einstein obtained his equivalence law.[39] Careful examination of both situations reveals that
these stupendous results were not achieved by any method remote
from closely interbehaving with events. No, as Mach indicates, it
is only by knowing the interdependence of events that one can
dispense with particular experiments.[40]

[39] The Story of Atomic Energy, pp. 46, 58.
[40] The Science of Mechanics, p. 6.

7

SCIENCE AND MATHEMATICS

Mathematical Character of Science

BEYOND experimentation the next most fundamental feature of modern science is surely the mathematical. One of the most prominent institutions is the view that numbers rule the world, hence that mathematics is one of the foundations of science.

Yet there are vast differences between the mathematical and the so-called content sciences, such as physics, chemistry, biology, and psychology. The latter deal with things in interaction—definite objects—even if they are as subtle and as small as vibrations or particles. The mathematical sciences, aside from directly referring to or representing relations, are concerned with constructs, whether propositions or equations. These differences have been aptly expressed by Mach:

> Although we represent vibrations by the harmonic formula, the phenomena of cooling by exponentials, falls by squares of times, etc., no one will fancy that vibrations *in themselves* have anything to do with the circular functions, or the motion of falling bodies with squares. It has simply been observed that the relations between the quantities investigated were similar to certain relations obtaining between familiar mathematical functions, and these *more familiar* ideas are employed as an easy means of supplementing experience.[1]

Perhaps an even sharper differentiation between equations and events is made by an eminent student of numbers:

> It is impossible to prove by mathematical reasoning any proposition whatsoever concerning the physical world, and only a mathematical crank would be likely now to imagine it his function to do so.[2]

And finally we may refer to Einstein's separation of geometry and experience:

> Insofern sich die Sätze der Mathematik auf die Wirklichkeit be-

---

[1] The Science of Mechanics, p. 492f.
[2] Hardy, The theory of numbers. Cf., also Claude Bernard, An Introduction to the Study of Experimental Medicine, p. 46.

ziehen sind sie nicht sicher, und insofern sie sicher sind, beziehen sie sich nicht auf die Wirklichkeit.[3]

May we not conclude that the relationship between mathematics and science requires considerable clarification. The first step is to observe that mathematics itself is a science—in no sense, then, just a language or a mere tool for carrying on nonmathematical investigations. Since as an independent science mathematics fills a number of cooperative roles alongside the content sciences, our aim is (1) to assess the nature of mathematics and (2) to relate it accurately to other scientific work and results.

Quantitative Aspects of Events

To the question why science should be dominated by mathematics there is one stable answer—namely, the quantitative aspect of events. Considering how important this aspect is it is inevitable that number and the symbols of quantity should occupy an enormous place in the scientific domain. Even in everyday contacts with things we cannot avoid their quantitative features. How much more prominently, then, do quantitative aspects appear in science where the need is so great for definiteness and precision. In dealing with things we cannot escape attending to their lengths, sizes, distances, frequencies and rates. Those who are at least sympathetic toward philosophical thought doubtless approve of the logician's preoccupation with quantity as one of the category classes along with quality, relation, and modality.

The scientist is also interested in quantity as abstracted from things. A refined form of Pythagorean principle thus finds a home in science, since order, proportion, and ratio are of the essence of scientific subject matter.

Still, the importance of quantity and number should not encourage us to make quantity a more significant aspect of things than quality or modality. No less must we shun the glorification of numbers because they are products of abstraction and lend themselves conveniently to the construction of formulae and models.

The Quantitative and the Mathematical

Given the fact that the quantitative treatment of scientific data is a first and rudimentary step, what follows immediately is

---

[3] Geometrie und Erfahrung, p. 3f.

a more analytic and abstract treatment of magnitudes. The obvious example is the use of averages and summations. Accordingly, the quantitative becomes elaborated into the mathematical. This implies a complicated set of activities in which number, quantity, magnitude, and, in general, mathematical constructs are prominent features occurring on a hierarchy of levels.

Number, however, is only *one* department of mathematical science. It must share the mathematical field with order phases of relations—in other words, with topology. Before dealing with the nature of mathematics and its place in the larger domain of science we turn to several preliminary considerations.

First, we should realize that there are various particular mathematical aspects and that scholars differ in their views concerning the character and function of mathematics in general. To illustrate, scientists frequently assert that they follow Gibbs in his view that mathematics is a language for the expression of physical events. It is highly doubtful, however, that Gibbs intended to reduce mathematics to an assemblage of signs, symbols, or terms.[4] Rather, he probably believed that mathematics is an auxiliary discipline serviceable in physics, chemistry, astronomy, and in other content-science contexts.

Secondly, we must distinguish between the linguistic or symbolic features of mathematics and the relations they represent. Numerals, signs, or symbols standing for units and for operations must be separated from the things represented. The linguistic aspects constitute specific kinds of signs, marks, and characters employed for purposes of designation. The actual things of mathematics are definite relationships—for example, order, magnitude, etc.

Finally, mathematical enterprises and the operations of counting, calculating, constructing, and analyzing must not be confused with the products of such operations, nor with the references and symbolizations connected with the products.

Mathematics as Concrete Enterprise

A direct approach to the mathematician's work yields the necessary conclusion that mathematics is the science of relations.

---

[4] Cf., Lewis, The Anatomy of Science, p. 21; also Wheeler, Josiah Willard Gibbs, p. 173.

The relations, of course, with which mathematicians interbehave are of many different sorts. Now because of the many natural and contrived sources of relations and the different applications of the results of encountering these relations, there are many fields of mathematics. For our purpose we need only indicate a few, on the ground that they are closely related to work in the other sciences.

Calculation. Calculation may be characterized as an activity interrelating various items considered as units. It also includes the construction of methods for carrying out the interrelations. Such calculating systems the mathematician calls algorithms or algorisms. There are no better examples than the early Euclidean algorithms for calculating common denominators and estimating the limits of prime numbers. Obviously such techniques are extremely valuable when scientists investigate events.

Graphic Description. A unique department of mathematics connected with scientific work centers around the techniques of analytic geometry. In a general way the mathematician in this domain interbehaves with spatial relations, though we must not limit the spaces involved to the common three dimensions. What we have here is a process of locating and describing points (or other entities) in relation to other points. For this reason the primary construction is the frame of reference, the coordinate system. Whether the mathematician employs Cartesian, polar, Gaussian, or other types of coordinate systems he is indicating the interrelationship between elements.

Geometric forms of mathematical activity we have called primarily descriptive. The term *description*, however, is not to be taken in too narrow a sense. We have already indicated that description is more a matter of identification and location rather than simple reference. Items are interrelated on the basis of ostensive specifications and definitions. But since geometry is analytic a tremendous amount of description and definition can be made in terms of equations and propositions, as well as in terms of spatial organization. We assume here that the equation or function correlates precisely with the geometric relation.

Systemization. Mathematical situations, no less than others, can be analyzed and separated by stressing some single relational feature. For example, the comparatively recent development of the symbolic or logical branch of mathematics emphasizes relational structures. Logical or symbolized relations are more or less completely abstracted from concrete things. To a formalistic mathematician it might seem a mockery to claim that emphasis on form is not retreating from things but getting closer to them. The formalist sets up systems of relations which pertain to a wider range of things than do the equations of a content or applied science. Otherwise, formalistic mathematics would lapse into a sheer game.

Light is cast upon the systemizing trend in mathematics by the efforts of biologists and psychologists to mathematize their domains. They assume that physics has become so successful because it has reduced or elevated its principles to mathematical relations. Why not follow this procedure in biology and psychology? Here is a typical statement of this kind of program:

> The aim of mathematical biology is to introduce into the biological sciences not only quantitative, but also deductive, methods of research. The underlying idea has been to apply to biology the method by which mathematics has been successfully utilized in the physical sciences.[5]

Doubtless the deductive type of system appeals tremendously to content-science workers. Through relational systems they hope to develop firm and absolute structures.

Statistics. Mathematicians who incline toward "purely aesthetic relationships" tend to misprize the statistical aspect, an attitude repugnant to anyone interested in the interrelations of mathematics with the other sciences. When the relations of things are important one does not bother about the purity and elegance of the structure one builds. Anyone absorbed in the practical side of interconnecting things and events does not reject utilitarian means. From a systematic standpoint statistical mathematics may well be inelegant. Calculation, description, logical organization, are all intermingled in order to achieve certain investigational results.

Mathematics in Science

Assuming then that mathematics is a type of work, yielding definite products in the way of knowledge and principles, we may

---

[5] Rapoport and Landau, Mathematical biology. For a criticism of the attempt to mathematize sociology, see Grebenik's review of Rashevsky's Mathematical Biology of Social Behavior.

now examine the points of contact between it and the other sciences. Clearly the connections are specific and operational. We cannot allow any metaphysical interpretation of mathematics, even that of Kelvin, who, in order to decry the verbalistic variety, declared that "mathematics is the only true metaphysics."[6] How close it was to everyday things he meant to indicate when he said "it is merely the etherialization of common sense."[7]

Mathematics in science is no transcendent discipline which engenders abstruse theories capable of explaining everything in general. Conversely it is the merit of mathematics to be utilizable in scientific situations. This implies a functional mutuality. Scientific history shows that many times one needs to search for a suitable mathematics (p. 132). When, as often happens, no existing mathematical processes are available, new mathematical inventions have to be made.

By the same token some kinds of scientific enterprises are much more amenable to mathematical treatment than others—astronomical events, for instance. Recall how Kepler tied up the laws of planetary motion and the elements of our solar system with the theory of conic sections. Generally speaking, the explanatory employment of mathematics in science accords best with those branches concerned with abstract data. Where motions, accelerations, and changes in magnitude and direction are under investigation, there we find favorable conditions for employing mathematical processes. *Per contra*, wherever qualities, origins, and evolutions are the focus of attention mathematics can only approach with extreme caution.

The contacts of mathematics and science are both intrinsic and extrinsic. In the former, mathematics is employed to aid the various features of the scientific enterprise. Extrinsic contacts are on the whole less legitimate connections and involve evaluative rather than operational phases of mathematics.

A. INTRINSIC CONTACTS

1. *Mathematics and Data.* Here we differentiate between contacts with crude and with refined data. In the former the place

---

[6] Thompson, Life of Lord Kelvin, p. 1124.

[7] Ibid., p. 1139. Compare Kelvin's remark with Laplace's: The theory of probabilities is at bottom only common sense reduced to calculus. A Philosophical Essay on Probabilities, p. 196.

of mathematics is not always salutary. For example, there is danger of making mathematics a false criterion in the sense of emphasizing quantitative features. Since first contacts with crude events consist of selection and identification it is unwise to stress one feature or one type of characteristic. Especially to be avoided is the substitution of mathematical relations for the properties of things. Splendid illustrations of such hazards abound in the past and present practice of scientists with color, sound, and other patent characteristics of objects.

Probably a more serious range of errors occurs in the opposed views of physicists with respect to data in the field of quantum mechanics. Note how Einstein, who is credited with formulating the leading ideas in the quantum domain, fails to go along with those physicists who value it as a sound body of theory. The ground is that Einstein refuses to accept a mathematical or statistical description of the basic and primary data.[8] His attitude has been accounted for by his adopting a philosophy which clashes with that of other workers.

It is certainly questionable whether we should regard quantum mechanical data as crude. No question exists, however, that, when abstractional materials are approached, insistence upon individual and isolable units cannot have the same appeal. Rare is the case in which refined data are unadulterated with quantitative or other mathematical factors.

2. *Mathematics in Investigation.* Even the most elementary scientific manipulations may require mathematical techniques as aids. It is hardly likely that precision, or even accuracy, can be achieved without the quantitative procedures of applied mathematics. Though calculating techniques are often indispensable, they should not be overrated as compared with other procedures —for example, experimental design and manipulation.

The functional relationship between mathematics and investigation is indicated in an anecdote concerning Coulomb: despite his ability as a mathematician he carried out his experimentation in electricity and magnetism without putting the results into mathematical form, a procedure he left for Poisson.[9]

---

[8] See Schilpp (ed), Albert Einstein: Philosopher-Scientist.

[9] Still, Soul of Lodestone, p. 172.

Even more striking is the situation of Faraday, whom Kelvin called the greatest physical genius of all time.[10] It is said that this eminent electric and magnetic experimenter and founder of electromagnetic science professed a certain innocence of numbers, asserting that only once in the course of his life did he perform a mathematical calculation—namely, when he turned the handle of Babbage's calculating machine.[11] Yet Kelvin points out that Faraday was perfectly able to carry on extraordinary investigations:

> Faraday, without mathematics, divined the result of the mathematical investigation; and, what has proved of infinite value to the mathematicians themselves, he has given them an articulate language in which to express their results. Indeed, the whole language of the magnetic field and "lines of force" is Faraday's. It must be said for the mathematicians that they greedily accepted it, and have ever since been most zealous in using it to the best advantage.[12]

Compare the parallel work of Faraday and Clerk Maxwell. As is well known, Maxwell is presumed to have translated Faraday's findings into mathematical form. Maxwell, however, did not differentiate between the mathematical and experimental methods. He explains that he refrained from reading mathematical works on the subject of electricity until he had first gone through Faraday's *Experimental Researches on Electricity*. He then goes on to say:

> I was aware that there was supposed to be a difference between Faraday's way of conceiving phenomena and that of the mathematicians. So that neither he nor they were satisfied with each other's language. I had also the conviction that this discrepancy did not arise from either party being wrong. I was first convinced of this by Sir William Thomson to whose advice and assistance, as well as to his published papers, I owe most of what I have learned on this subject.
> As I proceeded with the study of Faraday, I perceived that his method of conceiving the phenomena was also a mathematical one, though not exhibited in the conventional form of mathematical symbols. I also found that these methods were capable of being expressed in the ordinary mathematical forms, and thus compared with those of the professed mathematicians.

---

[10] Campbell, The Principles of Electricity, p. 63.
[11] Still, op. cit., p. 210.
[12] Quoted from Still, op. cit., p. 210.

For instance, Faraday, in his mind's eye, saw lines of force travers-ing all space where the mathematicians saw centers of force attracting at a distance. Faraday sought the seat of the phenomena in real actions going on in the medium; they were satisfied that they had found it in a power of action at a distance impressed on electric fluids.

When I had translated what I considered to be Faraday's ideas into mathematical form, I found that, in general, the results of the two methods coincided, so that the same phenomena were accounted for and the same laws of action deduced by both methods, but Faraday's methods resembled those in which we begin with the whole and arrive at the parts by analysis, while the ordinary mathematical methods were founded on the principle of beginning with the parts and building up the whole by synthesis.

I found, also, that several of the most fertile methods of research discovered by the mathematicians could be expressed much better in terms of ideas derived from Faraday than in their original form.[13]

So far we have considered only the so-called exact sciences, those investigative situations presumed to be sufficiently abstrac-tive to accommodate mathematical techniques. Now we turn to the biological domain where the employment of mathematics is primarily of the technical sort. Organization and calculation are decidedly instrumental in eliciting properties and characteristics of events which cannot be abstracted far from original qualities.

Measurement and calculation can be best applied, of course, to simpler and more mechanical happenings. For this reason we may be misled into believing that such events are more real than other kinds and that science is reducible to these formal opera-tions. From the very dawn of modern science the emphasis of mathematical application placed a greater value upon the then measurable and thus obstructed the investigative path of the organic and psychological sciences—a disability from which we have not yet recovered. We still suffer from the conception that only the measurable, the rigorously calculable, are scientific, though the wiser of even physical scientists do not share this view. For example, Professor G. N. Lewis definitely rejects such a notion:

I have no patience with attempts to identify science with measure-

---

[13] A Treatise on Electricity and Magnetism, Preface. As an example of Faraday's fertile methods, Maxwell gives the theory of the potential as a quantity satisfying a certain partial differential equation.

ment, which is but one of its tools, or with any definition of the scientist
which would exclude a Darwin, a Pasteur, or a Kekulé.[14]

To his list can be added Harvey, Linnaeus, Schwann, Schleiden,
Mendel, Virchow, and many others. To overemphasize measurement and calculation is to overlook the place of hypothesis-making
and experimentation which mathematics only aids but does not
supplant.

But what about statistics in biology and psychology? In both
these sciences statistics are indispensable tools. Claude Bernard,[15]
probably the most striking opponent of statistics in biology, never
dreamt of objecting to statistics as investigative aids. Rather, he
disapproved of the replacement of data by numerals or formulae.
Mach and Einstein, we have seen, make this same point relative
to physical events. Even when such substitution is not intended,
the wrong emphasis on method, rule, and formula—in short,
technical device—obstructs investigation. Discussing the statistical situation in America, E. B. Wilson says:

> It is not the illuminated and generalizing minds of Farr and Galton
> that guide us on our way, but the cheerful chatter of the Hollerith tabu-
> lator and the Millionair calculator.[16]

Now no one would be so bold as to decry the use of mechanical
aids in any sort of achievement. It would be a peculiar form of
egomania to suppose that the human organism can get along
without technical extensions of its activities. We must increase
our seeing powers by microscopes and telescopes, our hearing
powers by vacuum tubes. But extension is not substitution. In the
field of statistics we can use more and more devices, an increasing
number of formulae, more and more tabulators and calculators,
but they can only be utilized to execute ideas representing sound
reflection.

The scientist is prior to the machine. Machines cannot initiate
or direct an investigation. Only the scientist can do that. We
must admit, even insist, that certain techniques or formulae make
it possible for the scientist to achieve things otherwise impossible,
but these aids are only of value when properly directed. Correla-

[14] The Anatomy of Science, p. 6.
[15] Principes de Médecine Expérimentale.
[16] Statistical inference, p. 291.

tion coefficients or functional equations are powerful tools in scientific accomplishment; they can also be worthless or even misleading devices. A functional equation indicates the degree of relationship between events only when we can first experimentally or otherwise determine that there is a relation to measure.

Professor Wilson admirably states the case for man versus statistical techniques:

> A method is a dangerous thing unless its underlying philosophy is understood, and none more dangerous than the statistical. Our aim should be, with care, to avoid in the main erroneous conclusions. In a mathematical and strictly logical discipline the care is one of technique; but in a natural science and in statistics the care must extend not only over the technique but to the matter of judgment, as is necessarily the case in coming to conclusions upon any problem of real life where the complications are great. Over-attention to technique may actually blind one to the dangers that lurk about on every side—like the gambler who ruins himself with his system carefully elaborated to beat the game. In the long run it is only clear thinking, experienced methods, that win the strongholds of science.[17]

To sum up the place of mathematics in investigative situations: Mathematical techniques are equally indispensable along with other techniques; that is, whenever and however they can further the achievement of knowledge, the control of events, they are essential features of the scientific enterprise. Still, there is no substitute for events as the basis of investigation. They can neither be displaced nor reduced to anything else. Events are not equations or formulae except in the specialized mathematical domain.[18]

3. *Mathematics in Theory Construction.* Theory construction in science is particulate and multiple. Since the events to be interpreted are many and varied, theory construction is correspondingly heterogenous. In some cases theories may well be mathematical in nature, even extreme in the abstractional character of the relations summed up. Laws may be stated in terms of n-spaces, infinitely minute or enormously large time intervals. One rule is stringent: The theory must be derived from and applicable to the events.

Probably because mathematical formulae and equations are

---

[17] The statistical significance of experimental data, p. 94.
[18] Cf., Stigler, The Mathematical Method in Economics.

creative products they are frequently employed to build up laws and interpretations distantly removed from events. As a pertinent exhibit we quote Jeans:

> Our knowledge of the external world must always consist of numbers, and our picture of the universe—the synthesis of our knowledge—must necessarily be mathematical in form. All the concrete details of the picture, the ether and atoms and electrons, are mere clothing that we ourselves drape over our mathematical symbols—they do not belong to Nature, but to the parables by which we try to make Nature comprehensible. It was, I think, Kronecker who said that in arithmetic God made the integers and man made the rest; in the same spirit, we may add that in physics God made the mathematics and man made the rest.[19]

This is an extreme form of attributing characteristics to the things of science. Even Eddington who does not blanch in the face of creative powers which produce the entire "external world" insists that the mathematics employed to create theoretical physics is put there by the scientist.[20] Surely the imaginative processes so warmly commended by Tyndall, Rutherford, and others are carried to an inglorious extreme.

Not so far fetched, though no more effective, is the view that by means of mathematical formulae one can attain a high form of rationality and certainty. It is argued that mathematical explanation accords scientists a deductive power not to be surpassed. At once we ask: Are not equating and premising propositions obtained by definite manipulative contacts with things? If so, how can the formulae, which at best can be used to refer to or describe events and their transformations, accord more scientific power than the original manipulations?

Concealed in the background of the faith in the deductive principle is the time-honored doctrine that the procedure of Euclidean geometry constitutes the essential reasoning process. Today it should be common knowledge that the compelling powers and validity of the syllogistic-geometric procedure lie in nothing else than its structure. From our present point of vantage Euclidean definitions, axioms, and general rules are arbitrary. The same argument applies to the more recent formal reasoning of symbolic logic.

---

[19] The new-world picture, p. 356.
[20] The Philosophy of Physical Science.

B. EXTRINSIC RELATIONS

The extrinsic connection of mathematics with science lies in the sheer use of numbers, formulae, and equations as slogans and propaganda. Such is the attempt to employ mathematics for establishing a general philosophy—for example, a realism instead of an idealism. To formulate an epistemology in this way involves a double impropriety. First, one misinterprets mathematics; secondly, one implies that to develop scientific abstractions to the point of mathematical formulae justifies far-fetched metaphysical extrapolations. The notorious universe created by a supreme geometer signalizes the scientist's flight into theology.

Reciprocity between Mathematical and Other Sciences

History provides an array of instances in which mathematics has been indispensable for the progress of observation and experiment, while the development of contacts with events has stimulated the invention of algorithms and calculi of all sorts.

Mathematics Aids Science. In the early days of modern science it was the geometric form of mathematics that proved so beneficial for scientific development. It is a familiar story how Kepler made use of conic sections developed by the Greeks centuries before his time. Nor can one overestimate the importance of Descartes' formulation of analytic geometry.

Of the more definitely calculative and analytic mathematics useful for scientific development we mention imaginary numbers and the theory of complex numbers erected on the former as a base. A common illustration is the use of $\sqrt{-1}$ for describing facts of alternating electrical currents.

Coming now to the great developments of science in the 20th century, we cannot pass up the story of Einstein consulting his mathematical colleagues Pick in Prague and Grossmann in Zürich when constructing his relativity theory.[21] They informed him of the invention by Ricci and Levi-Civita of a general differential calculus. Also, in connection with quantum mechanics it is illuminating how effectively Jordan and Born applied matrix algebra. Born relates how when the need arose to interpret wave

---

[21] Frank, Einstein, His Life and Times, p. 103.

mechanics[22] he was reminded of once hearing about this type of mathematics.

Science Stimulates Mathematics. If the natural sciences are so greatly indebted to mathematics for aid, the compliment is returned in full measure. Think only of the development of the differential and integral calculus through the study of mechanics. In his *Development of Mathematics* Bell considers the results of the impact of scientific problems on the evolution of mathematics. He lists: (1) the vast domain of differential equations, (2) the analysis of many special functions arising in potential theory and other situations, (3) potential theory itself, (4) the calculus of variations, (5) integral equations, (6) functional analysis, (7) statistical analysis, and (8) differential geometry.[23]

Another writer[24] points to strategic developments in both pure and applied mathematics arising out of the impulse given by science to the study of trigonometric series.

Fourier in his studies on the "flow" of heat likewise demonstrated the importance of trigonometric series. Heat conduction involves wave motion, thus variations in the amplitude of the components of a wave form. Fourier also developed the theorem that every wave motion, no matter what the form of the advancing disturbance, can be represented as the superposition of component sine waves of different wave lengths. Harmonic analysis of the varying amplitudes of wave components comprise the more applied aspects of Fourier's work. The intense interest in trigonometric series has led to the development of the theory of functions of a real variable, to Cantor's point set theory, and to Riemann's integral.[25]

If, as we have pointed out, the influences are really mutual, we should expect a correlation of mathematics and science. It is superfluous to speculate how mathematical formulae harmonize with the relations of events. Langevin puts the matter in the form of a magical fitness of abstract mathematical products and practical scientific needs:

---

[22] The Restless Universe, p. 132, also Experiment and Theory in Physics, p. 17f.

[23] P. 335.

[24] Moore, Mathematics and science. See also Bell, Development of Mathematics, p. 270.

[25] Moore, p. 29.

It is nevertheless just and necessary to emphasize here the remarkable fact that among the abstract constructions realized by mathematicians, while taking for an exclusive guide their need for logical perfection and increasing generality, none seems to remain useless to the physicist. By a singular harmony, the needs of the mind, desirous of constructing an adequate representation of reality, seem to have been foreseen and provided for by the logical analysis and the abstract esthetics of the mathematician.[26]

Considering the common matrix of scientific and mathematical work we can understand Dirac's observation how so-called mathematical fictions can be adapted to the data most recently developed:

The steady progress of physics requires for its theoretical formulation a mathematics that gets continually more advanced. This is only natural and to be expected. What, however, was not expected by the scientific workers of the last century was the particular form that the line of advancement would take, namely, it was expected that the mathematics would get more and more complicated, but would rest on a permanent basis of axioms and definitions, while actually the modern physical developments have required a mathematics that continually shifts its foundations and gets more abstract. Non-Euclidean geometry and non-commutative algebra, which were at one time considered to be purely fictions of the mind and pastimes for logical thinkers, have now been found to be very necessary for the description of general facts of the physical world.[27]

There are abundant illustrations reinforcing the notion that abstruse mathematical relations can be matched by concrete events. Moore refers to Perrin's correlation of the trajectories of Brownian particles with continuous functions without a derivative. Perrin writes:

The entanglements of the trajectory are so numerous and so rapid that it is impossible to follow them and the trajectory noted is infinitely simpler and shorter than the real trajectory. Likewise, the mean apparent velocity of a particle during a given time varies widely in magnitude and direction without tending to a limit when the time of the observer decreases, as we see in a simple fashion by noting the positions of a particle in the camera lucida, first from minute to minute, and then every five seconds, or better still by photographing them each twentieth of a second, as has been done by Victor Henri, Comandon and de

---

[26] Moore, p. 30.

[27] Dirac, Quantized singularities in the electrochemical field, p. 60.

Broglie, in order to cinematograph the movement. One can no longer fix a tangent, even in approximate fashion, at any point of the trajectory, and we have a case where it is truly natural to think of those continuous functions without derivates, which the mathematicians have devised and which one would regard erroneously as mere mathematical curiosities, since Nature suggests them as well as functions with a derivative.[28]

Perrin argues that formulated systems of mathematicians are closer to reality than the more practical propositions of physicists:

> We all know how, before a rigorous definition is given, we point out to beginners that they already possess the notion of continuity. We trace for them a beautifully smooth curve, and we remark on placing a ruler against the contour: "You see that at each point there exists a tangent." Or again, to communicate the still more abstract idea of the true velocity of a moving body at a point of its trajectory, we say: "You surely perceive, do you not, that the mean velocity between two neighboring points of this trajectory becomes approximately constant when the points approach each other indefinitely?" And many minds, indeed, remembering that for certain familiar movements it appears to be so, do not see that the situation involves great difficulties.
>
> The mathematicians, however, have well understood the defect in rigor of these so-called geometric considerations, and how childish it is, for example, to attempt to demonstrate, by tracing a curve, that every continuous function possesses a derivative. Functions with a derivative are the simplest and the easiest to deal with, but they are nevertheless an exceptional case; or, if we prefer geometric language, curves which have no tangents are the rule, and the very regular curves, such as the circle, are very interesting but very special cases.
>
> At first glance such restrictions seem to be only an intellectual exercise, ingenious without doubt, but definitely artificial and sterile, involving the pushing to a mania of the desire for complete rigor. And, most frequently, those to whom one speaks of curves without tangents or functions without derivatives, begin by thinking that Nature does not present such complications or even suggest the idea of them. The contrary is nevertheless true, and the logic of the mathematicians has kept them nearer to reality than the supposedly more practical representations of the physicists.[29]

Mathematics and Science as Interbehavioral Fields

On an interbehavioral basis mathematics is deprived of all absoluteness and omnipotence. It is both a scientific and non-

---

[28] Les Atomes, ch. 4, quoted from Moore, Mathematics and science, p. 29f.
[29] Ibid., Preface, quoted from Moore, Ibid., p. 30.

scientific enterprise. The casual manipulation of relations—such as amateur number work[30] or playing with magic squares—the serious application of calculations, and the systemizing procedures in scientific investigation are activities of persons performed in connection with stimulus objects which happen to be relations. And the kind of manipulations depends upon the individual's interbehavioral history. The things interbehaved with—namely, mathematical relations—are developed mostly by the worker. True enough, there is an autonomous basis for many relations in *rerum natura*, but no other scientific domain is so full of unique and complete (independent) construction as is mathematics.

Scientific mathematics is strictly limited with respect to things and events unless it is employed in a purely descriptive or simply analogous manner. Otherwise it must be controlled by the worker's contacts with the investigated events. This fact justifies the assertion that numbers in science result from measurement; it also explains why it is just as essential to have texts, as well as equations, and a comparable analysis of both.[31]

In a letter to Maxwell, Faraday points out perfectly the relationship of (a) mathematical work and description, (b) experimental work, and (c) events (physical actions). He makes plain why mathematical equations must conform to the events calculated or described. The relevant parts of the letter merit quotation:

> There is one thing I would be glad to ask you. When a mathematician engaged in investigating physical actions and results has arrived at his conclusions, may they not be expressed in common language as fully, clearly, and definitely as in mathematical formulae? If so, would it not be a great boon to such as I to express them so?—translating them out of their hieroglyphics, that we also might work upon them by experiment. I think it must be so, because I have always found that you could convey to me a perfectly clear idea of your conculsions, which, though they may give me no full understanding of the steps of your process, give me the results neither above nor below the truth, and so clear in character that I can think and work from them. If this be possible, would it not be a good thing if mathematicians, working on these subjects, were to give us the results in this popular, useful, working state, as well as in that which is their own and proper to them?[32]

---

[30] In his brief book on the Greeks (p. 191) Kitto mentions his discoveries of number relations.

[31] Cf., Bridgman, The Nature of Physical Theory, pp. 59, 69, 72.

[32] Campbell and Garnett, Life of James Clerk Maxwell, p. 290.

Pertinent here also is the reaction Faraday reports to Maxwell upon receiving a copy of the latter's paper on "Lines of Force":

> I received your paper . . . I was at first almost frightened when I saw such mathematical force made to bear upon the subject, and then wondered to see that the subject stood it so well.[33]

No more powerful scientific instrument than mathematics in its measuring and calculating features has as yet been devised for making contacts with events definite and accurate. It remains our choice, however, to stress either (a) the work of the mathematician and the situation which makes his work possible or (b) the product of his work and the effectiveness of its application. In the latter case we risk making the mathematical factors into magical or mystical things.

The interbehavioral approach to the significance of mathematics in science bears fruitful results in the study of the statistical aspects of science. Consider the following by Planck:

> It is now generally agreed that heat movement of molecules and conduction of heat, like all other *irreversible phenomena*, do not obey dynamical laws but *statistical laws*. The latter are the laws of probability.[34]

Passing over such stylistic use of words as "phenomena obeying laws" we may ask what differentiates between dynamic and statistical laws? Assuming there are events to begin with, interbehavior with solid particles in mechanical interaction necessarily yields different kinds of data and requires different operations. An interbehavioral approach enables us to distinguish between events and the results of enumerating, measuring or describing them. For instance, it allows for interest in an individual's survival, as well as in the wager that he will or will not survive on the basis of various facts ascertained about him. We make no error if we limit our interest to sheer numbers, since the background situation does not permit us to revert to pure Pythagorean-Platonic essences. Sensitivity to concrete circumstances helps to differentiate between medical and physiochemical statistics, prevents us from overstressing the methods of any one type of situation.

---

[33] Campbell and Garnett, loc. cit., p. 519f.
[34] Where is Science Going?, p. 190.

Mathematics as Operational and Rational Institutions

In the scientific domain mathematics plays several dramatic roles. We are familiar with its operational character (p. 124f.). Now consider its contrasting role as the rational and deductive principle in scientific enterprises. Curiously enough this aspect of mathematics is supported by the assertion that since prediction is an important means of confirming propositions the propositions themselves must be deductive. This prediction potency of propositions, their power to confirm anticipations and justify hypotheses, is presumed to lie in their mathematical and deductive traits.

Overlooked, of course, is the fact that prediction implies no mathematical fixity. Predictability is a feature of concrete events, not of eternally fixed relations or sentence coupling. To assume that prediction involves mathematical deduction distorts the assertion that the function of a competent theory is to obviate experimentation, because the theory can foretell the results experimentation will yield.[35]

In what sense does prediction imply deduction? The answer calls for close inspection of the differences between scientific prediction and mathematical deduction, a distinction not to be blurred by verbally equating the two.

This brings us to the question whether mathematics itself is a deductive science. Here we must differentiate between mathematical investigation and the setting up of closed deductive systems. Is it true that the "perfect rigor no one dreams of doubting" which Poincaré attributes to mathematics is[36] nothing more than a constructional organization of propositions? We say nothing about the inseverability of related things, even such abstract things as artifactual points. Is mathematical induction free from the influence, for instance, of the objects forcing themselves upon the constructor of an n→n+1 system?

And what about recent developments in the logic of mathematics? Developments which indicate the proper nature of axioms and teach us, moreover, that we must dispense with absolutes. Are we not forced to consider the worker's mutual relations to the things upon which he works? Perhaps, then, we are not con-

---

[35] Jordan, Die Physik und das Geheimnis des organischen Lebens, p. 37, also Mach, The Science of Mechanics, p. 6.

[36] Foundations of Science, p. 31.

cerned, after all, with rigid deductional systems in science, even if they exist in mathematics. Rather, we are occupied with an organization of data and laws.

It happens that rationalism and deduction are fostered less by the workers in well established and productive domains, such as physics and chemistry, where the tradition has developed that mathematics is an auxiliary discipline. Here mathematics is regarded as a language, serviceable for stating precisely the findings research reveals. Consider at this point the view of a mathematician:

> ... discovery after all is more important in science than strict deductive proof. Without discovery there is nothing for deduction to attack and reduce to order.[37]

We conclude that what passes for powers of prediction and deduction—in short, any long-range connection with all types of *a priori*—boils down to the practical processes of generalization. Science by various means enables us to control, analyze, and synthesize things, whether in their molecular, atomic, or subatomic form. But this always signifies interbehavior. By hitting upon a stable object or event, by calculating the probability based on contact with many events, we construct a general law. Again we suggest that it matters not whether we call this generalizing procedure *deduction* so long as we keep before us the interbehavioral situation.

---

[37] Bell, Development of Mathematics, p. 76.

CHAPTER

8

SCIENCE AND MEASUREMENT

Measurement: Science or Method?

MEASUREMENT justifiably occupies an exalted position in science. Even more than experimentation it dominates the investigative domain. We have mentioned the allegation that measurement is the very essence of science, that science *is* mensuration. This is plain confusion. Mensurational operations are certainly essential to investigation. But measurement is not identical with observation, with research, not even with manipulation. Why confound one type of means with the character or end of science? Worse still, the idolator of measurement confounds the means with the things investigated. Thus is born the fallacy that the numeral which refers to or describes a quality or dimension of a thing is the thing itself. Matters stand little better when a number as the product of a measurement is identified with the thing measured.

Scope and Importance of Measurement

To reject the identification of measurement and science is not to minimize the scope and importance of measurement. However rash it may be to declare that physics is the mensurational science, except in the practical sense that the physicist concerns himself with things and events available for mensurative operations, we nevertheless cannot overestimate the value of such operations when it is possible to carry them out. These operations constitute elaborate manipulations which stress first the properties and relations of objects and events and secondly the precise means for ascertaining the required knowledge.

Measurement in Practice and Theory

Mensurational interbehavior developed earlier than experimentation. Comparison and calculation operations have been available longer than the transformational procedures of experimentation. Still, mensuration has been less well understood and more distorted in theory.

Like experimentation, mensuration is frequently regarded as magical, thus made a weapon of intellectual combat. In addition, through its connection with number, it has been hailed as an open sesame to truth and reality. Quantity, which is identified with number, is readily obtained through measurement. Those who are impressed with the potency of number to penetrate to the heart of reality and seek certainty and absoluteness, glorify mensuration beyond any legitimate limit. In thus making science kin to religion they distort the scientific enterprise.

By a peculiar paradox of history mensurational theory has evolved under stress of two opposed influences. The first includes the character of things and the investigator's interest. An immense series of practices has developed out of the crudest techniques, yielding information about things, their shapes, structure, linear and mass dimensions. The second influence consists of the traditional views concerning the superiority and greater reality of quantity in comparison with quality. Again the dichotomy of the extensional versus the intensional! A brief survey of the history of this second influence supplies an important clue to valid and invalid measurement theories.

Quality and Extension

Scientific theories disagree concerning the origin of the idea that somehow numbers are more real than things. What motivated Renaissance scientists to declare that the Book of Nature is written in the language of number? It has been suggested that the influence was Neoplatonic and Pythagorean, that numbers constitute the essence of things as the Pythagoreans established in their numerology.[1] There was also the medieval glorification of number as part of a grand theological tradition. Lastly it is argued that the glorification of numbers is a natural result of the aspiration to achieve precision and accuracy through mensuration.[2]

One thing cannot be questioned: Numerological influence has promoted a sharp separation between qualities and numbers.

---

[1] Burtt, The Metaphysical Foundations of Modern Physical Science; also Method and metaphysics in the science of Isaac Newton.

[2] Strong, Procedures and Metaphysics.

Strangely enough this separation became wider as modern science progressed. While Kepler did not deny reality to nonmathematical qualities, he nevertheless relegated them to a minor position in the reality scale. Galileo vigorously denied the natural existence of qualities and claimed reality only for quantities. Newton, definitely following Galileo, assumed a position which Descartes formulated as the opposition between thought and extension.

Those who argue that it was procedure rather than metaphysics which dictated this development can find a platform to stand on in the great success of the numerative view in the early stages of modern scientific evolution. Think first of Kepler who put the geometry of conic sections to such excellent use in formulating his three famous laws. Other important scientific results seem to justify the numerical viewpoint. Actually, very little advance could have been made at this early period in manipulating the *qualitative* aspects of things—hence the importance of the numerical; it had no competition. This is the elementary period of matter and motion, the age when Descartes declared he could construct the world, given only movement and space.

The extensive scientific development since that time proves that it was not at all necessary to dissect objects and events on the basis of extension and intension. An objective handling of things excludes reality variations among the qualities of things. It is baseless error to regard measurement as a means for discriminating between the properties of things, and then to elevate some of these aspects to a superior status. We have here a subversion of the entire procedure and purpose of mensurational operations. The result in scientific circles is the theory that measurement is applied mathematics.

Measurement as Applied Mathematics

This theory is responsible not only for misprizing actual objects, their qualities and properties: it glorifies the rational aspects of scientific situations; it exalts the reasoning powers presumed best to deal with them. The techniques we are about to list vary enormously; the bad result is the same.

Overemphasis on Mensurable Events. Obviously some things and events are easier to manipulate than others. This facility of number-yielding operations is then exploited to establish the stability of science.

Take Kelvin's remark about measurement:

> In physical science a first essential step in the direction of learning
> any subject is to find principles of numerical reckoning and methods
> for practicably measuring some quality connected with it. I often say
> that when you can measure what you are speaking about, and express
> it in numbers, you know something about it; but when you cannot
> measure it, when you cannot express it in numbers, your knowledge is
> of a meager and unsatisfactory kind: it may be the beginning of knowl-
> edge, but you have scarcely, in your thoughts, advanced to the stage
> of *science*, whatever the matter may be.[3]

This statement, always taken out of context, is made to serve
as authority for the applied mathematical theory. Actually, Kelvin
is referring to particular situations, in which case his point is well
taken. Moreover, he in no wise is overevaluating measurement
because it yields numbers as compared with manipulations yielding
knowledge. Furthermore, he speaks of knowledge, not of existence.
Even his stress upon measurement would no doubt be modified
for other investigative domains. Biologists and biochemists, for
instance, could hardly place so high an estimate on measurement
as the generator of numbers.[4]

Measurement Based on Numbers. Helmholtz is one of the
foremost proponents of the applied-mathematics theory of measurement. In his writings we can trace the basic technique of
stressing numbers rather than operations upon things. He goes
at once to the point that mensurational operations require some
rationale.[5] This is not strange. A strong believer in the rational
role of mechanics, he thought that a source of scientific certainty
could be found in mathematics. The laws of measurement he
therefore attempted to reduce to the laws of arithmetic.

Measurement as Interbehavior

The applied-mathematics theory of measurement has become
crystallized into the formula that measurement consists of as-
signing numbers to things. This proposition obviously simplifies
a complex procedure. Even the most abstract formula: "Measurement is a form of symbolization"[6] hints at the work of the meas-

---

[3] Popular Lectures, Vol. 1, p. 73.

[4] See George, The Scientist in Action.

[5] As Planck (Where is Science Going?, p. 84) quotes Helmholtz, measurement is a sign which must be interpreted.

[6] Craik, The Nature of Explanation, p. 75.

urer. The notion of numeral assignment clearly indicates the operations upon things measured. What is required is the specification of (a) the circumstances of mensurational situations, (b) the work performed and (c) results obtained. What measuring operations achieve is illustrated by the following four results:

1. *Equilibrium.* By use of a lever system or balance a suitable comparison can be made between various magnitudes or degrees of massiveness. The result is obtained in the form of an equilibrium established between selected units of the things to be measured.

2. *Equivalence.* Mensurational interbehavior yields equivalence of objects as in measuring specific gravity and in making color comparisons.

3. *Effect Production.* The widest range of mensurational operations is concerned with producing effects which serve either as simple indicators or as more definite determiners. Examples are (1) torsions and deformities, as in the practical domain of strength-of-material determinations; (2) chemical reactions, where reversible and irreversible changes are brought about: electrolytic deposition, for example, is not only a measure of electrical activity but serves also to evaluate and estimate properties of things; effects upon instruments, such as galvanometers, ammeters, etc., may be regarded as results or simply as indicators of electrical activity; and (3) the mensurational result that brings about behavior through various sorts of stimulation, such as applying tests.

4. *Item Ordering.* Ordering and scaling items, placing things and events in series, represent another form of mensurational interbehavior.

A distinctive feature in all these situations is the development of symbols and equations to represent the results. We cannot, however, overlook the difference between (a) the necessary manipulatory processes involved, (b) quantitative or qualitative information obtained and (c) the terms by means of which (a) or (b) are described or referred to.

Mensurational Specificity

From an interbehavioral standpoint mensuration is functionally dependent upon (1) the objects, events, and relations measured, (2) the operations and techniques employed and (3) the mensurative situation as a whole. Mensuration then cannot be a single type of operation.

1. *Specificity of Measurement.* Measuring operations obviously correspond to the things measured. But the products of the operations must not be identified with the original objects. The product—number or other indicator—derives its character from the conditions stimulating the operations and varies according to the availability of scales. Considering that some things at a given period are not effectively or at all measurable, mensuration does not lay down laws for nature or for science. For practical purposes we may separate mensurants into three classes: (a) objects, qualities, and relations, (b) interactions of things, and (c) the measurer's behavior with respect to (a) and (b).

2. *Specificity of Operations.* The enormous range of operations required to obtain, for instance, the lengths of boards, electromagnetic radiation, and galactic distances indicates the specificity of mensuration. Again, when weights instead of lengths are required we see how different both these operations are from ascertaining metabolic rates or drug tolerance.

3. *Specificity of Mensurative Situations.* The purpose of measuring depends upon the problem at hand. The situation may be theoretical or practical, scientific or nonscientific. In every instance the accuracy of the results and the operations for obtaining them are different. Each situation in its own way simultaneously coordinates mensurants and operations.

Range of Mensurational Situations

Routine and Problematic. Compare the scientific situation in which (a) highly refined weight determinations are required, as in chemical investigation with (b) the comparisons and estimates in nuclear physics, in the measurement of biological, psychological, and anthropological events. The operations in the (a) situations are not only routine but more or less incidental. These immediate scale operations are always features of larger situations. The measurements made may be exceedingly important but, after all, remain casual.

Typical problematic situations are those in which measurement is itself a warrant for the existence, say, of a particle or wave of some sort, a chemical element, a physiological reaction. The problem need not be so far reaching, however, but may involve merely the best type of scale or adequate technique. In general, mensurational problems arise when things to be measured are intractable or techniques unavailable.

Direct and Indirect. Direct measurements are obtained by comparing readily available properties. Rulers, scales, calipers can be immediately applied. These are routine situations. Stretching a chain between two given points is a direct technique. When, however, the thickness of an object has to be determined by weighing, as in the case of Faraday's determining the thickness of gold leaf, or when time is measured by weighing water, as Galileo had to do, we have measuring situations which are essentially indirect. Another indirect measurement is illustrated by the attempt to determine the temperature at the center of the earth or of some distant star.

Whether the situation is direct or indirect is frequently a function of the historical period in which measurements are made. Roemer's attempt to estimate the speed of light by timing the eclipse of Jupiter's moons at different times of the year contrasts with the more direct methods developed later. His incorrect figure of 22 minutes for light to travel across the diameter of the earth's orbit was in part owing to his indirect technique. In short, whenever measurements require extrapolated or interpolated calculations the operations are necessarily indirect.

Fundamental and Derived. Among physicists the tradition is solidly established that certain types of measurements are fundamental, whereas others are derived. An example is the CGS system. As a matter of fact, scientists go farther and look upon linear measure as the *only* fundamental one, all others considered as derived. Sometimes weight measurements, as well as electrical resistance, are also regarded as fundamental, but because of the character of the scales used, the basic characteristics of weight and resistance are reduced to length.

Dimensional systems are probably the most direct and basic measurements. But with the elaboration of contacts with things calling for vectoral units, angular scales, and non-linear motion of various sorts the field of derived scales appeared. Thus the mensurative bounds of science are made to extend far beyond such derived measurements as density, compressibility, viscosity, temperature, and hardness.

Simple and Complex. The terms *simple* and *complex* may be used to separate important from less important mensurative systems. The complex situation not only involves all types of scale applications but various sorts of calculations.

Concrete and Abstract. Concrete mensuration keeps close to original things measured, while preoccupation with relations is more abstract. Actually, of course, every measurement situation includes ascertainment of relations, since measuring always entails comparison. Either the thing measured is directly compared with an instrument or scale, or two or more things, scales, or instruments are indirectly equated. As long as the measured object is kept in view the abstractness is limited. There are situations, however, in which the character of the thing is suppressed and the relations emphasized. The extreme of abstraction occurs when the scientist stresses interbehavior with mathematical items; number ratios are manipulated instead of the concrete objects originally stimulating the mensurational problem.

Mensurational Products

From the very nature of measurement it follows that the resulting products depend essentially upon the original problem. The following, named after different scientific situations, comprise the primary product types.

Magnitude. Products derived from information concerning the sizes and dimensions of things are called magnitudes. Magnitudes have to do with spatio-temporal situations in which there is a relative constancy of time and a variability in the spatial aspect. Lengths distributed in various dimensions and arranged according to shape and organization of objects sum up such information. Magnitude measurements imply operations upon wholes. The problem is the number of units or parts within the whole. We may well find that the whole is itself a part, as, for example, a simple dimension of an object.

It is essential in dealing with measurements of magnitude to differentiate between the units of the measured object and the units of the measuring scale. For example, when we are interested in an animal's size or length, we employ units of scale and operation rather than strict units of length, because the organism's length is naturally divided into head, thorax, abdomen, and appendages.

A second form of mensurational operation results in ascertaining a magnitude by comparing two wholes or objects. Naturally we draw a sharp line between magnitude as an operational product and as a purely verbal (metaphysical) construction. Though we assume that things and events possess size or length properties independent of the measurer, we reject completely any magnitude as an absolute or Platonic essence. It is admitted that the properties of things are only partly known, even when suitable instruments and procedures are available. Still, the entire mensurational situation is far removed from absolutistic dimensions.

Quantity. In general, quantitative information consists of the amount or numerosity of items (multiplicity of dimensions) in a series or class. The items may be qualities as well as things. The requirement is the availability of analyzable units. In the simplest situations quantitative products are obtained primarily by counting or multiplying. In more complex circumstances the use of apparatus may be necessary in addition to the process of computing.

Pattern Products. Metrologists who cling to the number-assignment tradition overlook pattern structures as mensurational products.[7] Pattern-results constitute elaborations of the simple structures obtained from ordinal scales which give only monotonic series. Complex pattern products are derived from the spatiotemporal relationship of two or more variable quantities such as rhythm, accent, and resonance. To include pattern products is merely to take account of the heterogeneity of mensurable materials. From a mathematical standpoint many forms of functional equations represent pattern products, but, in general, they are most typically connected with topological rather than with simple geometric or calculative models.

Intensity. Intensity products yield information concerning the interrelationship of several heterogeneous factors. For example, the measurement of colors involves the determination of

---

[7] Cf., Kantor, Psychology and Logic, Vol. 2.

the proportion of brightness to hue. Comparisons are made between varying brightnesses with constant hues as over against constant brightnesses with varying hues. Similarly, density determinations furnish information concerning the proportion of mass to volume.

Rate. Consider velocity as an instance of rate determination. The operations are designed to discover the ratio of two varying event phases. Whether we take as our products $t = s/v$, $s = vt$, or $v = s/t$, we have in each case a measure involving a ratio of two related heterogeneous factors. It is typical of rate determinations that the variables are motional (changes) rather than fixed structures or qualities. These are sometimes only apparent polarities, as in the case of observing the decay rate of radioactive substances. Changes are properties.

Periodicity. The product in this instance consists of information concerning the recurrence of certain events. In one sense we may regard this information as a record of the multiplication of equal intervals, in which some things or characteristics are duplicated. By interval we mean here a quantity of time. Within these recurring intervals there is a constant arrangement or pattern of quality and quantity of things.

Units, Intervals, Limits

Measurement being a method to ascertain the properties of things, the basic units represent the things measured. Moreover, the units are not designed primarily on the basis of some mathematical model. We can therefore set aside the two opposing views (a) that units and standards are absolute and (b) that they are completely arbitrary. This is not to deny that there are certain options in the choice of units, ranges, standards, and limits. But, after all, one's choice is regulated by the enterprise at hand. Again, units and other mensuration factors are utilizable only when they are relatively stable. And the criterion for stability stems from the things measured and the accompanying conditions.

Mensurational Instruments

Conventional metrologists implicitly entertain the idea that there is only one instrument of measurement—elementary arithmetic. Of course, they discuss calipers, compasses, scopes, and meters of every variety, but numerical magnitudes or quantities dominate their thinking.

In contrast we propose a functional treatment of mensurational instruments. Those who hold an interbehavioral view freely admit that to discover and record the characteristics of things and events requires every possible type of instrument, not just numbers, but objects of all sorts, scaled, graded, and calibrated. Metal, paper, even rats, guinea pigs, and other organisms including man and his behavior serve as mensurational tools.

Indeed, it is a notable fact that physics, a scientific field largely responsible for the simplified and mathematical views of measurement, in its modern conquests of new domains has brought to the fore a vast number of novel and generally unassimilated mensurational apparatus. Think of the numerous forms of automatic and electrical counters—for example, Geiger apparatus for recording electronic radiation and Wilson cloud chambers. This enlarged scope of mensurational tools suggests that in physics mensuration articulates closely with experimentation and general methodological enterprises.

Measurement and Experiment

Mensurational and experimental procedures sometimes fuse since both center around the common point of investigation. Often the work of ascertaining the properties of things constitutes an experimental operation. Thus, mensuration becomes enlarged to a system of interbehavior. Hypotheses are stimulated by the problems at hand; techniques are suggested for solving the problems and verifying the hypotheses. Finally, mensurational laws may be set up.

Levels of Measurement

For convenience we break up the mensurational continuum into the three levels of practical, technical, and metrological situations.

Practical Level. Practical measurements occupy the interval in which things are immediately handled for the ordinary purposes of everyday life. There is generally no problem here of fitting means to ends, no necessary awareness of metric issues. Nevertheless, this range is extremely large, as the following list indicates; in each case the object to be measured is paramount rather than the measuring operation.

1) Things and properties (size, length, area, volume).
2) Relations (number, quantity, magnitude).
3) Strength or intensity in relation to (a) function (electrical resistance) or (b) effect on other things.
4) Rates (frequency according to various criteria): period, time interval, speed, velocity, acceleration.
5) Behavior (what a thing does under various circumstances).

Technical Level. These measurement situations are bounded by technological circumstances. Objects as measurable are not the immediate focus of attention; rather, the operations and instruments necessary for dealing with complex things are emphasized. Also, since the measurement processes themselves present problems for solution, the kind of scales prepared, the way they are applied, become focal. Such a series of activities as were required to develop thermometers, galvanometers, ammeters, and other instruments for electrical measurements are typical.

Metrological Level. The theoretic mensuration level may be quite remote from the other two. Problems only distantly related to practical interests or technological enterprises are involved. The problem we mentioned earlier—namely, the relationship of mensuration and mathematics—is a good example. We have already intimated that theoretical mensurational problems may become decidedly mathematical, even metaphysical, and hence leave far behind the concrete operations of experimental science.

Interrelation of Levels. Despite the great differences between these three levels they represent intervals on a single continuum. Not only do the central problems of each level overlap: we may even see connections between the remotest mathematical theory and some overt weighing and measuring procedure. The individual items of scientific interbehavior are never sharply separated.

Measurement and Scientific Theory

Measurement touches on scientific theory mainly in such elaborate situations as those of quantum mechanics. With its opposition of causation and statistical rule, quantum mechanics has provoked discussions concerning the nature of objectivity, of cause, and of reality. Let us consider these problems individually.

Objectivity. So tenaciously have physicists held to the particle institution that energy interrelation appears to disrupt their techniques and theories. The necessity to deal with energy systems precipitates upsetting problems concerning the nature of measurement. The old classic particles, observed or inferred, were regarded as objective. Likewise, the objectivity of measuring techniques according to conventionally established scales and standards was unquestioned.

The development of such constructs as mass, energy equivalence, and ambivalence of photons and light waves stimulated physicists to inject into their work problems of subjectivity and mental creation. From the psychologist's point of view physicists are confusing (a) the things measured with the act of measuring, (b) the instruments and the abstracted units with the properties of the energies to which they are applied.

Granting the difficulties of measuring energy, the refinements necessary to deal with nonvisible, nonsolid, nondiscrete entities, we are still concerned with the ineffaceable *field*. This field involves the worker and the things with which he interbehaves, plus all the apparatus he uses. The worker's inevitable participation in a measuring field projects no question of objectivity or subjectivity.

Causality. Faced with the technical problems of measurement in studying relativity and quantum mechanics, many scientists have suffered the consternation of seeing causation—the alleged cornerstone of science—shift from its presumably impregnable position. Moreover, measurement, so long regarded as a criterion of existence, has become the fulcrum for displacing causation. Alternatively, the causal problem is treated in Kantian fashion as a mental process designed to introduce order into the ephemeral entities called sensations.[8]

Reality. Finally we come to the paradoxical circumstance that mensuration—a technique for making knowledge concerning the properties of things definite and precise—has turned the scientist in the direction of reality metaphysics. After long entertaining the dogma that science is measurement and that physics,

---

[8] For example, Bohr, Causality and complementarity.

because built upon mensurational operations, is the primary science, workers in quantum mechanics have come to the following conclusions: (1) measurement cannot be regarded as operations performed upon independent things with unique inherent properties and (2) measurement is the process of creating the things measured.

IV

THE SUBDOMAINS OF SCIENCE

9

EVENTS AND CONSTRUCTS IN PHYSICS (I)

I N THE preceding chapters we have treated the sciences as general interbehavioral enterprises evolving in cultural complexes. We have indicated that scientific operations (experimentation, mensuration, mathematical treatment) and instruments (activities and apparatus) are interbehavioral happenings. The goal of science, we have seen, is the construction of intellectual products (descriptions, explanations, laws, theories); and such products are derivations from the scientist's interbehavior with events. These points follow from our hypothesis that science is a specialized type of contact with things, a contact which eventuates in an orientation basic for prediction and control.

Our task in this and the five following chapters is to test the interbehavioral hypothesis in the particular sciences, to exhibit the procedures leading to system structurization. Our approach is primarily historical, since scientific situations are always developmental. Though we are guided by the general systemic pattern delineated in Chapter 2, it is hardly necessary to follow so formal a plan. Less constricted exposition suggests far better the spontaneity of the scientist's operations.

But even this nonformal procedure does not obviate expository problems because of the enormous diversity of scientific situations and consequent specializations of system construction. Despite the common core in all scientific enterprises they are differently organized because of variation in (1) events studied, (2) investigational circumstances, and (3) the manner they are affected by their cultural background. We attempt to surmount this difficulty by making use of our coordinate grouping (p. 90) of all the sciences into four departments: the physiochemical, biological, psychological, and anthropological.[1] In each depart-

---

[1] An obvious omission is the mathematical and formal sciences. These we have considered in ch. 7. While we regard mathematics as science in the same sense as the other branches, the objects and events dealt with are to a great extent constructs.

ment we search for the unique way in which scientific workers move from events to constructs.

The achievement of descriptions and laws marks the advancement from crude to refined interbehavior. For example, the science of magnetism evolved out of elementary contacts with a lodestone; the mighty science of electricity developed from ancient contacts with amber. Of course, an authentic magnetic or electric science resembles the primordial handling of a lodestone or the amber no more than a corn plant resembles the germ of a maize seed. Even the early expansion of any science involves so many developments in a linear and areal direction that it is difficult to trace the continuity of the different interbehavioral stages. In the case of a complex, mature science it is impossible. Nevertheless, it is only through such zigzag stages that any science evolves.

Physiochemical Sciences in Evolution

In our study of construct evolution in the physiochemical sciences we are able to follow the simple plan of *from–to*—namely, the emergence of complicated constructs from simpler ones. In no instance, however, can we do more than indicate the high points, nor need we expect to recover any but the most sketchy evidences of interbehavior. Depending upon the circumstances we shall stress (1) findings about things and events or (2) final judgments and assessments.

A. FROM CONFIGURATIONS AND MOVEMENTS TO COSMIC MACHINES

Physicists who say they study matter conceal what they actually do, for matter is nothing more than an abstractive product of their work. Despite their experimental investigation and mensuration, physicists and chemists describe their activities in constructional rather than behavioral terms. The source of the abstractions is missed. But for logical purposes we need to stress that the physicist works with specific things, with objects in stationary configuration and balance or moving in relation to spatiotemporal coordinates, alone or in configuration with other things.

Out of such interbehavior physicists have constructed the most ingenious principles. Their descriptions and models of the bodies they have observed in independent action or manipulated by means of levers, screws or inclined planes have become magnified into nature's laws and general principles of existence.

Our task now is to trace the long and tortuous history of mechanics through its statical and dynamical phases. This we shall do by studying the worker as he interbehaves with interbehaving things and events. Notice that the worker's contact with these interbehaving things is in principle similar in all respects to the interbehavior of two chemical reagents. In other words, the reaction of the observer to the thing observed is the same type of event as the interaction of any two things.

Statics

The statical arm of mechanics is an outgrowth of everyday contacts with levers and wedges. As Mach says:

> Long before theory was dreamed of, implements, machines, mechanical experiences, and mechanical knowledge were abundant.[2]

Now, once we slice away from mechanical science the impeding constructs about the senses, concepts, and reason, we see that the cumulative contacts with things under auspices of practical necessity eventuate in a set of laws or formulae. The earliest of these results comprise the laws of the lever and the inclined plane: $\Sigma W_1 L_1 = \Sigma W_2 L_2$ and $L_1/L_2 = W_1/W_2$. Such formulae sum up the results of arranging and balancing things; they may also be used as guides for further manipulation.

Dynamics

It is generally conceded that the initiation of dynamic laws had to wait upon the development of tools for interbehaving with time intervals and durations. Thus the ancients were limited to the statical features of mechanics. When it became possible for Galileo and others to estimate and compare time intervals, interbehavior with things in motion came under formulative and predictive control.

Do not overlook the essential cultural factors in the transition from statics to dynamics. The apparatus Galileo used to measure time could easily have been constructed by an Archimedes capable

---

[2] The Science of Mechanics, Introduction, p. 2.

of inventing a worm gear. Not attempting at this point to compare Greek and Renaissance civilizations, we merely point to the small, tidy, and fixed character of the former; the immense, indefinite, and adventurous culture of the Western European world after the Middle Ages.

Galileo stands out in the history of the dynamical branch of mechanics as its founder. It was he who demonstrated that heavier bodies, or those with greater weight, do not fall more rapidly than lighter bodies. Moreover, this discovery is enhanced by the precise quantitative determination of the rate of freely falling bodies. The formula $S = \cdot 5gt^2$ is a landmark in scientific development.

But by far the most outstanding achievement of Galileo was the development of the construct *inertia*, the central point not only of mechanics but of all modern science. Inertia sets aside the notion of external pushes and internal forces making bodies move or otherwise act. Basic to the inertia construct is the inter-behavior of sets of factors. To describe or account for a change in the motion of a body—namely, acceleration—one has to take a set of specific circumstances into consideration.

The immense technological and engineering evolution of Western European culture in the Renaissance period corresponded to a novel initiation of scientific principles. By the use of new instruments men such as Huygens, Descartes, von Guericke, Hooke, Boyle, and Varignon developed a stock of scientific laws.

When Lagrange felicitated Newton on his good fortune that there was only one universe about which to construct laws he assumed an absolutistic view. In contrast, Newton may well be celebrated as the efficient formulator of findings and principles which had been developing for some centuries. Thus the law of gravitation which has figured so magnificently in the history of mechanics completed a structure developed by Kepler and Galileo. By his effective formulation of the nature of force and mass, by his statement of action and reaction and the parallelogram of forces, Newton completed and organized "the formal enunciation of the mechanical principles now generally accepted."[3] It would be supererogation to recount Newton's great achievement. We must be reminded, however, that his work seals the establishment of an immense scientific culture.

---

[3] Mach, The Science of Mechanics, p. 187.

The Mechanical World View

That chapter in the history of science which recounts the advance of the mechanical world view is packed with incidents. Consider (1) the exacting work of Lagrange, D'Alembert, Jacobi, John and Daniel Bernoulli, Euler, Gauss, and others in refining and elaborating the Newtonian principles and (2) the eminently successful application of mechanical principles to other things and events than were originally included in the department of mechanics. We need but mention the use of mechanical laws and models for elucidating problems in heat and thermodynamics, for explaining the basic facts of electricity, of gases, liquids, even units of energy. Particles in motion have become thoroughly established under rigorous laws.

Historically the power of the mechanical-world view has lain in the scope it afforded for interpreting things and events in an elementary causal fashion. This situation is excellently illustrated by Helmholtz.

> Finally, therefore, we discover the problem of physical material science to be to refer natural phenomena back to unchangeable attractive and repulsive forces whose intensity depends wholly upon distance. The solubility of this problem is the condition of the complete comprehensibility of nature.
>
> And its (science) vocation will be ended as soon as the reduction of natural phenomena to simple forces is complete and the proof given that this is the only reduction of which the phenomena are capable.[4]

B. FROM STATIC CONSTELLATIONS TO AN EXPANDING UNIVERSE

Of the 85 or more constellations currently entered in astronomical records early man must have known a considerable number. Granted that the 48 or so constellation names used by prescientific observers were improper designations for star groups, there is no denying that astronomic bodies themselves were raw materials for records which later became astronomical science.

It is an interesting fact that early interbehavior with constellations was tinged as much with cultural as with observational and experimental factors. Primitive myths and legends may well be regarded as poetic appreciations of attractive objects. How far back in the history of man notice was taken of the stars in their

---

[4] Quoted from Einstein and Infeld, The Evolution of Physics, p. 58.

groupings it is impossible to know, but we may safely assume that it might have happened soon after the evolution of man, something more than a half million years ago.

Emergence of Constellational Science

Simple observation of the constellations led to studies of position, number, brightness, and relative magnitude of astronomical bodies. The earliest contacts were, of course, made upon crudely visible objects necessarily assumed to be stable and limited. What then could be more natural than the immediate accumulation and classification of crude facts? The results are represented by the early star catalogues, the first of which historians of astronomy attribute to Hipparchus. Though dated about 125 B.C., this catalogue is known only through Ptolemy's Syntaxis or Almagest. Hipparchus listed 1080 stars by their measured positions and arranged them in six brightness orders from the first brightness downwards. While his brightness magnitudes were determined by direct visual judgment, his positional determinations were aided by his own improvements on the plane and spherical astrolabes.

Ptolemy's catalogue, prepared three centuries after Hipparchus, contained 1030 stars which were placed in their constellation groupings, as well as in their magnitude orders and longitude and latitude positions. Catalogues similar in extent to Ptolemy's were prepared by the Persian Al-Sufi in the tenth century, by Ulugh Beg of Samarcand in the fifteenth, and by Tycho Brahé in the following century (1590).[5] In 1677 Halley extended Tycho Brahé's catalogue of 1005 stars to include the South Pole.

With the invention of the telescope the work of enumerating and locating stars increased tremendously. The first catalogue to include telescopic stars is attributed to Hevelius' *Prodromus Astronomiae*, posthumously published in 1690. Telescopic catalogues run into hundreds of thousands of items. An example is Argelander's *Bonn Durchmusterung* which includes 324,000 stars down to 9.5 magnitude. Telescopic astronomy, of course, not only enlarges the scope of catalogues but also facilitates accuracy of observation.

---

[5] Cf., Duncan, Astronomy, p. 319.

The next astronomical inventory involved the use of photography. Photographic catalogues could be made showing some millions of stars, since it was estimated that the 22,000 plates required to survey the heavens would register from eight to ten millions.

An interesting development of constellation study is the naming system established by Bayer in the early years of the 17th century. Taking the constellation members in order of descending brightness magnitude, the letters of the Greek alphabet are applied to them. Thus Sirius is Alpha Canis Majoris, Algal is Beta Persei. When a larger number of stars is discernible than the list of Greek letters, the Roman alphabet is used to supplement them.

Astronomy Matures

While the dominant note in early constellation study was fixity and completeness, the relative changes in star positions and constellation structures could not be overlooked. Indeed, it is said that Hipparchus' first interest in cataloguing stars arose from the fact that as early as 134 B.C. he noticed the appearance of new temporary stars.[6] Moreover, early observers could differentiate sharply between the relatively static constellations and the vagabondage of the planets. Estimating magnitudes constitutes but the first step in astronomic science. Its maturation depends upon (1) things and events and (2) observational techniques.

(1) *Things and Events.* The intensification of scientific activities changes completely the treasury of data with which astronomers interbehave. To begin with, to the approximately 5000 stars visible to the unaided eye were added the million made available by telescopic and photographic procedures, and beyond these the billions of astronomic objects contained in the many star systems, whether they form clouds, rotatory structures or spheres. Comparatively recent additions are binaries, clusters, giants, dwarfs, and many variable stars.

Perhaps still more striking additions are all sorts of nebulae and nebular events. The observer's progressive acquaintance with astronomical things is illustrated by the fact that the term *stella*

---

[6] Schlesinger, Astronomy, p. 139.

nebulosa was used before authentic nebulae were known. Bright fixed astronomic spots were included in star lists. Ptolemy includes in his Almagest six star clusters and other loose star groups as nebulae, among them Praesepe and some elements of the Scorpion and Orion. Even Bayer and Flamsteed listed nebulae as stars.

The distinction of making the first telescopic discovery of an authentic nebula is accorded to Peiresc of Provence who found the great nebula of Orion in 1610. Two years later the German Simon Marius reported the Andromeda nebula. Messier, primarily a student of comets and an astronomer who indiscriminately listed more star clusters than nebulae in his 103 objects, produced the first catalogue of nebulae in 1781. It was Sir William Herschel, however, who made the first systematic study of the heavens in 1783. Sir William and his sister Caroline listed 2500 new nebulae, including clusters. The acquaintance with astronomic things was further increased by Sir John Herschel, whose list contained 5000 objects. By 1888 Dreyer expanded the list to 13,000.[7]

(2) *Observational Techniques.* A minor but not insignificant addition to the knowledge of the astronomical cosmos was made by the improved method of estimating star-brightness magnitudes. The progressive development of telescopic and photographic observation enabled workers to distinguish between brightness order in scale and size. The influence of such factors as temperature and distance could then be taken into account. The development of the Herschel-Pogson scale in the 19th century provided an accurate quantitative means of moving on from directly visible to instrumentally mediated data.

Nothing, however, surpasses in importance for astronomical investigation the application of physiochemical principles. The progression from the calculative techniques of geometry through the observation and measurement of temperature, density, radiation, and, in general, energy content and modification has altered the entire history of astronomy.

Without question the outstanding observational technique is spectroscopic. The study of spectra not only yields information concerning the chemical constituency and structure of astronomic objects but also data for their classification, comparison, and basic

---

[7] For most of the above details on nebulae I am indebted to Duncan, Astronomy, ch. 19.

interrelation. Through the interbehavior with light in its various properties and relations knowledge is obtained both of individual things and their organic systems (solar, galactic), up to what is commonly referred to as the universe.

Indeed, modern astronomy has come a long way from the tidy little universe of the ancients. From the tiny cosmos extending hardly beyond the solar system and the visible boundaries of Euclidean space the universe has become enlarged to indefinite dimensions. Galactic and trans-galactic nebulae, with their recession reckoned in thousands of kilometers per second, characterize the astronomic universe of today. The numbers and dimensions employed by modern astronomers could have no possible significance for earlier students. Imagine Hipparchus or Ptolemy encountering calculations involving millions of light years! To say that the diameter of the universe may be estimated as 3,500,000,000 light years would overwhelm anyone not conversant with current astronomy.

The Expanding Universe

The astronomer does not work in isolation: his scientific colleagues are working too. Geometers have discovered the cracks in the tidy rectangular walls of the early mathematicians. Space may be curved. Possibly there are no limits to the actual motion of things in astronomic space. The universe is not only enormous in extent but actually permanently expanding. Let it be admitted that since the scientist's interbehavioral possibilities are sharply bounded, he may be entering upon a path more speculative than factually interpretative. Still, a plenitude of evidence justifies such constructions as astronomers of old never dreamed of. A proper coordination between constructions and contacts with things is the prime requisite.[8]

C. FROM PATENT MATERIALS TO ENERGY STATES

More than other sciences chemistry displays an immediate interest in things and events, inasmuch as the chemist searches for the composition and transformation of objects. Even the most

---

[8] Relevant literature: Hubble, The problem of the expanding universe, The Realm of Nebulae, The Observational Approach to Cosmology; Finlay-Freundlich, Cosmology.

abstract chemical theories center about the analytic and synthetic manipulation of the constituents of things. This is why chemistry is essentially the science of elements (p. 81 f.). The chemist, as a rule, accounts for the actions of things and their interrelated effects by their constitutional changes in coordination with temperature, pressure, and so forth. It follows then that chemical speculation and research are tightly interconnected. With the greatest ease we can trace the evolution of the most complex investigative procedures of contemporary chemists back to the earliest inquiries into the nature and stability of things.

The roots from which current chemical science has developed may be enumerated as (1) agricultural: problems centered in the gathering and production of food; (2) general technological: interest in raw materials—metals, clays, pigments—used for utensils, tools, weapons, and instruments; (3) medical: preparation and use of drugs; and (4) alchemical: problems connected with transmutation of metals. In all these situations questions of composition and modification lead to the manipulation, information, and speculation which comprise chemical science.

Greek Cosmochemistry

Because of the comparatively simple scientific culture of the Greeks their inquiries concerning the basis and origin of things took on a cosmic character. The earliest chemistry, antedating the use of the name, was concerned with the general nature and sources of things. A scientific interest evolving from the chemical roots mentioned above motivated the search for the primary and durable constituents of all objects.

What characterizes Greek chemistry above all else is the simplicity and directness of its constructions. Whether the early thinkers adopted all four of the ancient constituents of things (Empedocles and Aristotle); only one (water, Thales; air, Anaximenes); or two (fire and earth, Parmenides; water and earth, Xenophanes), they regarded these primordial things as the manifest materials of immediate observation. Obviously they were dealing with constructions; their air, fire, water, and earth principles were more or less idealized factors. Apparent air, visible water, they knew as a solvent and mixture, but they did not go beyond the things with which they were in contact. The four elements were the actual abiding bases for all processes of mixing, synthesizing, combining, and reducing things, and consequently were the substrata for all bodies coming into being (generation) and passing away (degeneration). They were also at the base of all growth and organic alteration. Another formulation derived directly from manifest things is the qualitative combination of the four basic principles. Fire is hot and dry; water wet and cold; air hot and moist; earth dry and cold.

The simplicity of Greek chemistry, however, does not prevent it from soaring above the dead level of apparent visibility. The obvious illustration is the antagonism between Leucippus and Democritus, the atomists, and Anaxagoras concerning the character and function of the substratum of things. Whereas Anaxagoras found the substratum in the "homoeomeries":

> ... viz. bone, flesh, marrow, and everything else which is such that part and whole are the same in name and nature.[9]

the atomists say:

> ... there are indivisible bodies infinite both in number and in the varieties of their shapes, of which everything else is composed—the compounds differing one from another according to the shapes, 'positions', and 'groupings' of their constituents.[10]

Those who agreed with Anaxagoras regarded air, fire, water, and earth as comparatively second-order elements, as it were. This view brought Anaxagoras into line with the atomists and in opposition to the Empedocleans and Aristotelians.

Specialized Operational Chemistry

As early as the Alexandrian period diffuse contacts with things were developing into specialized chemical techniques. From the various technological arts and practical trades an interest evolved leading to problems concerning the origin of things and their changes. The knowledge developed in various human situations and in different cultural units became more and more pooled.

---

[9] Aristotle, De Generatione et Corruptione, 314 a, 19.
[10] Ibid.

This marked a striking upsurge in the chemical department of civilization.

The various interests in practical chemical processes we mentioned above, such as (a) preparing concoctions for medical purposes, (b) making dyes for treating clothing and ornaments, (c) adding to or imitating metallic or other types of raw or finished products, are reflected in such classical works as the writings of Aristotle, Pliny, Galen, and the chemical papyri of Leyden and Stockholm.[11] The general complication of life in Western Europe brought to the fore not only a greater acquaintance with things, but also the operations necessary to handle them. On the whole, however, we are still concerned with a period in which manipulative skill is featured far more than analysis of underlying principles.

Our thesis that it is impossible to overvalue the importance of culture in studying the evolution of any science is strongly substantiated by the history of chemistry. If chemical science is continuous with everyday practices we can take account of the contributions of China, India, Babylonia, Egypt, as well as of Greece, Rome, and more westerly located peoples. Unquestionably the Alexandrian conquests and resulting interrelation of cultures have influenced scientific evolution, in addition to the Roman and Arabic developments.

Well known specialized operations were the widely practiced alchemical manipulations for transmuting mercury to gold and for producing the elixir of life. The recipes were circulated from group to group, including Egypt, China, India, Arabia, and many European countries.

According to Paracelsus, the steps of alchemy are:

> ... distillation, solution, putrefaction, extraction, calcination, reverberation, sublimation, fixation, separation, reduction, coagulation, tinction, and the like.[12]

Even though the alchemists manipulated particular objects, they assumed the existence of essences. As we have seen, they transformed salt, sulphur, and mercury into ethereal principles with subtle and imponderable properties. Such substrata as they dealt

---

[11] Partington, A Short History of Chemistry, ch. 2.
[12] Partington, op. cit., p. 43.

with were in complete contrast with the crude principles of the ancient four elements. Air, fire, earth, and water elements were at most idealized forms of immediate things, whereas alchemical principles remotely, if at all, stemmed from actual things. Thus the Sceptical Chymist vigorously attacked the doctrine of four elements and three principles.[13]

Airs, Gases, and Solids

Of the greatest moment in chemical evolution were encounters with airs and gases. For one thing the scope of contacts with chemical substances was tremendously increased. For another, the discovery of gases, which was quite a slow development,[14] not only completed the states of substances, but provided a basis for chemistry's practical and theoretical advance.

Invisible and intangible substances such as air and ether were a subject of speculation from the time Anaximenes made air the single ultimate element. Naturally, a concrete chemical view could not have developed before the alchemists and chemists busied themselves with such processes as combustion and calcination. Another significant item was the occupation of chemists with respiratory processes. It is interesting to note that the gases van Helmont dealt with were carbon dioxide (gas sylvester) and marsh gas (gas pingue). Hales, too, among the early students of gases (which he called air), made some respiratory experiments on himself by way of treating air with potash before inhalation.

The scientific realization of the importance of the gases developed slowly but surely. Boyle early demonstrated that gases can be collected; also it was appreciated that air has weight. Sources of gases were sought. Hales studied the amount of air which could be extracted from various substances by heating. Black concluded that gases were among the constituents of the alkalies. As is well known, Priestley was a diligent and successful investigator of air, and in consequence one of the discoverers of oxygen.

Still more trenchant perhaps was the discovery that water

---

[13] Boyle, The Sceptical Chymist.

[14] The name *gas* stems from Van Helmont in 1630, though it did not come into its proper use until Lavoisier and Macquer employed it about 150 years later.

was composed of inflammable air (hydrogen) and dephlogisticated air (oxygen). This conclusion was the apex of numerous manipulations performed by Priestley, Warltire, and especially Cavendish. It was the last who perfected Priestley's experiment of synthesizing water by means of an electric spark. With gases taking their place as constituents of solids and liquids the range of elements and compounds increased extensively.

This history of gas investigation symbolizes both (1) the expansion of interbehavior with other than the most palpable substances and (2) the hazards of such expansion. Not only did early workers struggle pitifully to separate, identify, and describe their airs and gases, but they connected them with purely hypothetical and nonexistent substances. The single reference to Priestley's description of oxygen as dephlogisticated air, and nitrogen as phlogisticated air, hints at this unfortunate episode in chemical history. It is not an improbable speculation that Becher, Stahl, and their succeeding phlogistonists were misled into believing that if things were impalpable and invisible they could be imponderable or negatively massive.

Atoms, Molecules, Compounds

With the completion of the circle of chemical states into solids, fluids, and gases the chemist at the same time rounded out the range of his gross contact with things. The next step was to intensify his acquaintance with and understanding of the intricate details, including the progressive accumulation of substances as represented by the 98 elements known today, in addition to the hundreds of thousands of compounds, both original and synthetic, in the inorganic and organic classes of things.

From the standpoint of present-day chemistry the historical development of the categories of atoms, molecules, and compounds is a minor though important achievement. The development of the atomic theory by Dalton, Higgins and others enabled chemists to penetrate into the specific organization and interaction of substances, and further to develop formulae, especially in the organic field. By formulae we mean, of course, not merely the symbol or description of the structure of a compound: we mean the actual results of handling compounds.

Since chemical things and events are of a piece with other

happenings, the development of chemistry complements that of biology, physics, astronomy, and the other sciences. Note particularly the culmination of chemical science in the environment of electromagnetic radiation and radioactive transformations.

Atoms, Ions, and Radiation

From the time that electrical methods were employed to investigate chemical events, as by Cavendish, Priestley and Davy, it was a foregone conclusion that electricity should be closely integrated with chemistry. The slow but certain development starting from the electrochemical theories of Davy and Berzelius, through Arrhenius' more concise and accurate ideas concerning ions, culminated during the 20th century in the unified construction of the electrical nature of matter. As a consequence atoms assumed properties not available to them simply as fixed and eternally existing particles. Electrical charges and resulting reactions became integral features of the basic components of things. But even ionization as a process in the electrical conductivity of chemical materials was but a step in the complete transformation of chemical particles or units into radiation.

Twentieth century chemistry, associated with the elaboration of theories of relativity and quantum mechanics, appeared to reduce the fixity and continuity of chemical objects (p. 85 f.). But this was only a symptom of the scientist's need to become adapted to the more subtle and central characteristics of things. Even the possibility of breaking down the barrier between things and events did not challenge anything but culturally established constructs.

Historic March of Chemical Constructions

Chemical constructions derived from complex circumstances represent a comprehensive integration of data and investigations. Since the essential chemical problem concerns the nature of objects in the form of chemical compounds—namely, the reactions of component atoms and radicals—we expect the constructs to become progressively more technical and abstruse. From the crude characterization of things to the complicated formulae of inorganic and organic chemistry, on through such elaborate units as elements, atoms, radiation, etc., the chemist's constructions proceed to abstract principles such as spectral emission and absorption, even wave probability.

Such theories as Prout's protyle are symptomatic of the range of constructions. Construct builders now leave far behind the simple consideration that all constituents of things are reducible to hydrogen or some other universal thing or principle. Ambivalent waves or particles round out the theoretical picture. Laws stated in such terms do not, however, transcend the interbehavioral situation in which chemists work. It is a confirmation of the corrigibility of science that investigative interbehavior sooner or later eliminates erroneous constructions.

D. FROM HEAT TO ENERGY QUANTA

Availability of Heat Events

Mach[15] objects to the wide-spread view that thermodynamics as the basic science of heat began when scientists first realized that heat is a form of motion. He points out that long before thermodynamics was known men of the middle ages already had the motion idea. No wonder, since even primitive men, who produced fire by drilling, rubbing, and striking stones and metals against each other, must have observed the connection.

In a unique way the science of heat is continuous with the original events of heating and cooling. Warmth and cold constitute the most obvious of natural events, such as the changes from liquid to solid by freezing; glowing, lighting, melting and transforming by heating. Even before the cultural advent of fire making, organisms were in contact with the warmth supplied by the sun's rays. Nothing more need be said in view of the fact that the sun is the sole source of all the earth's light, heat, and energy. The ubiquitous availability of heat events is symbolized by the inevitability with which heat becomes one of the four basic qualities of substances.

Despite the comparative simplicity and easy availability of heat events a satisfactory description of heat has been achieved only through a tortuous development. Heat has been regarded as a quality, a motion, a substance, finally a form of energy. These various interpretative constructions exist, of course, on different though interrelated levels. For our present purposes we shall differentiate constructions on (1) the level of everyday circum-

---

[15] Principien der Wärmelehre, p. 211.

stances, (2) the technological level of industrial contacts with heating problems, and finally, (3) the level of scientific experimentation.

1. *Naive Encounters with Heat.* Ordinary interbehavior with warm and cold objects and conditions has resulted in a number of descriptive constructions. The most definite is naturally the notion of the property character of heat and cold. Perhaps the first step was to move away from the naive idea that heat and cold are two different kinds of properties. We count it a distinct achievement to have put heat and cold elements on a single continuum.

The next step in advance was the development of objective means of discerning and fixing degrees of temperature. The historical evolution of temperature scales and instruments is an instructive part of the history of physics. From Galileo's elementary thermoscope to the thermometer, thermocouple, and bolometer there is an excellently worked out series of steps in which things were manipulated for measurement purposes. Air, water, mercury, and other metals have all been experimented with in order to gauge temperature under various circumstances.[16]

A fascinating and paradoxical feature of the physics of heat is the early development of ideas which, though later abandoned, finally turned out to be exceedingly satisfactory. These are the variants of the notion that heat is, or is connected with, motion or agitation of particles. Beginning with Bacon (1620),[17] Descartes (1637),[18] and Hobbes (1635),[19] the following philosophers and scientists proposed this view, though for different reasons:[20] Amontons (1702),[21] Boyle (1738),[22] Cavendish (1783),[23] Locke (1706),[24] Newton (1692, 1717),[25] Huygens (1690),[26] Hooke (1678),[27] Daniel

---

[16] Mach gives an excellent summary of the historical development of thermometry in his Principien der Wärmelehre, pp. 3–48.

[17] Novum Organum.

[18] Les Meteores.

[19] Elements of Philosophy.

[20] This notion has been traced back to Levi Ben Abraham (1246–1315) in the 13th century, see Mark, *Isis;* also Pledge, Science Since 1500.

[21] Cajori, A History of Physics, p. 100.

[22] Of the Mechanical Origins of Heat and Cold.

[23] *Philosophical Transactions Royal Society,* Vol. 73.

[24] Elements of Natural Philosophy.

[25] De Natura Acidorum, Opticks.

Bernoulli (1738),[28] Lavoisier and Laplace (1783)[29] and Davy (1799).[30]

2. *Heat and Chemical Science.* By a strange coincidence the first developments of the modern physics of heat resulted in an unsatisfactory interpretation. With the growth of chemical science, heat came to be regarded as a substance. When Black, through his own and others' experiments, developed some definitely scientific ideas about heat he looked upon it as matter in the form of weightless fluid. Thus arose the construct of caloric which has played a large and obstructive role in physics and chemistry.

An interesting problem is posed by those who defend the caloric doctrine on the ground that it furthered the scientific treatment of heat. How can a false construction be helpful in science except in an accidental manner? Where the caloric incident is really useful is in separating (1) contacts with things from (2) constructions about those things and (3) from interbehavior with the resulting constructions. If wrong constructs are associated with authentic contacts it is still possible that the false construct will not obstruct further interbehavior with familiar events. Nevertheless these are exceptional situations. It is much more effective to work with constructions derived directly from events.

3. *Development of Thermodynamics.* The evolution of heat physics admirably illustrates the influence of technological expansion upon scientific constructions. The growing use of power in industry was a result of the invention first of the steam engine and later of the electric engine, as Joule called the electric motor. Technological and economic problems involved in the most effective way the transformation of heat into mechanical and electrical energy; utilization of the energy obtained stimulated the development of the kinetic theory of heat, as well as general thermodynamics.

An important step in the growth of the kinetic theory was the development of the equivalence of heat and work. This prin-

---

[26] Traité de la Lumière.
[27] Lectures de Potentia Restitutiva.
[28] Hydrodynamica.
[29] Mémoires de l'Académie; cf., Cajori, A History of Physics, p. 123.
[30] An Essay on Heat, Light, and the Combinations of Light.

ciple was derived from observing the effects of mechanical processes in producing heat and from the attempt to use the best
means of converting heat into mechanical energy. Historians of
science have brought together a vast amount of material bearing
upon the evolution of the equivalence construction, including
Rumford's observations on cannon-boring in the Bavarian arsenal.
Then there was Joule, the Manchester brewer, who entered dili-
gently into experiments leading to a quantitative determination
of the ratio between heat and work.

Though Mayer based his study of the equivalence of heat
and motion on the casual observation of the difference between
venous blood under different temperature conditions—in other
words, was motivated by a general philosophical conception: *causa
aequat effectum*—he was also influenced by the general stock of
physical information.[31] As a consequence of his adherence to the
scientific culture he became a contender, along with Colding,
Carnot, Joule, and Helmholtz, for the credit of discovering the
law of energy conservation.

Undoubtedly Carnot's construction of the heat cycle provides the connecting link between the technological development
of heat engines and the basic theoretical constructions concerning
heat. As physicists generally acknowledge, the Carnot cycle is of
fundamental importance not only for the development of a scientific theory of heat engines, but also as a model for interrelating
heat supply and energy product, for linking work and energy.

Thermodynamics as the science of heat constitutes an ultra
refinement of constructs closely connected with definite events.
The basic laws are of two general sorts: the mechanical and the
quantitative.

The mechanical laws are three in number. The first simply
sets forth the equivalence of work and heat, as stated by Clausius
who is credited with the early development of thermodynamics:
"The energy of the universe is constant." He also set up the
equation: $dQ = K(dU + pdV)$. This law is simply the principle of
the conservation of energy applied to thermal events.

Clausius' second law: "The entropy of the universe tends
toward a maximum" more directly than the first is related to

---

[31] See p. 24.

concrete happenings. From one angle the point may be made that no machine for converting heat into work ever attains complete efficiency. No ideal Carnot cycle can exist. Energy is bound to become unavailable. Inevitably there is a condition which Kelvin called the degradation of energy. For the most part, then, the second law refers to fairly isolated systems. Clausius indicates as much in his statement:

> Heat can never pass spontaneously (i.e., without external influence) from a colder to a hotter body: a temperature difference can never appear spontaneously in a body originally at uniform temperature.[32]

The loss or increasing unavailability of energy Clausius called *entropy.* The extrapolation of the basic fact that when energy gets into the form of heat it is not altogether retrievable has led to the notion of *Wärmetod.* This extrapolation may well be questioned both as a technical scientific procedure and as a sample of deductive argument.

Nernst in 1906 formulated what is called the third law, which in effect puts a limit to the amount of entropy. Nernst declared that in the neighborhood of absolute zero the unavailability of energy loses its trend. In that situation accordingly all processes become reversible. By analogy with the form of the first two laws Nernst's heat theorem can be expressed as follows: "It is impossible to obtain absolute zero by any process whatsoever."

The mechanical view of thermodynamics is based upon the assumption that heat concerns the dynamics of molecules. Heat and its intensity depend upon the relative motion and velocity of particles. The physicist's necessity to set up laws governing the velocity of particles obviously takes him beyond the range of direct observation. The agitation of particles, their mean free path, and the correlated factors of viscosity, diffusion, and conductivity can only be statistically treated. Development of the necessary calculations and premises is credited to Maxwell and Boltzmann. The latter formulated the following statement of the second thermodynamic law: "Nature tends to pass from a less probable to a more probable condition." Mechanical thermodynamics has thus assimilated probability and converted the purely mechanical theories of particles into statistical mechanics.

---

[32] Cf., Grimsehl, A Textbook of Physics, Vol. 2, p. 126.

Heat as thermal energy is obviously not limited to mechanical action or continuous motion of particles. There is also radiation. Through the attempts to connect changes of radiation with the motion of oscillating bodies the principle of quanta of action or energy emerged.[33] The quantum aspect of thermodynamics, as in all cases of new constructions, at first appeared to be remote and even disconnected from concrete events. The necessary intellectual adjustments, however, soon revealed that energy is actually discontinuous and that constructions could be established to describe and explicate the facts.[34]

E. FROM POLLEN-GRAIN AGITATION TO MOLECULAR KINESIS

The events known as Brownian movement and the historical scientific interbehavior with it provide an excellent illustration of the natural history of science. The motions or agitations of pollen grains first came under fortuitous notice. Their study as events developed by means of appropriate manipulations. Later through explanatory construction they became integrated with many other types of happenings.

The Discovery

In 1827 Robert Brown, an eminent botanist whom Humboldt called *botanicorum facile princeps*, was busily engaged in the study of pollen, particularly the particles contained in pollen grains. Brown's interest at this time centered in the sexual character and function of plants. By means of a simple microscope he was examining the comparatively large particles or granules, in length 1/4000th to 1/5000th of an inch, obtained from pollen of *Clarckia pulchella* while immersed in water. He noticed that many of the particles were in motion, changing places in the fluid, also turning on their longer axis, as well as altering their shape. The particles with which Brown began his investigations, and which he called molecules, were derived from the pollen of ripe *Clarckia* antherae before bursting. Later he examined pollen from antherae immedi-

---

[33] Soddy (The Story of Atomic Energy, p. 66) objects to the construct *energy quantum* on the ground that the quantity of kinetic energy involves two factors *v*h by comparison with the single action quantum or atom h.

[34] Planck gives an interesting brief account of the development of the quantum construct in his Scientific Autobiography.

ately after bursting. In the former case the bodies were subcylindrical, in the latter smaller and more spherical. The smaller bodies were observed to be in rapid oscillatory motion.

The next step was to determine that the pollen particles or molecules of other living plants showed the same type of movement. This plan of investigation was enlarged to include particles obtained from dead plants and from the tissues of dead and living animals.

Finally Brown entered upon the question whether such particles and movements occurred also in inorganic things. He proceeded to pulverize all sorts of minerals—earths, metals, and their combinations. He examined rocks of various geologic ages, even a Sphinx fragment. In every substance which he could reduce sufficiently to suspend in water he discovered particles and their motions.

It would be tedious, says Brown,[35] to mention all the mineral substances in which he found agitated molecules; he lists travertine, stalactites, lava, obsidian, pumice, volcanic ashes, meteoritic substance, manganese, nickel, lead, bismuth, antimony, and arsenic.

First Construct Stage

Perhaps because Brown was primarily a taxonomist and anatomist he stressed the molecular character of organic and inorganic substances. He was a successful plant geographer, also the discoverer of the nucleus of the plant cell.[36] But since he did not move on from the presence of a nuclear structure in the plant to its biological significance, he simply established the existence of complex agitated motion in particles of every variety. This, however, is no mean achievement from the standpoint of the interbehavioral history of scientific work; moreover it reveals the clear division between the worker's encounter with events and his task of constructing complex and adequate descriptions of them.

---

[35] Our report of Brown's work is drawn from his pamphlet, "A Brief Account of Microscopical Observations made in the Months of June, July, and August, 1827, on the Particles Contained in the Pollen of Plants; and on the General Existence of Active Molecules in Organic and Inorganic Bodies" reprinted in part in Magie's *Source Book in Physics*.

[36] Nordenskiold, The History of Biology, p. 391f.

The Theory of Brownian Motion

The peculiarly agitated movements of such molecules as Brown observed became the focal points for impressive physical theories. How can such particles maintain their motion so persistently? In 1865 Cantoni and Oehl observed that the movement persisted unchanged for a whole year when the liquid containing the particles was sealed between two cover glasses.[37] How can one reasonably account for such apparently random and zigzag motion?

In his notes to Einstein's papers on the Brownian movement Fürth[38] mentions a number of hypotheses concerning these events. For example, Regnault (1858) attributed the movement to irregular heating by incidental light; Weiner (1863) denied the influence of impact forces of the particles upon one another, of temperature differences or evaporation. On the other hand, S. Exner (1867) believed that the smaller the particles the greater the movement which is increased by light and heat rays. In 1870 Jevons proposed that Brownian movement may be accounted for by electrical forces. This was promptly rejected by Dancer.

Exactly a half century after Brown's first observations acceptable theories began to be formed. In 1877 Delsaux suggested that Brownian movements originated in the impacts of the immersion-liquid particles on the solid particles. Eleven years later Gouy of Lyons published the results of his precise investigations; he concluded that Brownian motion is caused by the irregular movements of the molecules of the immersion liquid. Gouy found that the tempo of the motion is universally dependent upon the viscosity of the liquid. This investigator denied the influence of illumination intensity effects, or of a strong electromagnetic field. In another report of precise investigation F. M. Exner (1900) concluded that the velocity of Brownian movement is inversely proportional to the size of the particles and directly proportional to the temperature.

Before Einstein learned about the observations of Gouy,

---

[37] From Fürth p. 87, in Einstein, Investigations on the Theory of Brownian Movement.

[38] See note above.

Siedentopf, and others[39] concerning the effects of thermal molecular motion upon particles he had developed a theory of Brownian movement based upon the molecular theory of heat. Einstein assumed that the calculations of kinetic energy for gas molecules should be the same for all particles including bodies of microscopically visible size suspended in liquids. It is to be expected, for example, that the average kinetic energy of Brownian-movement particles should have the same value as the molecules of a gas.

By refining the statistical formulae of Maxwell and Boltzmann with respect to the displacement and velocity of molecules Einstein was able to construct the accompanying formulae which indicate the following results.[40]

$$\Delta x = \sqrt{\frac{2LTt}{9\pi\eta r}} = \sqrt{\frac{RTt}{3\pi\eta rn}}$$

The mean displacement of a particle in any dimension is directly proportional to the square root of (a) the absolute temperature and (b) of the time of observation, and inversely proportional to the square root of (a) the viscosity of the medium and (b) of the radius of the particle.

The Verification

Einstein first formulated his theory in 1905. Later Perrin at Paris made accurate and thorough measurements on gamboge and mastic particles. He was able to measure both translational and rotational movements. His verification of the theoretical formula is taken to provide direct proof of the existence of molecules, also the number of them in a unit volume. The measurements likewise conform to the Maxwell-Boltzmann law of equipartition of energy for rotational motion.[41]

As to the difference between Brownian and gas molecules Grimsehl says:

> Brownian movements differ from molecular motions only in their extremely small velocities and their extremely small mean free paths, which are due to the great mass of the observed particles.[42]

---

[39] See Investigations of the Theory of Brownian Movement, p. 19.
[40] Grimsehl, A Textbook of Physics, Vol. 2, p. 56.
[41] Grimsehl, loc. cit.
[42] Op. cit., p. 57.

With Westgren's extension of Perrin's investigation (1913–1916) to particles of colloidal metals Einstein's construct appears to be well incorporated in the current system of molecular science. The study of Brownian movement is outstanding in its demonstration (1) of the confluence of localized observations, (2) of the coordination of discovery, and (3) that experimental investigation goes hand in hand with theory construction.

10

EVENTS AND CONSTRUCTS IN PHYSICS (II)

F. FROM AMBER TO PROBABILITY WAVES

ELECTROSTATICS began its development when the ancients fortuitously encountered amber. The discovery that amber had the power to attract straw and other light objects was the earliest link in a chain leading to such extreme abstractions as waves or particles of probability. A second step was taken when in Elizabethan times Gilbert indicated that other objects besides amber, when rubbed, attracted light bodies such as metal, wood, leaves, water, and oil. Electricity thus became independent of amber when it became connected with glass, sulphur, sealing wax, resins of all types, rock crystal, precious stones, alum, rock salt, etc. The scientist, however, was still in immediate contact with the elementary event of attraction. Even repulsion had not yet been discovered.

Similar crude contacts with things led DuFay to the conclusion that all bodies can be electrified. Hence Gilbert's distinction between "electrics" and "nonelectrics" became nullified.

Another step on this level is von Guericke's observation that electrical "virtue" developed by friction can be exercised at a distance of at least an ell or more from the charged object, provided a thread of that length is attached to the charged body.

By comparison with von Guericke's conduction observations the work of Gray exemplifies a marked individual variability of contacts. Whereas the former interbehaved simply with the conduction event, Gray elaborated his observations sufficiently to learn some of the conditions favorable for conduction. Though he himself missed the fact that the dampness of his twine favored the transmission of electricity, he tried out various materials and lengths, the latter up to 765 feet.[1]

---

[1] Taylor, Physics, p. 606f.

Another early discovery was the collecting and storing of electricity with its subsequent dissipation or discharge. Historians point out that this phase—namely, experiments with Leyden jars and planes of glass covered on both sides with tin foil—flourished more in Holland and Germany than in England and France where the conduction phases were first studied.

Even at this simple investigative level electrical effects were well described. Cavendish developed two methods: shock and spark effects for determining the amount of discharge on a condenser. In the former he discharged the condenser through himself and estimated the severity of the shock. In the second he estimated the distance through which a spark from the condenser would jump.

About 1786 the first gold-leaf electroscope was invented by Abraham Bennet. The divergence of the leaves when an electrified body is brought near the instrument indicated that both are charged with electricity of the same sign; the amount of divergence signifies the approximate amount of charge. The instrument lacks only two features which could transform it into an electrometer: it only roughly measures the quantity of electricity with which it is charged and it lacks a scale.

A significant quantitative approach to electrical problems was made by Coulomb. By a technique such as Cavendish used to measure gravitational attraction, Coulomb, using a torsion balance, determined the fundamental law of electricity:

> The repulsive force between two small spheres charged with the same sort of electricity is in the inverse ratio of the squares of the distances between the centers of the two spheres.[2]

First-Level Constructs

DuFay observed the differentiation between what he called vitreous and resinous electricity. Materials of the latter sort, such as amber, sealing wax, and hard rubber, when rubbed with woolen substances interacted differently with light objects from the case when vitreous or glass-like substances were rubbed with silk. For example, light bodies, such as pith balls, put into contact with electrified amber, repelled each other. The same thing occurred if

---

[2] Magie, Source Book in Physics, p. 411.

pith balls were brought close to rubbed glass. On the other hand, a pith ball which had been in contact with glass and one which had been in contact with amber attracted each other. From this observation DuFay concluded there are two kinds of electricity—resinous and vitreous—which operate on the basic principle that like kinds repel each other; unlike kinds attract. When the two kinds of electricity were present in equal amounts, bodies showed neutral instead of electrical effects.

Here, theory construction remained on the lowest level. Du-Fay assumed that electricity consisted of two kinds of fluids. Franklin opposing this theory claimed there was but one kind, an extremely subtle and elastic substance universally distributed. Unless there was an inequality in the electrical distribution of bodies they were neutral. An excess of fluid made a body electrically positive; a deficiency electrically negative. Neither the one- nor the two-fluid theory represented a very elaborate construction. Further contacts with electrical events were necessary.

Electrodynamics. While the accidental discovery of electrical events continues apace, the very quantity of prior acquisitions changes the process. Prior knowledge modifies the mode of discovery, gives it the characteristic of inevitability, channels it in a certain direction. Beyond this the scientist invents or develops events by refining and transforming them.

The evolution of current electricity is closely connected with Galvani's discovery (1791–1792) of animal electricity. He observed that muscle contractions occurred in a frog's leg if a scalpel touched the exposed nerve when an electrical machine was discharging, even when there was no connection between the machine and the frog. While Galvani realized that junction of dissimilar metals was concerned in the contractions he did not conclude that this was the basis for the electrical effect rather than some property of animal tissues. In the meantime, however, he bumped into current electricity.

The development of the electric-current domain achieved tremendous strides when Volta opposed Galvani's ideas and developed electrolyte batteries. Achieving control over events follows contacts which certify their existence and relation. To produce currents and the techniques of regulating their flow leads at once to their interrelation with other things and events. This increased knowledge resulted in applying currents to the fusion of metals, to the dissociation or electrolysis of substances, to long-distance communications, artifical lighting, and use of power.

Oersted's discovery of the magnetic action of electric currents (1819) marks a new and memorable development in electrical science. Through Ampère's refinement of Oersted's work, and his own and Arago's electrical researches, the powerful science of electromagnetism came into existence.

The quantization of electrical events at this stage includes the determination of the dielectric constant, Ohm's law of resistance or conductivity, and the various specifications and refinements of the units which came to be named the ampere, farad, coulomb, volt, etc. In this development the invention of many mensurational instruments was of paramount importance, since they served to provide the numbers required for various mathematical formulae. Among these may be mentioned the galvanometer, the voltmeter, the ammeter, the Wheatstone bridge, etc.

The apex of this stage was the completion of the cycle bringing electricity and magnetism together. With Ampère's establishment of the electrical nature of magnetism the way was opened to reciprocate Oersted's induction of magnetism by electricity and to bring about the induction of electricity by magnetism. This achievement by Henry and Faraday led not only to extensive technological and engineering applications, but also to the practically complete assimilation of electrical events into the domain of scientific data.

Second-Level Constructs

This level centers around the determination of the complex effects of electrical events—in other words their essentially dynamic aspects. These aspects concern electrical and magnetic happenings which were originally regarded as separate events, but on this level are interrelated. Maxwell developed equations summing up and refining the data; he formulated sets of propositions which indicated relations between electrical and magnetic qualities, as well as quantities inherent in all sciences—namely, length and time. These equations accounted for changes produced in given places and times as a result of comparable occurrences and other space and time localizations, depending upon the electrical character of the media between the two sets of coordinates.

Electronics. The closing decade of the 19th century signalized a developmental trend which helped to provide orientation concerning the nature of electricity. The zealous search for an interpretation in terms of material substance led increasingly to the identification of electricity with energy. Indeed, in the final accounting, matter has become electricity instead of electricity being identified with matter.

Once the electromagnetic theory was established scientists were quick to recognize the supreme importance of radiation in electrical studies. Not that they merely associated light with electricity. This happened: they observed that energy is essentially active as waves and that waves are connected with particles or corpuscles.

Since Faraday had made plain that electrical events should not be regarded as contained in charged bodies, but as involved with the media between them, the importance of dielectrics played an increasing part. It was natural, then, for Maxwell in 1873 to declare how important for electrical science and for the knowledge of gases it was to investigate further the discharge of electricity through gases.[3] This type of investigation, coupled with studies of radiation, revolutionized electrical science.

We indicate a few high spots. In the first place, in 1894 Thomson discovered his corpuscles, later called electrons, which evolved from gas-discharge research. Then in 1895 Roentgen, through his interest in cathode-ray discharges, discovered the x-rays. In 1896 Becquerel discovered radioactivity, to be followed in 1898 by the discovery of radium and thorium by Pierre and Marie Sklodowska Curie.

Development of knowledge about electromagnetic waves most likely goes back to Henry's observation that the spark discharge of a condenser produces electrical oscillations. He saw a resemblance between these oscillations and light. Maxwell, however, had really established the basic electromagnetic hypothesis by predicting in 1856 that such oscillations would resemble light and travel through space with the velocity of light. The hypothesis was confirmed by Hertz in 1888. The subsequent development of radio communication served to establish the wave nature of electricity beyond the confines of a laboratory situation.

---

[3] Treatise on Electricity and Magnetism, p. 58.

This colossal achievement was only the beginning of the fundamental analysis of the nature of electricity. Evidence began to appear that while electricity did constitute electromagnetic waves, it might also be atomic—that is, composed of particles. This development centered around research with cathode rays.

Maxwell's prediction that the study of electrical discharge through gases would be highly significant turned out to be true. Evolution of procedures for producing vacua furthered the research. The most important effects of electrical discharges occur when gases are rarified or exist under low pressure. This means that the best results are obtained under conditions of maximum exhaustion. Physicists credit some of the beginnings of cathode-ray discharge to Geissler who first developed an effective tube.

Geissler was a craftsman working with Plücker, professor of Physics at Bonn University. Plücker observed that discharging electricity through a rarified gas resulted in green fluorescence; further that an electromagnet influenced the glow to shift its position from one side to the other with a change of polarity. Goldstein, by the way, who named these events *cathode rays*,[4] asserted that they consisted of electromagnetic radiation similar to light.

Goldstein, stressing the wave properties of cathode rays, developed a theory that they were a kind of ether. A rival hypothesis was sponsored by Crookes who accepted a suggestion made by Varley in 1871 that cathode rays were tiny particles or corpuscles projected in straight lines from the cathode. Furthermore, following another suggestion made by Faraday in 1816, Crookes called these corpuscles *radiant matter* or a fourth state of matter.

In line with the historical inclination of the Continental workers toward continuity ideas and the British toward particle or discontinuity ideas a rivalry set in with respect to the proper interpretation of cathode rays. Is it possible to deflect cathode rays by a magnetic field? That was the question. Important experiments by Hertz and Lenard made it appear conclusive that cathode rays are not corpuscular. Thomson, repeating this experiment, obtained the same result. Later (1897) he improved the

---

[4] On a suggestion of Wiedemann. Cf., Taylor, Physics: The Pioneer Science, p. 774.

tube by making it capable of high exhaustions and found that the cathode-ray stream was deflected by an electrostatic field. He was convinced that cathode rays consist of charges of negative electricity, carried by particles of matter.

Further studies on electrons yielded the result that they constitute components of atoms; the traditional atom therefore could no longer be regarded as an indivisible unit. The upshot was that both matter and electricity were reduced to electronic charges.

The elaboration of research brought in its wake refinement of analysis concerning the electrical nature of matter. Atoms became analyzable into a positive nucleus consisting of a positively-charged particle called a proton and a neutron. Around the nucleus are shells of various numbers of negatively-charged electrons.

Third-Level Constructs

Constructs on this level are clearly the most remote from crude data. Physicists have divided their science into the macroscopic and microscopic divisions, the former involving events not subject to any sort of direct observation. But at no point is there any break between the most abstruse constructions and the original data stimulating the problem. Admittedly, the investigational operations may appear to make those original data into very tenuous entities.

Probability Waves. For example, the entire question of waves versus particles, both for light and other kinds of events, has resulted in the development of enormously complex and apparently arbitrary equations. We need only refer here to the Schrödinger ψ function, when interpreted as probability waves. It is not surprising that writers indicate the great distance between these constructions and original events. But even the brief synopsis we have suggested concerning the experimental operations leading to the final abstruse equations points to a definite continuity throughout scientific operations. Original contacts with amber and lodestone, in other words, have led to interbehavior with cathode rays and the products of the betatron and cyclotron.

Even eminent scientists overlook the continuity between constructing an average from a set of measurements and formulating descriptions and laws in terms of statistical probability. What obviously bothers the physicist is that, unlike the factors which enter into the averages, the items making up the probability are originally subtle and invisible. However, from the standpoint of manipulating events by one means or another, the apparent difference is normal: it fits into the scientific range.

Waves of probability, no more than the simplest average (of lengths, masses, or any other variable), project problems of reality. As we have constantly stressed, reality problems stem from unscientific protopostulates concerning the dualities of mind and matter, sensations and vibrations, experience and nature. It is on such bases that physicists argue for (a) real external worlds and (b) irreal and internal states of mind and other constructs derived from traditional theology and philosophy (p. 38 f.). So important are these issues for the logic of modern science that again we bring them into our present discussion of the construct levels in electrical science.

A reality construct can only be employed for interbehaving with the multiplicity of things and events encountered, described, and formulated according to the individual's contacts with such things. There is no break between crudely manipulating a thing and creating a naming word or descriptive formula concerning directly or indirectly ascertained characteristics of the most recondite objects, relations or calculated magnitudes. Taking account of the variations in interbehavior is the one requisite.

Notice how subtle and damaging metaphysical protopostulates are when scientists occupy themselves with construction problems. Quite laudably scientific workers consider the important role which construction plays. Then what do they do? They reduce the constructive process to the traditional creativity of mentalistic psychology. The central feature of this sleight-of-hand procedure is to assume that science like all observation begins with some "immediately-given experience." This "experience" consists of the "verifiable" psychic states—"sensations"—which by acts of "construction" are made into external things.[5] In this manner all things, ranging from trees to wave lengths, are created from Berkeleyian and Humean sense impressions intermixed with a rational element supplied by the Kantian "mind."

On such a basis molecules, electrons, genes, among other

---

[5] Cf., Margenau, The Nature of Physical Reality, especially chs., 3, 4, 8, 15, 21.

things and their properties, are *realized*. Thus a metaphysical cauldron is created to prepare a broth in which the inventions of historical metaphysicians become equal ingredients with the data and operations of science.

G. FROM LUMINOSITY TO WAVE PROBABILITY

Visibility and the Science of Light

Light science has developed through a series of meandering interbehaviors. Although the final goal is the same as in the study of electricity and magnetism the beginning is quite different. The primordial contacts are not with tangible objects, such as pieces of amber or bits of lodestone, but with a state or condition which may be called luminosity or visibility. In tracing the evolution of the science of light, therefore, we stress more the contact than the thing contacted.

Though light can hardly be classified as a thing in the everyday sense there is nothing more familiar. From a commonsense standpoint encounters with light events are of the most ubiquitous, since in a way light is basic to visibility. And visibility is normally a constant condition of human interbehavior.

Records of interest in light events are extremely ancient. Archaeological evidence indicates an early use of mirrors and burning glasses. It is reported that in the ruins of Nineveh a converging lens of rock crystal was found.[6] Beyond the obvious contacts of primitive man with periodic light and darkness, such a cultivated people as the Egyptians knew and remarked upon elementary optical illusions, as, for example, that the sun at the horizon appears larger than at the zenith.[7]

It is not to be wondered then that elementary light constructs appear early in scientific history. Historians point out that even in ancient times observers had recorded a number of findings concerning light. For example, light travels in straight lines—that is, an object is seen in the direction in which it lies. Reflection also was observed very early, as evidenced by the existence of mirrors. Layard's discovery of a convex lens of rock crystal at the site of the palace of Nimrud apparently indicates that the ancients knew that light rays could be focussed. The Greeks are credited with

---

[6] Cajori, A History of Physics, p. 9.
[7] Ibid.

knowledge of the fundamental law of reflection—namely, that the angles of incidence and reflection are equal. To Hero of Alexandria is attributed the proof that the path of a light ray is the shortest possible.

Light Constructions on Scientific Levels

Although it is undoubtedly true that the ancients were more familiar with optics than other scientific phenomena, light science did not develop appreciably until the later part of the 17th century. Whether this fact is attributable to the intangibility of the materials dealt with, rather than to cultural factors, is difficult to determine. The records of science do show that light events have yielded few constructs or even construction levels. We shall concern ourselves with but two: the levels of action and of the nature of light.

Level of Action. Constructions on this level comprise two important types: (a) concerning the speed of light, and (b) concerning its interbehavior with other things. These events are both relative, of course, to each other.

(a) *Speed of light.* Speculations concerning the speed of light can be traced from early Greek times. Opinions oscillated between the instantaneity of light and its finite speed. Galileo is credited with the first attempt to measure the speed of light by an experimental manipulation. Stationing two persons with lanterns on hills a mile apart, he estimated the time it took to flash light back and forth.

By a combined observational and calculative procedure Roemer, a Danish astronomer working in Paris, achieved a significant first approximation to the speed of light. Working with Jean Picard, Roemer observed that the eclipse intervals of Jupiter's moons were shorter when that planet and the earth were approaching than when they were receding from each other; he attributed this effect to the different distances light had to travel, and calculated that 22 minutes were required for light to cross the diameter of the earth's orbit. Considering the time and conditions the difference between his result of 227,000 kilometers per second as compared with 300,000 is in no sense disproportionate. While his contacts with light events were rather indirect his general procedure was essentially interbehavioral.

A more direct procedure was designed by Fizeau in 1849. He used a rapidly rotating disc with 720 teeth which alternately blocked and let light through. This apparatus was situated about five miles from a point where a mirror reflected the light back to the disc. By a suitable arrangement of telescopes at each end of the light path, results could be observed in the form of brightness or eclipse of the luminous point. By measuring the speed at which the disc rotated, the time required for the light obtained from a lamp to travel the double distance could be computed. The mean value from 28 observations he reported as differing only a little from that accepted by astronomers.[8] The figure was about 5 per cent greater than that usually accepted today.

In 1862 Foucault reported results obtained from measuring the velocity of light in space with the same apparatus he used in his famous experiment of 1850 to determine the differential light velocities in media of varying densities.[9]

Foucault's apparatus comprised some striking improvements over that used by Fizeau. Instead of a toothed disc Foucault used a rotating mirror. For the measurements reported in the second experiment he was able to incorporate improvements for the better determination of the velocity of the mirror's rotation—namely, 298,000 kilometers per second.

Improvements in interbehavior with such an impalpable event as light naturally consist primarily of emending apparatus and operational techniques. In the century since its development Fizeau's method has been more and more refined by such an outstanding worker as Michelson, first associated with Newcomb, later with others. The following are samples of Michelson's results obtained through many years of research on the light-velocity problem: 1879, 299,910 km/sec; 1882, 299,853; 1927, 299,796 ± 4 km/sec.

(b) *Interbehavior*. Determinations of the velocity of light obviously involve the reactions of light to other things—for example, light sources and reflecting surfaces. One may, however, emphasize isolated light as primary or the things in contact with it. We prefer

---

[8] Cf., Magie, A Source Book in Physics, p. 341f.

[9] This is the experiment by means of which Foucault proved that light traveled less rapidly in a denser medium, a result which has been taken to upset the corpuscular theory of light.

to differentiate between the behavior of light under certain conditions and the effects produced in its speed and direction when in contact with air, glass, and other types of things. For instance, consider the type or amount of refraction or bending when light strikes such substances. The results obtained are formulated as the index of refraction. What the scientist has to do is illustrated by Snell's conclusion that the behavior of light upon refraction is better represented by a ratio of trigonometric functions of the angles involved than by a simple ratio of the angles themselves. What is called Snell's law, as Descartes set it up, is represented in the following formula: $\sin i / \sin r = \mu$.

From the standpoint of knowledge accumulation the application of the light refraction law to the construction of optical instruments has been rather fruitful. The results of contacts with events at one stage have become instrumental for facilitating inter-behavior with events on higher and more intricate levels.

Nature of Light. The interpretative and explanatory level of light constructs concerns the nature of light. As it happens, the history of this phase centers around the question whether light is continuous and undulatory or a stream of discontinuous particles.

(a) *Particles or Waves.* Historians of science make Newton and Huygens the main opponents in the battle waged by the undulationists against the corpuscularists. Newton was so impressed with the rectilinear propagation of light and in general so inclined toward particles that he minimized the facts of rays and the presence of an ether, which he did not doubt.

Huygens, on the contrary, putting greater store on the facts of reflection and refraction, regarded light as a continuous undulation. The history of physics indicates that probably the great authority of Newton, among other factors, influenced the scientists of the 18th century to accept the corpuscular theory.

In the 19th century it became increasingly apparent that the wave theory advocated not only by Huygens but by Hooke, Linus, and Pardies among others had more evidence on its side. For one thing the Foucault experiment showed that Newton was wrong in supposing that the ratio of the speeds of light for media of varying densities, which corresponded to the ratio of the sines, would show a slower speed in the rarer medium.

Further evidence favoring the undulatory theory was supplied by the interference experiments of Young. When Fresnel refined and amplified this work the wave theory became prominent, indeed took a dominant position.

(b) *Light and Electromagnetism.* When in the latter part of the 19th century light waves became identified with electromagnetic waves the science of physics plunged ahead. After Maxwell constructed his equations to describe light as well as electric and magnetic events (p. 35) the science of light merged with the science of electricity and magnetism. The opposition, moreover, between the proponents of waves and of particles became strangely mitigated in the 20th century with the evolution of wave mechanics and the probability theory of light and electricity.

H. FROM COLOR, THROUGH FREQUENCY, TO COLOR

Color science is a prime illustration of the interbehavioral continuity of research with things and events. Color science early turns away from contacts with color surfaces or color properties toward things and events which only represent and substitute for color, and finally in the 20th century comes back to actual contacts with color happenings. This variation in interpretative construction is accounted for by the facts that (a) colors have been regarded as only properties or qualities of things and not as things or events in themselves, (b) color theories have been complicated by traditional dualism which has deprived color and other so-called secondary qualities of reality, and (c) color has never been separated into (1) a quality or thing on one side and (2) a reaction or result of reaction on the other.[10] In other words, colorologists have not accurately distinguished between the physics, the physiology, and the psychology of color.

Color Constructions on the Direct Contact Level

Records of the earliest scientific color contacts go back to the Greeks. Aristotle observed that the color of the primary rainbow is found likewise in spray; he observed also the greater size, lesser intensity, and color reversal in the secondary bow. He generalized that rainbow colors could be accounted for by varying intensities

---

[10] Traditionally scientists have distinguished only between sensations—nonobjective phenomena—and light waves or frequencies as objective events.

of reflection. Seneca is credited with the observation that rainbow colors were produced by the same sort of process as the colors seen when sunlight is reflected by irregular edges of glass. The primary rainbow he regarded as an imperfect image of the sun, fringed by colors and magnified by the image-reflecting action of clouds.

In his *Optics* (1629) Vitellio advanced the theory of rainbow formation by declaring that refraction as well as reflection is involved. He did not, however, know that the process was based upon individual drops of water; rather he held that only the gross moisture-laden atmosphere was concerned.

That rainbow color events were produced by the effects of light on individual drops of water was a view developed by a series of theorists, including Qutb-al-din, Theodorich of Saxony, Maurolycus, de Dominis, and Descartes. Maurolycus saw the analogy between the color sequence of the rainbow and the spectrum produced by the reflection of light by a glass prism. It was Descartes, however, who worked out the theory of the rainbow on the basis of experiments made with a spherical globe filled with water. With great detail he developed a set of propositions concerning the presence and absence of color and color hues based on the size of angles of incidence and refraction.[11]

Color Construction on the Indirect Contact Level

It is a curious and disturbing observation that as color science progresses and the colorologist masters the facts of color his constructions imply the irreality of color things and events. The beginning of the indirect contact phase may be dated to the time when Newton established the proposition that the nature and existence of color depend upon the dispersion of light rays by prisms. Newton made prismatic colors, which were not unknown before his time, the general basis for a refraction theory applying to all color. Accordingly in Newton's opinion it was not only raindrops and prisms which accounted for rainbow colors: color itself he believed to be a quality corresponding to rays filtered out of the great compound which is light.

[11] For historical details cf., Mach, The Principles of Physical Optics; Taylor, Physics.

The theory of color which Newton brought to a peak he elaborated in his articles in *The Royal Society Transactions* and in his *Opticks*. He points out that the differently refrangible rays are potential color producers when they initiate effects in the eye and brain. Color he definitely declares to be sensation, a mental process. The rays in themselves are in no sense to be regarded as colored.[12]

Since Newton's time physicists have developed numerous modifications in the physical correlate of color. For example, it is no longer regarded as established that different color-making rays are contained in white light which the prism simply separates out. Light is not regarded as a sum of varying wave lengths or frequencies. The periodicity is produced by the prism. Not even such harmonic analysis as the Fourier principle allows can be resorted to in order to substantiate Newton's idea of the composition of light. But in one respect Newton's theory is still regarded as the only one; in fact, the theory that color is mental process, not existing in *rerum natura*, is never questioned. Actually, of course, this is not Newton's theory, but an item of folklore which existed centuries before Newton and which continues today. What Newton achieved was simply ordering of facts of light dispersion and spectrum manufacture according to the age-old dichotomy of mind and matter.

Newton's generalizations not only reduce all kinds of color to one source but also so transform colors as to take them out of the domain of natural things. In the association of white and other colors with light rays we have an effective demonstration of the split between the material and the spiritual. Physics forthwith endorses the view of the spiritual, hence the unreal character of colors.

Physiological Substitutes for Color

As the history of science indicates, colorology has been a domain of physics. And the physicist has reduced color to wave lengths or frequencies. Color qualities themselves, which cannot be equated or identified with light properties, they relegated to the limbo of inextensional mind. Still the colors of the world make their presence felt, their beauties appreciated. Even though

---

[12] Cf., *Opticks*, p. 108.

the physicist asserts:

> The beauties of form and color, so constantly recurring in the
> varied phenomena of refraction, diffraction, and interference are...
> only incidentals.[13]

he cannot escape the fascination of:

> ...beauties of coloring, the exquisite wonders of symmetrical form
> and combinations of forms which are encountered at every turn.[14]

The physiologist goes farther: he tries to do something about
it. He makes colors at least partially real by replacing them with
the organic mode of their production. Accordingly he has made
brave adventure of his dissections: he has attempted to show the
"color mediating cones" in the retina, the optical paths for "color-
rousing light waves," the "brain spot" where the color sensations
are "complemented." That all this substitution is a wall shutting
color out of science seems to make no difference to the physiologist.
Better an exact description of a portion of the brain than an attempt to seize upon the elusive chromaticity of things!

Color Events and their Defenders

Where the scientist fears to tread the poet and philosopher rush
in. Thus the science of color is the scene of one of the most dis-
creditable of all controversies. Goethe attacks Newton with all the
vehemence with which he could arm his usually temperate and
courteous behavior. Newton, he thundered, could not be more
wrong than to reduce all color to whiteness: Is not the most brilliant color obviously darker than white light? But the real crux
of his argument was his vigorous opposition to any view that
robbed the world of the magnificent array of seen color.

If no one matched Goethe in the intensity of his defense of color
as a natural fact, he had powerful sympathizers in the eminent
physiologists Johannes Müller, Purkinje, and Hering. Strangely,
too, one of his recent detractors could accuse Goethe of nothing
more damaging than scorning a spiritistic tradition. Says Sherrington:

> ...Goethe himself seems to study colour as if colour itself existed as
> such in nature. He could not, as it were, divest himself, during his

---

[13] Michelson, Light Waves and their Uses, p. 2.
[14] Ibid, p.1f.

scientific work, of the practical habit we all have of accepting the external world in terms of our senses and colour as part of it.[15]

Sherrington goes on to quote Magnus (Goethe als Naturforscher) as arguing:

> ... there were times when Goethe did not succeed in bearing in mind that the physical, although it correlates with the psychical, does not necessarily resemble it.[16]

Color Pervades Science

That colorology limited itself to the spectral colors was an accident of scientific history which was bound to correct itself. Colors, which Michelson thought had only esthetic significance aside from the underlying light waves, assumed the importance of events on their own account. To be sure, color had to wait until chemistry evolved and brought pigment colors into prominence. But physics itself had to accord colors a large place when radiation problems became focalized. Light is most easily derived from heated solid bodies. The measure of heat radiation is indicated by the correlation of wave frequencies with color. From red, through orange, then blue, and finally to blinding white the colors shift with increase of frequency. The astrophysicist, too, has discovered that colors and their shiftings are reliable data, constituting an authentic basis for important work.

Probably the most effective entrance of color events as material for scientific activity was through the chemical avenue. There were several distinct developments.

The first centered around color as pigments and dyes. Here one is reminded of Perkin's discovery of analine purple or mauve while working in the organic chemistry laboratory directed by Hoffman. From this discovery developed a large industry employing many specific chemical processes for the production of dyes and drugs. Color and its nature became problems in the analysis and synthesis of definite chemical substances.

The second development stems from the work of Willstätter and his collaborators in the early part of the 20th century, and resulted in the discovery of the composition of the essential green

---

[15] Goethe on Nature and on Science, p. 10. This remark is omitted from the 1949 edition.
[16] Ibid.

substance *chlorophyll*. With increased knowledge concerning this substance, which is the basis both of the ubiquitous green hue of our environment and of the fundamental biological processes involved, color things and events became significant in a way never dreamed of by those scientists who regarded color as an unreal phantasm projected from the no less unreal mind. The attempt to separate the chemical properties of chlorophyll—for example, those which (a) operate to build up carbohydrates in plants from atmospheric carbon dioxide and moisture and (b) those which correlate with the color characteristics of plants—is an utterly gratuitous performance.

Another noteworthy advance was the discovery of the relationship between haematin and chlorophyll. Only those who make immediate jumps to metascientific generalities can overlook the fact that so basic a physiological compound as that of haematin and globin—namely, haemoglobin—has a characteristic color different from that of chlorophyll which it closely resembles in chemical makeup and properties. Who can deny the scientific significance of the chemical fact that these two powerful factors in organic life result from a difference in *one* atom. Whereas an atom of iron provides the red color of blood, an alternate atom of magnesium enters into the composition of chlorophyll.[17] This difference really suggests how palpable and manageable color events are.

A fourth development of color chemistry concerns the plant pigments basic to the great variety of colors found in flowers and fruits. This evolution begins with the isolation in crystalline form of one of the anthocyanins by Griffiths in 1903. When 10 years later Willstätter and his pupils began the systematic study of these substances a new era in the science of color was initiated. Color things and events were investigated on the same level as other scientific materials. It became possible, for instance, for chemists to determine that the blue color of the corn flower and the red of the rose are each owing to a substance called cyanidin combined with two molecules of glucose, while the color of the cranberry is owing to the same substance combined with but one sugar molecule. In similar fashion the chemist has discovered that

---

[17] Cf., Findlay, A Hundred Years of Chemistry, p. 173.

carotene xanthophyll is the basis for the yellow color of flowers and fruits, whereas lycopene provides tomatoes and rose hips with their red color. The enlargement of chemical colorology will in time take account of other color-forming substances, such as those found in the cell saps of plants and in various iron salts, the tannins, and other compounds.[18] The contribution of enzymes and their actions in color production cannot be underestimated.

Colors as events, then, will not be suppressed. Problems in astrophysics, chemistry, and biology demand that colors be treated as things and events constantly encountered among the interrelated factors making up temperature, chemical and radiational similarities and differences. With the development of various colorimetric and chromatographic methods, colors as stable and autonomous things have assumed a satisfactory place in scientific laboratories.[19] No longer is it arguable that color is unmeasurable, unamenable to the treatments applicable to other sorts of scientific data.

New Scientific Attitude toward Color

The scientist's rejection of color events is the strongest possible evidence of the power of the dualistic tradition which condemned psychology to be the domain of psychic principles and processes. Today a new attitude toward color reactions has arisen. With the passing out of psychic states (sensations), contacts with color events are described as interbehavior (observations and experiments) with colored objects. On such a basis psychological constructions fit in perfectly with such new color facts as we have been surveying.

Consider the accompanying typical correlation of color qualities and wave lengths:

Wave Lengths	Color Qualities
380–436	Violet
436–495	Blue
495–566	Green
566–589	Yellow
589–627	Orange
627–780	Red

[18] Findlay, op. cit., p. 173f.
[19] Cf., Bouma, Physical Aspects of Color; Zechmeister and Cholnoky, Principles and Practice of Chromatography; and Partition Chromatography.

How could color and frequency be correlated unless a worker were actually in contact with these two phases of color events? Scientific workers, gradually freeing themselves from absolutisms, are no longer disturbed by the difficulties of measuring color nor by the fact that color is ordinarily encountered as a quality or condition. They fully realize their job is to describe and relate events, further that such work is always set in concrete circumstances. And so despite the great number of difficult conditions to be taken into account when evaluating colors, a science of chromatology has evolved.

I. FROM LODESTONE TO MAGNETIC ATOM

Discovery of the Magnet

The science of magnetism in its evolution from the crude observations of the lodestone through successive myths, on up to scientific concepts, vividly exemplifies the myriads of interbehaviors making up a scientific enterprise. Acquaintance with the lodestone, the mineral magnetite, consisting mostly of iron oxide FeO,Fe_2O_3, goes back to hoariest antiquity. Early literature teems with legend concerning the stone that attracts metal and appears to act through empty space. This impalpable magnetic force has been the marvel of the ages.

Theoretic constructs about magnetism developed first on the basis of unadorned data. A second step led to the discovery that lodestones are polarized.[20] Magnets brought into contact with iron filings attract the metal at each end, leaving the axis portion between them bare. The space surrounding the polar regions have been construed as the fields of magnetic force.

Although the basic attraction of magnetism had undoubtedly been encountered before recorded history, only two magnetic events, aside from attraction, were known as late as the end of the 15th century.

The first dates from Greek times—namely, the fact that a magnet can impart its attractive powers to other suitable objects. Socrates says to Ion:

> ... there is a divinity moving you, like that in the stone which Euripides calls a magnet, but which is commonly known as the stone of Heraclea. For that stone not only attracts iron rings, but also imparts

[20] The term *pole* was introduced by Gilbert.

to them a similar power of attracting other rings; and sometimes you may see a number of pieces of iron and rings suspended from one another so as to form quite a long chain: and all of them derive their power of suspension from the original stone.[21]

Magnetic induction and repulsion are referred to by many Greek and Roman writers, including Aristotle, Galen, Lucretius, and Pliny. We quote the following from Lucretius:

> And I'll begin to treat by what decree/Of nature it came to pass that iron can be/By that stone drawn which Greeks the magnet call/After the country's name (its origin/Being in country of Magnesian folk)./This stone men marvel at; and sure it oft/Maketh a chain of rings, depending, lo,/From off itself! Nay, thou mayst see at times/ Five or yet more in order dangling down/And swaying in the delicate winds, whilst one/Depends from other, cleaving to underside,/And ilk one feels the stone's own power and bonds—/So overmasteringly its power flows down.[22]

Lucretius, notice, not only considered the attractive force of magnets but the repellant action also:

> It happens, too, at times that nature of iron/Shrinks from this stone away, accustomed/By turns to flee and follow. Yea, I've seen/ Those Samothracian iron rings leap up,/And iron filings in the brazen bowls/Seethe furiously, when underneath was set/The magnet stone.[23]

The second magnetic event, date unknown, was that a freely suspended magnet would always come to rest with its poles turned in a north-south direction. Because this is the basic principle of the mariner's compass it has always attracted great interest. Where and when the compass was first developed has stimulated the writing of one of the most fascinating paragraphs of technological history.[24]

What is reputed to be the first description of a pivoted-needle type of compass is found in Peregrinus' *Epistola de Magnete*. By this time (1269) the compass was well known and extensively used.

---

[21] Plato, Ion, 533.

[22] Cf., Of the Nature of Things, p. 286.

[23] Ibid., p. 291.

[24] An interesting account of the search for compass origins, with bibliography, is given in Still, Soul of Lodestone.

To illustrate this point Still quotes an illuminating passage from Neckham's book *De Naturis Rerum* of about 1207:

> The mariners. . . when in cloudy weather they can no longer make use of the light from the sun, or when the world is wrapped in darkness and they have lost all knowledge of the part of the horizon toward which they are sailing, touch the needle with the magnet which is then whirled round in circles, and when the motion ceases, the point of the needle looks toward the north.[25]

A distinctive step in the development of magnetic science was the enlargement of the observer's horizon. Magnetization was discovered to be a property of other things besides iron and its alloys (including steel). In the class of ferromagnetic objects cobalt and nickel were prominent members. Especially striking was the fact that such alloys as Heusler proposed—namely, a mixture of copper, aluminum, and manganese—were equal to iron in their magnetic properties.

Lodestone to Earth Magnet

As late as the 17th century magnetism was still thoroughly laid over with mystical belief and legend. Gilbert is celebrated for advocating naturalistic treatment of magnetic facts. His fame, however, rests more solidly on his enlargement of the magnetic domain; he is credited with the discovery that the earth is a magnet and exhibits numerous magnetic properties. One immediate deduction was that the suspended needle was north-south polarized because it was part of the earth magnet. While in a sense terrestrial magnetism serves as a means of accounting for many other facts, the origin and nature of the earth's magnetic field is itself still unknown.

In the meantime this domain is a rich mine of important events. The type, amount, and range of magnetic dip, magnetic declination, and magnetic forces, as well as the diurnal and other variations of these events at different parts on the earth's surface, are facts readily encountered and recorded by comparatively simple instruments like magnetometers, declinometers, inclinometers, and magnetographs.

---

[25] Still, Soul of Lodestone, p. 55.

Electromagnetism

The early part of the 19th century marks a period of sophistication in magnetic science. Technology and the natural sciences had by then reached a high peak of experimentation, instrumentation, and mathematical formulation. The accumulation of basic observations was weighty enough to require definite search for useful theory.

So comparatively slow has been the development of magnetic science that one of the fundamental facts about magnetism—namely, its basic relationship to electricity—had to wait until the accidental discovery by Oersted in 1819 that an electrical current could produce effects in a magnet. This discovery did not occur until the field was well prepared for it. When Oersted's magnet set itself perpendicularly across the wire which carried the current, a new era in understanding electricity and magnetism was ushered in. Almost immediately Ampère, Arago, Sturgeon, and others began a development which culminated in the work of Faraday and Maxwell. Numerous experiments were soon made by a large number of workers upon the reciprocal effect of inducing currents from magnets. The result: electromagnetic science evolved. The outcome of this development proceeded in two directions; on the one hand, the studies of Faraday and Henry led to an extensive electromagnetic technology, in which electrical energy was utilized for power and communication; on the other hand, through the work of Maxwell and others the highest peak of modern electrical theory was attained.

Magnetic Constructions

In dealing with magnetism the student of the logic of science confronts an exceptional situation. The magnetic domain is extremely restrictive. Constructions remain for the most part on the descriptive level. Magnetic events are unique; so electromagnetic happenings stand out sharply, but without the characteristics common to other types of events which allow for explanatory interrelation.

Nevertheless, theories concerning attraction and repulsion have been constructed. To the question how the magnet attracts bodies the answer is essentially that it is made up of small magnets. As Maxwell pointed out:

> Still, however, we have arrived at no explanation of the nature of
> a magnetic molecule, that is we have not recognized its likeness to any
> other thing of which we know more.[26]

Numerous valuable facts, however, have been discovered concerning the relationship between magnetism, electricity, and light. An interesting feature of magnetic constructions is the closeness with which the historical succession mirrors the general state of science and intellectual culture at the time.

As late as the 17th century Descartes and his followers—for example, Rohault—imagined corpuscles with screw threads which could percolate the pores of magnetized bodies. Then there were theories about magnetic fluids, such as Poisson's which resembled the fluid theories of electricity. These theories, together with various suggestions of flowing effluvia, mark the inept attempts to develop constructions on the thing level.

One of the more definitely event-level constructions concerned the law of magnetic force. The attempts made by Mayer in 1760 and Lambert in 1766 to determine this law were capped by Coulomb in 1785. By means of suitable apparatus Coulomb was able to establish that the force of attraction or repulsion between two poles varies universally as the square of the distance between them.

Coulomb's quantitative law was elaborated by Poisson, though he made his constructions entirely in terms of imaginary magnetic fluids. Magnetizable bodies he thought consisted of an indefinite number of particles, each of which contained equivalent amounts of the two fluids in free motion, limited only to the spherical particle. The intermixture of the fluids made the particle neutral; their separation resulted in magnetism.

Kelvin, later Neumann, Kirchoff, and Maxwell, emended and clarified Poisson's construction and separated it completely from the fictitious fluids. As a consequence, in the hands of Gauss and Weber was placed the opportunity to develop an experimental magnetic science with a full panoply of units and standards for achieving practical control over electromagnetic events.

A momentous step was taken when Faraday in 1845 observed

---

[26] A Treatise on Electricity and Magnetism, sec. 833.

that light polarization could be reversed by a magnetic field. That discovery marks the achievement of the power to interrelate magnetism not only with electricity but with light. The effect of a magnetic field upon light events brings magnetism into the light situation and stimulates the development of the currently accepted electrical theory of matter.

The peak of magnetic construction was reached when magnetism was connected with atomic properties. On the basis of observations made on the magnetic action of different substances Weiss developed the concept of a magnetic unit of action corresponding to the unitary nature of the electrical currents in atoms. These magnetic units were themselves thought of as magnetic atoms and were thus called *Magnetons*. Atoms of different chemical elements contain different numbers of magnetons.

With the increased understanding of the structure of atoms, especially through the work of Bohr, the magneton construction was refined. What came to be called the Bohr magneton differed in magnitude from the Weiss magneton, was more assimilable to the newer electrical and atomic constructs and also more closely aligned with atomic investigation, as, for example, the way free atoms orient themselves in magnetic fields. Results obtained by Stern and Gerlach in 1923 in projecting a parallel beam of silver atoms through a strongly divergent magnetic field provided evidence that the magnetic moments of these atoms equaled one Bohr magneton. And so the line connecting the lodestone at one end reaches at its other terminal a magnetic atom.[27]

J. FROM SOUNDS TO OSCILLATORY FREQUENCIES

Contacts with sound events are among the earliest and most intimate of the human organism. It is hardly necessary to mention the great variety of sounds produced by man's meteorological, geological, and biological environments. Moreover, considering that the outstanding matrices of sound consist of speech and music, it becomes evident how close acoustical science is to original things and events. It happens, too, that the evolution of culture has not transformed sounds and their sources as it has other kinds of happenings. Despite all the new sound-making objects our

---

[27] Cf., Loeb, Fundamentals of Electricity and Magnetism, sec. 89.

culture has evolved, the complexities of musical and speech sounds consist of the patterning of a limited number of unit tones.

It is to be expected then that the acoustic department of science is among the most favorable for observing the evolution of descriptive and explanatory constructs as products of interbehavior with sound, rather than with traditional beliefs. Logicians of science cannot overlook the plain fact that the construct system in acoustics is more directly linked with everyday events than is the case in electricity or thermodynamics.

How Sound is Produced

The earliest step in acoustic science concerned the mode of producing sounds and tonal variations. The first theoretical description of tone production is attributed to Pythagoras. It is probably nothing more than a legend that in passing a blacksmith shop he observed that the hammers on the anvils produced intervals of an octave, a fifth, and a fourth. The difference in the tone, he found, correlated with the weight in the ratio of $1:1/2:2/3$ and $3/4$. Cajori[28] asserts that the hammers with the indicated weights do not yield the sounds indicated.

It is similarly alleged that Pythagoras discovered that strings of the same material, equally long and thick, give the intervals mentioned above when made tense by weights in the proportion of $1:1/2:2/3$ and $3/4$. Cajori again points out that the pitch of tone varies not as the weight but as the square roots of the weight.

A more acceptable rendering is that Pythagoras by varying the length of strings became aware that pitch changes inversely as the length of the strings. This discovery has been acclaimed as the basis for one of the first constructions of a quantitative theory. Certainly it is the beginning of the tradition that sound is essentially a vibratory or oscillatory event.

Some individuals hesitate to connect the naive Pythagorean numerical philosophy with the modern science of acoustics. Such hesitation is not based, however, on the fact that modern physicists have achieved reliable and valid constructions concerning sound events. As we shall see, the current science of acoustics

---

[28] A History of Physics, p. 13.

contains a far larger proportion of propositions not derived from interbehavior with sound events than those so derived.

Nature of Sounds

Acoustic science now stands firmly on a broadening platform of acquaintance with sound-making objects and situations. In contrast to the formative years, writers on the present level of acoustic investigation are familiar with a vast variety of musical instruments and other types of sound sources. Acoustical scientists and engineers employ numerous types of oscillators for producing precise and controllable sounds. Moreover, thanks to the enlargement of telephonic techniques, many sorts of instruments and processes are now available for sound measurement.

We are not limiting the present stage to any particular chronological period. Investigations of the nature of sound cover the studies made by musicians, by such mathematicians as Euler and Bernoulli up to the 19th century, and, during that century and later, by the physicists. The scope of acoustics is indicated by the following experiments: Chladni on waves and their vibrations; Young on wave interference; König on manometric-flame sound analysis. Also, we must include Savart's work with his toothed wheel; Lissajous and his mirror-reflected figures, and Helmholtz's masterly studies. This list by no means exhausts the range of investigation. As in many scientific departments, the science of acoustics has evolved along with the general evolution of other sciences and technology. So in the 20th century we bring to bear upon acoustic problems electronically operated oscillators and refined instruments for making thorough analyses of sound waves in all their varied forms.

What unifies and slants all these studies is the conclusion that sound is essentially oscillatory frequency and amplitude. This view not only limits and contracts the events, as though all sound consisted of single tones or noises in many combinations: it also bespeaks a philosophical tradition concerning the "real" qualities and properties of things.

Conventional acoustic constructions imply that oscillations may be legitimately abstracted from vibrating bodies (strings, bells) and from the situations in which they are placed. But to abstract vibration frequencies from the complexes to which they belong prevents a field analysis.

The traditional view that acoustics is simply a special branch of the science of vibrations therefore shifts the ground from sounds as basic events of music, and of much else in man's surroundings, to a single component feature common to sounds and other events. Once again dualistic philosophy, which separates extension or mathematical properties from subjective (mental) properties, distorts events and their interpretation. Influenced by the dualistic view scientists divide sound events into vibrations on one side, tonal qualities on the other. The latter are transformed into *reactions* to sound.

Sounds as Reactions

Historically, physicists have followed the procedure of turning over properties of sounds, aside from oscillating frequency and intensity, to the philosophical psychologist. With the development of experimental psychology, physiologists and psychologists improved conditions by investigating reactions to sound. They studied the anatomy and physiology of the organism when interacting with sound. For our purposes it is sufficient to refer to the work of Helmholtz who perpetuated the tradition that the mental (extraspatial) properties of sound, historically referred to as sensations, could be studied, even experimented upon, by investigating their physiological correlates.

In the middle of the 20th century we should expect some alleviation from the medieval incubus which made necessary the shifting of ground from sound events to "psychic processes" and their alleged biological correlates. Still, in the current *Handbook of Experimental Psychology* the following statement appears:

> The external ear delivers sound waves through the external auditory canal to the middle ear, and thence they pass to the inner ear. There, in the cochlea, the sensory cells of the organ of Corti are stimulated and initiate nerve impulses in the fibers of the auditory nerve. The impulses pass through a series of nuclei and fiber tracts in the medulla and midbrain to the auditory area of the cerebral cortex; and *there, somehow*, they generate the sensations that we know subjectively as "sounds."[29]

Aside from the continued utilization of medieval constructs in modern science we have here a confusion of (1) the events inter-

[29] P. 1116 (our italics).

acted with—sound features of situations—and (2) one's reaction to the events. Only a naturalistic construct of the interbehavior of organisms with sound can correct this situation.

Interbehavior with Sound

This naturalistic stage of scientific construction now developing promises to yield an altogether different handling of sound events. To begin with, they are not reduced to vibrations nor divided into physical or extension qualities on the one hand and nonextensional psychic sensations on the other. An objective attitude enables the student of sound to distinguish two sorts of natural facts. Pitch and distinctive vowel or musical qualities of tones which do not require instrumental means for crude discrimination are taken to be just as objective as the vibrations which cannot be discriminated without instrumental aid. But in each case interbehavior with sound objects is required before they can be measured, described or explained.

An interbehavioral analysis of sound events comprises at least four factors: (1) sound events including sounding things, (2) responses to those events, (3) interbehavioral contacts, and finally (4) interbehavior with interbehavioral events.

(1) Sounds as natural events are properties of sounding bodies and situations; they are the sources of all oscillatory and qualitative descriptions. Factors of sound such as quality or timbre, pitch, loudness, source or location, even the feature of pleasingness, are the bases for scientific analysis. All these factors, along with oscillation and intensity, are derived from the original sound situation.

(2) Responses constitute the behavior of persons in their various contacts with sound events. Individuals interbehaving with sounds, discover problems about them, develop solutions. Responses also include the primitive behavior to the sounds made by hunted animals, the production and appreciation of sound patterns in speech and music, the scientific manipulation of sound, as well as the construction of theories concerning sounds and our reactions to them.

(3) Sound interbehavior constitutes the basic event for any scientific inquiry in this department. The primary stress is on the fact that sounds in any of their properties or analyzed qualities

do not depend for their existence on responses made to them. Responses to sound could not occur without the present or former existence of sounding objects with which to interact.

Furthermore, when we examine sound interbehavior we are able to understand all the myriads of complicated sounds issuing from invented objects like fans, blowers, locomotives, phones, industrial machinery, and musical instruments, events brought into existence through both deliberate and incidental interbehavior with things. Such a listing of sound situations suggests that the interbehavioral continuum comprises contacts with both natural sounds and those artificially produced.

(4) Interbehavior with sound interbehavior is excellently illustrated by what scientists do in manipulating sound objects and constructing theories about them. The behavior of analyzing (a) sound ranges, (b) audibility of sounds, and (c) the invention of sound-producing and sound-measuring instruments constitutes the raw material (crude data) for the logicians of science—namely those who interbehave with the scientist's interbehavior with sound.

Common Pattern Exemplified

Throughout our brief survey of the various physiochemical sciences we have found a similar pattern of evolution. No matter how different the events dealt with, the work of the various scientific specialists indicates a gradual evolution of constructs arising out of a matrix of elementary interbehavior with things. Inept and false constructions illustrate the pattern just as well as workable and verifiable ones. Nowhere is there evidence of a creating mind, soul or principle. The various stages of abstraction and law formulation constitute an increase of analysis and dissection and an interrelating of things with each other.

All physiochemical sciences specialize in mathematical constructs. This fact testifies to the character of the things with which the physiochemist works. While it is true that the reign of number in physics constitutes a cultural revolution,[30] we must assume that the revolution succeeded because physicists interbehaved in particular ways with events.

---

[30] Consider how Magnus spurned mathematics. See Cajori, A History of Physics, p. 144.

What is true of the physiochemical sciences is true of the others. All consist of constructs forged in the heat of interbehavior. Because of the different things dealt with, the sciences differ in the rigour and durability of construct making. But the model furnished by the physiochemical disciplines operates in each. The laughter of Galileo and Kepler at the professors who refused to look at the moons and planets through their telescopes typifies in all science and in all ages the separation of those who *do* from those who do *not* cling to actual things.[31]

The physiochemical sciences, where discovery is common, have perhaps had the least trouble about original events. The problems center more about classification, measurement, interpretation, explanation. Is heat a substance? Is electricity a fluid? Discovery itself is a complexly evolved procedure, as in the case of cosmic rays unexpectedly disturbing an electroscope. Even in the 13th century, Roger Bacon and Peregrinus insisted upon the need to observe, to experiment (p. 102).

---

[31] Lodge, Pioneers of Science, p. 106.

EVENTS AND CONSTRUCTS IN BIOLOGY

Study Pattern for Biological Systems

Biological events are constantly and copiously available as crude scientific data. Nor do they resist analysis more than other data of equal complexity. Whatever difficulties the biological system-maker encounters arise from the protopostulates he adopts. Free biological systems from the excesses of cultural imposition—vitalistic and teleological principles, abstractional chemism or mechanism—and they at once resemble all other scientific products.

The fact remains, however, that biological events differ from other types; accordingly we require a fitting pattern of study. Instead of isolating specific situations in order to trace out the evolution of constructs from contacts with events, as we did in the physiochemical subdomains, we shall make a broad survey of the entire biological field and examine general problems concerning its major system components—*data, investigation,* and *interpretation.*

A. BIOLOGICAL DATA

Organisms or Living Matter?

The abstractional urge to achieve ultimacy and generality has led the biologist to develop the construct *life* to parallel the psychologist's *mind* and the physicist's *matter.* In the physical sciences the term *matter* does comparatively little harm, since reference is soon made to things and events. In biology and psychology the situation is more serious because the terms *mind* and *life* are not treated as mere names for objects immediately encountered, but as symbols for occult principles which presumably account for observed events.

Although it is obvious that biologists study interacting organisms, they still claim credit for introducing the concept *living matter* as a replacement for the concept *life*.[1] Doubtless it is an improvement in thinking to discard the occult force called *life*, but we need to get still closer to concrete events. When biologists[2] define living matter as the totality of living organisms they approach concrete things but only at a distance.

For example, influenced by the *matter* construct, biologists assert that organic beings are made up of protoplasm. To protoplasm are attributed the basic characteristics of living things. Protoplasm as living matter is regarded as a complex of colloidal chemical compounds, in constitution primarily water. Other constituents include inorganic salts, proteins, fats, carbohydrates and extractives. But notice the difficulty with this chemical conception when it is necessary to describe the organism's adaptations. As we shall see, it is then necessary to create vital forces and powers in order to account for its structure and activities.

Traditionally, biologists have chosen either cells or total organisms as the refined or analytic unit. The cell theory, developed in the early part of the 19th century, gave impetus to the view that the cell is the basic biological unit. The observation that a large portion of the biological world consists of single-celled animals and plants was accepted as evidence. Moreover, all complex organisms begin their lives as single cells, which, through interaction with their environments, multiply and develop. Again, many single-celled organisms, such as the ameboid bodies, appear to maintain an independent existence even in complicated organisms.

Organismists, however, have pointed out that cells are not isolated units which in aggregation constitute complex organisms. Rather, cells are specialized, existing and acting as parts of a larger unit. For example, regeneration and transplantation facts indicate a priority in the general organization of the total organism.[3]

The supporting facts of either view are hardly sufficient to establish one against the other. Certainly it is impossible to deny that the cell for certain purposes is a unit. The same may be said for

---

[1] Vernadsky, The biosphere and the noosphere.

[2] Cf., Vernadsky, op. cit.

[3] Cf., Loeb, The Organism as a Whole; Child, Individuality in Organisms; Ritter, The Unity of the Organism; Bertalanffy, Problems of Life.

the organism. Each unit proposed is selected out of a larger field which, in its totality, must be regarded as the authentic biological event. However legitimate for investigational purposes it may be to make such an arbitrary separation as cells and organisms, the fundamental unit always consists of the organism-environment *field*. Except for local investigative enterprises—studying nerve or muscle preparations, maintaining a chicken heart or other organ *in vitro*—it is impossible to separate the organism as an autonomous unit from the internal and external environmental factors.[4]

Basic Interactions in Biological Events

Historically, biologists have overemphasized the organism. The structure of tissues, the interrelation of various organs, loomed so large that the plant or animal appeared to be the entire datum. Stressing morphology, however, is a comparatively minor error, since concrete things are still kept in view. A more serious problem is to approach physiological processes without regard to field factors. We suggest that the entire biological domain be treated as interactional, whether it is the form or function of organisms we study, or their maintenance, reproduction, and ecological inter-behavior.

Metabolism. Undoubtedly the most fundamental interaction is energy interchange and transformation; upon these events depend all others. The most typical example is the interaction of chloro-phyllic plants with solar energy, during which they utilize radiant energy to synthesize organic molecular materials for food and ultimately for cell growth. Metabolism is thus an interactional process whereby organisms interchange structure-function substances with the environment and maintain themselves by disintegration (catabolism) and reintegration (anabolism).

Since animals are unable to interact metabolically with solar energy they must rely entirely upon the metabolic products (foods) developed by other organisms. Some can use plant products as food; others need substances similar to their own cellular composition—for example, mammalian animals require protein, car-

---

[4] Herbert Spencer appears to have had a vague intimation of this fact when he asserted that the essence of biological events is the adjustment of inner to outer actions and relations. Cf., Principles of Psychology, sec. 53.

bohydrates, and fats. The ingestion of such substances serves to replace materials lost by waste and excretion.

Constructs concerning energy transformation and utilization are built directly from details observed in the interactions of securing, eating, and digesting food. The energy is disposed of in three ways: (1) by liberating heat of combustion—heat energy evolves while hydrogen ions and electrons are transformed through enzymatic action; (2) by the performance of work consisting of the various intraorganic actions such as conduction, contraction, and secretion; and (3) by storing fat, protein, and carbohydrate reserves which provide a basis for future energy expenditure. Organism-environment fields can be described as perdurative. Descriptions of biological interactions emphasize the stability and continuity of the organisms involved. There are three types of organismic maintenance.

(a) *Individual-Form Maintenance.* Through various interactions with internal and external factors organisms maintain themselves as unique individuals. Aside from the ordinary anabolic processes there are the regenerative processes resulting from injuries and mutations. Structures and patterns of unit organisms are maintained even when organisms are morphologically organized into clones, colonies, or groups.

(b) *Growth.* The intussusceptive assimilation of food material is a process initiated in the early embryological stages and continued throughout the individual's life. This process contrasts sharply with the accretional coherence of inorganic substances. Organismic growth constitutes an intimate and continuous series of interactions.

(c) *Immunization.* Interactions of organisms with others in the relationships of host-parasite, invader-resistor, are in many ways more definite than the interactions involving food objects or atmospheric conditions. The emphasis is usually placed upon the invaded organism, but an interactional description including both host and parasite is closer to the actual event, even when the resisting organism produces antibodies. In this case internal objects and processes are interacting within the larger interplay of the two clashing organisms. If we do not hold rigidly to structure and think, rather, in terms of functions or actions we can observe more readily the continuity throughout the chemical interactions of digestion, respiratory gas interchange, and symbiotic and parasitic commensalism.

Immunization events easily lend themselves to elaborate field analysis. On the side of the organism there are such prominent factors as structural and physiological type, size, susceptibility to certain invaders, and the ability to resist. In specific infection and immunity situations the type of virus or organism must be taken into account. Certain infections and diseases involve particular kinds and combinations of bacteria and microscopic animals. Then there are general field conditions which may concern primarily the organism as it interacts with temperature, for instance, or the availability of nutrient material, etc.

Biological Continuity. Bisexual reproduction involves typical biological interactions occurring on various levels. Either single cells interbehave as portions of large complex organisms or the interbehavior occurs between organisms of different sexual structure. Vegetative as well as bisexual reproduction is interactional. In the vegetative event the interbehaving factors are located in the same biological unit. Cell division or unicellular fission approaches chemical or physiological interactions.

Responsive Interactions. Under this heading we consider elementary ecological interactions—ways in which organisms shift their location in a field with respect to some other object, or otherwise adapt themselves to changes in their surroundings. Ecological interactions are of two types:

(a) *Locomotion.* Organisms interact with their surroundings by changing their location. Movement is relative to the type of organism: animals are more mobile than plants. These movements take place by walking, flying, swimming, floating, each depending on the structure, size, and other characteristics of both organisms and surroundings.

(b) *Irritability.* Sensitivity to the specific nature of the surroundings is one of the most striking interrelationships between living things and their environment. This sensitivity is generally referred to as excitation or responsiveness to stimulation. Any alteration in the surroundings, such as impact, heat, chemical action, light, sound, electricity, correlates with characteristic responses in the organism.

Structure and Function of Organisms

The fine balance of structures and functions—namely the organization and behavior of organisms—is an impressive happening. Exigencies of study have naturally led to specialization, with the unsavory result that biologists have separated structure too widely from function. Anatomical and general morphological studies, for instance, favor structure or organization rather than action or function. This separation of factors is illegitimate: Does the heart have its shape and organization because of the function it performs or is the function conditioned by the heart's morphology? Though taken in the large this is a hen-and-egg problem, there are specific instances in which the question is not so trivial. In all cases, however, the problem is illicit; it arises because organism-environment events are treated as though they consisted of parts rather than of an integrated field. For investigative purposes we might regard structure as prior to function, or vice versa. Actually, each depends on the adaptations of living organisms to their surrounding conditions.

Philosophically inclined biologists frequently object to the structure-function dichotomy and suggest that structures as separated from functions involve only spatial dimensions, whereas to make use of a four-dimensional manifold would obviate the separation. Time considerations alone, they urge, bring to the front function or actions. We reject this neat argument as insufficiently based on contacts with biological events. It does not differentiate between the kind of objects we encounter in a dissecting room or laboratory, where we are dealing with transformed biological things, and those same things when existing under typical circumstances. We know, for instance, that the size and structure of the isolated bone is a function in a mathematical sense of a large number of factors which have operated in its evolution.

The Origin of Living Things

Though all biologists agree that currently existing organisms have evolved from previously existing forms, they differ as to the actual steps. The evolutional hypothesis is not limited to the series of organisms open to direct or paleontological observation. Evolution processes go beyond the development of successively complex organisms and organic situations. Can we extrapolate the evidences at hand to the first stages of plant and animal origin? Can we reach some stage of transition from organic chemical molecules to organisms?

Biological origins, being beyond the limits of direct observation, invite idle speculation. The vacuum of ignorance is filled by pronouncements derived from myth and folklore. Philosophic assertions about creation, purpose, and vital principles proposed by such Romantic metaphysicians as Bergson and such Vitalistic biologists as Driesch, Haldane, and others have been ably answered by writers like Cohen[5] and Woodger.[6] Successful evolution study keeps close to the observation of definite organic transformations. Howsoever troublesome the fact that there are different kinds of evolutionary mechanisms and that biological development includes devolutional and retrogressive processes, there is no other procedure than to reconstruct evolutionary processes by cleaving to existing organism-environment events.

It is a likely assumption that this planet was a red-hot sphere of molten material two or three billion years ago. A gigantic cooling and solidification of the earth's surface must have taken place to make possible the existence of the chemical constituents of organisms—carbon, oxygen, hydrogen, nitrogen, sulphur, phosphorus, etc.[7] Only much later, after the development of a solid crust and the genesis of suitable habitats, could even single-celled organisms evolve.

Now there are two possibilities. Either the simplest basic materials for the evolution of organisms developed on the earth's crust, perhaps in the water-covered portion, or the earliest living things came to the earth from another location. A number of scientists have favored the latter theory. About 1865 Richter[8] proposed that living things were transported to the earth as *cosmozoans* or minute living spores. In 1871 Thomson (Lord Kelvin) formulated the hypothesis that living things came to the earth from meteoric sources.[9] Helmholtz, too, developed such a hypothe-

---

[5] Reason and Nature.
[6] Biological Principles.
[7] But see Urey, The Planets, Their Origin and Development.
[8] Zur Darwin'schen Lehre.
[9] Thompson, S. P., Life of Lord Kelvin, p. 1103.

sis.[10] Arrhenius calculated that a small plant spore, at the upper limits of the atmosphere, propelled by solar radiation could attain a velocity of 100 kilometers per second and reach the earth in 10,000 years from the nearest star.[11]

The above theories were propounded only on the presupposition that living things could not have evolved on the earth itself. Still, howsoever difficult terrestrial origin appears, the competing view is practically impossible, since any organic thing moving out of the protective environment of the terrestrial atmosphere would be killed by the sun's ultra-violet rays which the atmosphere ordinarily absorbs.[12] On the whole the hypothesis of living things originating somewhere else than on the earth's surface at best dodges the entire issue.[13]

Apparently the only acceptable view is that the earliest living things developed from simple chemical compounds. Primordial compounds may well have originated in the waters of the earth through processes of solution and various synthetic and catalytic reactions. There is no difficulty in assuming that the necessary chemical elements were present. The details of the development have been elaborately worked out by Oparin and Blum.[14]

B. BIOLOGICAL INVESTIGATION

Range of Biological Investigation. Because biological things and events possess so many unique characteristics there is a vast range of investigation. Though scientific traditions tend to undervalue field studies in comparison to the presumed excellence of laboratory work[15] *in situ* investigation may be both exact and important. On the other hand, much biological work conforms to the precise canons of controlled laboratory manipulation and measurement. Biologists also make use of elaborate statistical and mathematical techniques despite the resistance of biological events to abstractive simplification.

Think of the polarity of possibilities and limitations of biologi-

---

[10] Vorträge und Reden, Vol. 2, pp. 89, 418f.
[11] Gamow, Biography of the Earth, p. 156.
[12] Cf., Gamow, The Birth and Death of the Sun.
[13] Cf., Alexander, Life, Its Nature and Origin.
[14] Oparin, The Origin of Life; Blum, Time's Arrow and Evolution.
[15] For example, its fundamental and general character.

cal investigation. Biologists are able to dissect, analyze, and reduce complex and highly integrated data. They also construct large synthetic systems. At one pole the biologist can adopt chemical and physical procedures; at the other he must refrain from destroying or converting his events. Many of the events with which he is concerned require long-time periods for their consummation. Though this fact sharply limits experimentation it detracts not at all from the sovereign investigative principle of setting questions to natural things.

Biological things are pliable. More easily than physical things they can be bent to the worker's specifications. Witness the transformations man has brought about by domesticating and breeding animals and plants, denuding and restoring forests.

Specialization of Biological Investigation. In the following sections we indicate variations in (a) types of problems attacked, (b) techniques and instruments employed, and (c) precision and range of generalization.

Taxonomy. Biological events justify the old tradition that arranging and classifying things constitute simple preliminary processes in scientific investigation. Biological organisms are vastly different in their structure and behavior, yet alike in their fundamental characteristics. The difficult task of classifying them yields important material for basic biological constructions. The value of taxonomic studies has been questioned on the admitted ground that ordering things counts for less than analyzing them or discovering their quantity and origin. But the fact that more important investigations exist hardly robs taxonomic studies of their value. Did not evolution problems arise primarily from taxonomic investigation? Each biological specialty is necessary for an effective scientific enterprise. Furthermore, taxonomy is not limited to the discovery of types of organisms: it includes their comparison. For example, taxonomists differentiate and associate variables as a basis for quantitative and experimental researches.

The theoretical position reached by taxonomy is illustrated by problems concerning the reality of species, races, genes, and family groups—issues penetrating to the heart of the logic of science. Taxonomists begin with organisms having both common and divergent traits. For the most part differences between plant and animal organisms are obvious. But actually there are many instances in which the variations are so minute as to challenge the observer's acumen. When organisms display a continuum of homologies and analogies, descriptions become difficult, sometimes impossible. Even the lines of demarcation between animals and plants fade out. The same difficulty occurs at the juncture of organisms and inorganic things such as viruses.

Now because the constructs of the taxonomist possess a marked degree of uncertainty, even positive arbitrariness, many biologists are doubtful of the objective character of any description except that of individual organisms.[16] This view reveals a lack of appreciation that all constructs are derived from observations of individuals taken singly or in groups. Careful observance of similiarties and dissimilarities of traits, plus control of conventional impositions, affords a very satisfactory system of classification. The persistent search for properties and performances of organisms interbehaving with their surrounding conditions may not be good taxonomy, but it does lead to research results in other specialties.

Taxonomic devaluation is based upon two principles, one of which is (a) interpretative and legitimate, the other (b) philosophical and illegitimate.

(a) It is allowable to denigrate a taxonomy based on visible and other apparent traits on the ground that such traits are superficial and accidental. It is a legitimate plea that it is necessary to go deeper than taxonomy does to reach chemical and ecological mechanisms basic to surface characteristics. That antitaxonomists judge visible and apparent characteristics to be relatively less important than their underlying conditions is merely implied.

(b) It is illegitimate, however, to separate more from less basic traits on the basis of some philosophical assumption concerning levels of reality. When we assume that all trait differences are traceable to the adaptive interbehavior of organisms with their surroundings we do not impose unworkable constructs upon any feature of observed events. We can even allow for such traits as characterize supraorganisms—that is, multi-individual units, colonies, aggregations, and communities of animals or plants.[17]

Anatomy. Anatomical investigations stress the thing aspect of

---

[16] Cf., Dobzhansky, Genetics in the 20th Century, p. 579.

[17] Allee, et. al., Principles of Animal Ecology.

biology. In the interest of his specialized research the anatomist frequently overemphasizes form, structure, and, in general, morphology. No plausible objection can be made to such abstractive isolation as long as one remembers that to analyze any biological event is arbitrarily to select it from an interbehavioral field.

To a large degree anatomical investigations consist of peeling off layer after layer of a complex event. First the conditions of an organism's interbehavior are stripped away; next the organism is abstracted from its contacts with environing things; finally the organism itself is taken apart. Investigators proceed on the principle that the end justifies the means. In order to learn more and more about biological organisms anatomy is separated from ecology and from physiology; organisms, in other words, are regarded as dead objects. To discover the nature of living things it is legitimate to transform them, even to destroy them in part:

> Wer will was Lebendiges erkennen und beschreiben
> Sucht erst den Geist heraus zu treiben.

To dissect organs or tissues, to macerate them in chemicals, to induce pathologies, are essential for an understanding of the nature of biological events.

While it may appear that anatomy can be separated from the physiological department of biology, even from the ecological when hard tissues and organs are in question, actually this is not the case. Every operationally isolated unit is an artifact. The entire series of cells, tissues, organs, and organisms is abstracted from biotic events as complex field systems. Bones may be regarded as bits of minerals; their shapes and sizes described and measured, their chemical analyses made, but only for research purposes and the production of scientific constructs.

The fact that natural processes of tooth and claw leave remnants of former complex events for observers to discover simply enforces the pragmatic correlation of event and construct. Neither the artifact nor the construct can be confused with the original datum. Certainly there is no problem of creating any event, except by processes of transformation. Protoplasmic colloids, cells, tissues, and organs, whether gross or microscopic, treated or untreated with stains, are all products of investigative operations.

Physiology. More than most other biological specializations physiology is concerned with biological fields. When we study physiological events—namely, the development and maintenance of organisms in their environment—it is difficult to stress anything less than the entire set of complex factors. The copresence of innumerable component happenings testifies to the futility of distinguishing too sharply between forms and functions, between structures and actions, between organisms and environments.

Physiological researches may be conducted on two levels. The first or general biological level consists of investigations upon the continued existence of organisms through their adjustment to changes in external and internal environments. For example, organisms maintain a constancy of organization in blood chemistry (sugar content, acidity-alkalinity balance), bodily temperature, and fluid balance in response to the requirements of environing conditions. The constructs developed from these large-scale observations and experiments make up the general principles of biology as compared with the hypotheses of special researches. General physiological activities have been studied as long ago as the Greek biologists who set up the list of vegetative, sensitive, reactive, and locomotor functions.

On the second level, local processes of the organismic interior are investigated. Prominent among these intraorganic adjustments are interactions between the organism's various systems— nervous, muscular, digestive, cardiovascular, and so on. For the most part, knowledge about these events has developed since the 19th-century intense penetration into cellular and biochemical situations. Since then an amazing accumulation of detailed information has been achieved.

Preoccupation with precise details inevitably results in autonomizing them. Consequently physiologists have traditionally assumed that one set of tissues or organs—the neural, secretory or digestive, for instance— acts upon other systems. Furthermore, this assumption fitted the historical notion of cause according to which one detached object causes something to happen to something else.

Investigators specializing in physiological events assume that their contacts are either immediate or mediate. Immediate contacts result in information concerning the essential operation of cells, tissues, or organisms under specific conditions. Mediate contacts are presumed to yield knowledge about indicators or correlations. For example, the chemical and electrical records made when contraction or conduction is studied are not considered as the consequence of direct contact with the event of central interest. The distinction between mediate and immediate physiological contacts is definitely favorable to a field interpretation of biology.

Note that mediate and correlative studies modify the view mentioned above that physiology, as compared to anatomy, is always concerned with the living organism. Chemical and electrical studies can be made on tissues or segments which no longer can be classified as living things. An important consequence of correlative studies is their confirmation of the continuity between the actions of living things and the changes and transformations in inorganic objects.

Embryology. Investigators in this area specialize on two different types of events—the reproductive and the evolutional. Each group puts a different emphasis on developing organisms. Members of the first group consider their data as rooted in the past behavior of parental organisms. Embryology for them, at least in part, is the physiology of reproduction. Interest in the evolutional phase is centered in the future: the organism is observed as evolving from comparatively simple cellular materials into a complicated individual organism.

From whichever angle the embryologist starts he faces problems comprising an enormous series of detailed changes. A single cell not only evolves into a gigantic multiplicity of cells, but assumes the size, proportions, color, and behavioral characteristics of the species to which it belongs. Embryological investigation is designed to facilitate the biologist's contact with these changes. He exerts all his ingenuity to discover the steps leading to the individual organism's evolution. The more baffling the problem the keener the urge to solve it.

To a great extent, then, embryological investigation is observational. Experiments usually confirm the validity of working hypotheses but do not lead to strikingly new generalizations or laws. In consequence, embryological studies emphasize the need to reject traditional constructs imposed upon biological events—

for example, all the vitalistic principles alleged to govern the organism's evolution.

Embryological events may be compared to the items of a convergent mathematical series. The limits are set by the species characteristics of the reproducing parents and the matured progeny. Between these two points there are an indefinite number of elements—actually interactions of the developing embryo with its environing circumstances. But in contrast to the discontinuities introduced by the calculator, biological events form a single multiplex system. The entire embryological process comprises as a minimum (1) the union of gametes, (2) influences from prior events affecting the parental source of the gametes, and (3) the multiplicity of physiological and chemical details of embryological evolution. Could anything differ more from the universalistic notions implied in the traditional theories of epigenesis and preformation! Whatever the particular interpretation of these pseudo-processes, whatever their alleged connections with embryological events, they evaporate in the face of the great series of concrete interrelated processes summing up a reproductive event, even by the relatively simpler vegetative forms of replication.

Biochemistry. Because biological events are so complex as to incorporate chemical as well as physical events, the interbehavioral logic of science stresses the inclusion of what may appear to be only correlative facts. Obviously, from the standpoint of constitution, the organism is not reduced to its lowest terms until one reaches its chemical constituents. Not even the fragments obtained from dissection yield complete information concerning its makeup. The chemical study of biological events consequently furnishes indispensable knowledge.

Chemistry is perhaps most closely integrated with biology when actions and processes are under review. Probably the earliest association between technical chemistry and biology dates from the time that Lavoisier established the principle that respiration is a combustion event. Although the father of chemistry had few facts at his disposal, compared with a modern biochemist, he was so fortified by the promise of chemical investigation as to utter his ingenious declaration that "life is a chemical function." That promise, vague as it must have been in Lavoisier's time, since respiration-combustion is, after all, a limited sort of happening, became fulfilled beyond anything the great chemist could possibly have imagined.

Biochemistry, like any hyphenated science, forces the recognition that investigative procedures must follow the lead of events. The inevitable interrelationship of chemical elements, their mechanical and thermodynamical behavior in the organization and disorganization of living things, necessitated a science of physiological and biological chemistry. The continuous development of inorganic substances to form living things, only to revert back to their inorganic beginnings, evoked first the attitude of mystery, then the science of chemistry.

Lavoisier puzzled over this cycle of life: (a) the extraction by plants from the air, water, and the mineral kingdom of those substances necessary for their organization, (b) the development of animals from these inorganic substances by feeding on plants themselves or on other organisms which have fed on plants, and finally (c) the return of these substances to the atmosphere and to the mineral kingdom, through fermentation, putrefaction, and combustion. Lavoisier then exclaimed:

> What is the mechanism through which Nature brings about this marvelous circulation of matter between the three kingdoms?[18]

Biochemical investigation soon minimized the aura of mystery. Observers, however, took sides on the question whether the processes were exclusively chemical or biological. This conflict is excellently illustrated by the famous controversy concerning fermentation conducted by Liebig and his sympathizers on one side and Pasteur on the other (p. 84f.).

The integration of chemical and biological events which Lavoisier regarded as so mysterious was more elaborately stated by Pasteur as the details of biochemical events became better known. Dubos[19] points out that Pasteur grew rhapsodic about the life cycle which Lavoisier treated so reservedly. But the significant thing is that Pasteur's amplifications were made possible by an increased contact with biochemical situations. It is interesting to

[18] Quoted from Dubos, Louis Pasteur, p. 160.
[19] Op. cit., p. 160f.

compare his assertions with those of Lavoisier:

> It is necessary that the fibrin of our muscles, the albumin of our blood, the gelatin of our bones, the urea of our urines, the ligneous matter of plants, the sugar of their fruits, the starch of their seeds. . . be slowly resolved to the state of water, ammonia, and carbon dioxide so that the elementary principles of these complex organic substances be taken up again by plants, elaborated anew, to serve as food for new living beings similar to those that gave birth to them, and so on *ad infinitum* to the end of the centuries.[20]

The career of biochemistry constitutes a progressive penetration of the various subdomains of biology. It began with the study of the interchange of oxygen and carbon dioxide gases in respiration and their transformation in blood circulation. Significant as are the reversible reactions of hemoglobin with oxygen and carbon dioxide, and their indispensable function of facilitating the process of gas exchange and transformation, they appear very simple as compared with the complex catabolic and anabolic digestive processes. Hence the biochemistry of metabolism, work, reproduction, and therapy represents successive chemical conquests.

a. *Metabolism and Growth.* The prominence of chemical reactions in metabolic and growth situations has given rise to the fanciful model of animal organisms as combustion machines. We have seen (p. 216) how metabolic processes convert the latent energy of ingested foodstuffs into work and heat energy. Such models suggest what an expansive specialization biochemists have been able to develop. The breadth and depth of this development can be estimated by referring to some details of enzyme, vitamin, and hormone chemistry.

1. *Enzymes.* Knowledge of enzymes and enzymatic action had its inception from contacts with fermentation and putrefaction. Such processes have long been observed in the apparently spontaneous transformation of sugar into alcohol, cider into vinegar, in the souring of milk or the disintegration of organic materials. The obvious chemical changes are indicated by the production of such gases as carbon dioxide and malodorous putrefactive products. The first notable scientific step in understanding enzymes was discovering that fermentation processes involve the action of specific substances called fermates which do not themselves become transformed in the process.

---

[20] Ibid., p. 161.

The first isolation of an enzyme is credited to Kirchhof who in 1814 extracted by water a substance from germinating barley grains which could convert starch into sugar. In 1833 Payen and Persoz precipitated this substance with alcohol and gave it the name *diastase*. Two years prior to this, Leuchs discovered that saliva (ptyalin) can transform starch to sugar. In 1836 Schwann found in gastric juice the pepsin enzyme which could reduce albuminous substances. The various other digestive juices yielded trypsin in pancreatic juice, amygdalin, invertin, and others.[21]

The development of biochemistry was rapid after the discovery of the wide range of enzymatic events. Every possible variety of chemical conversion and transformation is mediated by enzyme substances. These are classified on the basis of the materials acted upon and the products produced. Certain enzymes act on proteins, starches, sugars, and fats; they serve to coagulate, split, oxidize, dehydrize, deanimize, and break up solid, fluid, and gaseous substances.

For the history and logic of biology nothing surpasses the enzymes in interest. It was problems connected with enzyme action which precipitated the memorable battle between the purely organic chemists and the physiologist Bernard, on one side, who insisted on an exclusively chemical interpretation of fermentation, and, on the other, the crystallographic chemist Pasteur who declared that the fermentation process was an activity of living organisms. As we know, the decision appears to have gone to the advocates of the chemical theory. Since Büchner demonstrated in 1897 that a fluid prepared by breaking yeast cells and subjecting it to high pressure facilitated the conversion of sugar to alcohol, the presence of live yeast cells was unnecessary. Büchner supplied evidence beyond zymase when he extracted enzymes from bacteria producing lactic and acetic acid. These extracts were as effective as the original bacteria. Though enzymes must still be obtained from living sources the central place of chemical reactions in biological situations is assured.

But now the question arises: What is an enzyme? How does it act? The fact that enzymes act without themselves being consumed points to a catalytic interpretation, one closely related to ideas first suggested by Berzelius and then definitely developed

---

[21] Cf., Cowgill, in Howell's Physiology, ch. 46.

by Ostwald.[22] Even though there is still so much to learn concerning catalytic processes,[23] enzymes as organic catalysts have been made into the fount, origin, and essence of all organic existence. A typical example is the description of a living unit or entity as:

> ... one that can direct chemical changes by catalysis, and at the same time reproduce itself by autocatalysis, that is, by directing the formation of units like itself from other, and usually simpler chemical substances.[24]

Again, the identity of biology and enzymology or organic catalytic chemistry is revealed in the following:

> ... the conception of *enzyme action*, or *specific catalysis*, provides a definite, general solution for all of the fundamental biological enigmas: the mysteries of the origin of living matter, of the sources of variations, of the mechanism of heredity and ontogeny, and of general organic regulation. In this conception I believe we can find a single, synthetic answer to many, if not all, of the broad outstanding problems of theoretical biology. . . . It is an answer, moreover, which links these great biological phenomena directly with molecular physics, and perfects the unity not alone of biology, but of the whole system of physical science, by suggesting that what we call life is fundamentally a product of catalytic laws acting in colloidal systems of matter throughout long periods of geologic time.[25]

2. *Vitamins.* Undoubtedly there are many potential sources of vitamin chemistry. The most frequently mentioned is the practical observation that the scurvy of sailors is relieved or cured by lime or orange juice. We are reminded here of Lind and his predecessors.[26] When as early as 1794 Huxham prescribed vegetables for the British fleet[27] the scurvy problem already revolved in the orbit of medical pathology. Indeed, Cartier found the American Indians using a preparation of spruce needles as a remedy.[28]

Knowledge of what became known as diet-deficiency diseases

---

[22] Lehrbuch der allgemeinen Chemie.

[23] Cf., for example, Bayliss, The Nature of Enzyme Action; Oppenheimer, Fermente; Willstätter, Problems of Modern Enzyme Chemistry.

[24] Alexander, Life, Its Nature and Origin, p. 79.

[25] Troland, Biological enigmas and the theory of enzyme action, p. 327.

[26] See Garrison, History of Medicine, p. 364.

[27] Pledge, Science since 1500, p. 244.

[28] Pledge, op. cit., p 243.

and their cure multiplied by the increasing contact of physicians with situations in which food problems existed. In the middle eighties of the 19th century Takaki eradicated beri-beri from the Japanese navy by prescribing a mixed diet under the mistaken notion that proteins were deficient. In 1897 Eijkman was able to produce beri-beri in birds by depriving them of rice husks, and cured them by alcoholic extracts of rice polishings. Grijns, a fellow worker of Eijkman, declared (1901) that this was a dietary rather than a general hygienic problem.

A second source of vitamin chemistry may be located in the laboratory studies of nutrition. Here there is a complex development which centers about the inevitable connection of physical and chemical processes with the life and health of organisms. We can refer to only a few features. About 1860 Voit and Pettenkofer began their work on calorimetric processes in metabolism. This included the comparative study of the properties and importance of fats, carbohydrates, and proteins. From the conclusion that proteins were especially significant stems the evolution of knowledge concerning the amino acids of which proteins are compounded. In the early part of the 20th century Thomas and Abderhalden, and more recently Rose and other chemists, investigated the synthesizing capacities of organisms for amino acids in order to determine dietary requisites. A central issue was the sufficiency of a chemical or artificial diet.

A typical demonstration was made by Lunin and Bunge; namely, young animals can live but not grow on synthetic milk.[29] Hopkins is credited with the idea of linking the facts of diet sufficiency with the problems of diet pathology. In 1906 he formulated the hypothesis that certain accessory food factors were necessary for health and growth. About 1912 Funk declared that the accessory food factors were definite chemical substances which he named *vitamines*. It was probably the lack of vitamins, as they were later called, which accounted for the diseases of scurvy, pellagra, beri-beri, and perhaps, rickets.

Until 1915 it was assumed that only one chemical substance was involved. Then McCollum and Davis demonstrated that there were two, called A and B, the former being fat soluble, the latter water soluble. The evolution of vitamin chemistry resulted in the

---

[29] Pledge, op. cit., p. 244.

multiplication of their number. To A and B were added C, D, E, and K, while B was subdivided into a series of substances. Even more important were the chemical analyses and syntheses. The following list of chemical names for the vitamins indicates the penetration of chemistry into the biological domain:[30] all the (B) series—Thiamine, Riboflavin, Niacin, Pyridoxine—Ascorbic acid (C), Ergosterol and Calciferol (D), etc.

Metabolic and growth chemistry becomes doubly impressive when we consider that beyond the complex compounds the organism is equally as much in need of inorganic substances, including metals. If we include hydrogen and oxygen as the basis of an organism's substance the list of required chemicals reads like a large sampling of the Periodic Table: radium, sodium, potassium, calcium, magnesium, chlorine, phosphorus, sulphur, iron, copper, iodine, manganese, cobalt, zinc, and nickel. No wonder the reductionists are encouraged!

3. *Hormones.* In hormone chemistry the original events are closely interrelated with biological structures and processes. Hormones are characteristically described as secretions of specialized glands—internally secreting organs which dislodge their products directly into the blood stream. Hormones, therefore, constitute uniquely organismic substances operating in the healthful and pathological conditions of organisms.

Hormone chemistry really constitutes a refinement of events vaguely known from the earliest records of biology and medical practice. In other words, there is an unbroken line from the hormonology which Bayliss and Starling established in 1902 back to the humoral doctrines of the Greek physicians.[31] Some writers even go so far as to associate modern endocrinological ideas with the most primitive organophagy and opotherapy.[32]

A more conservative view connects hormone chemistry with observations on organ excision, transplantation, and pathology. As to the first, we need but mention castration, known from early antiquity. The annulment of castration effects by transplanting testes of a castrated cock was experimentally demonstrated as early as 1849 by Berthold. Among prominent medical observa-

---

[30] Cf. Williams, et al., The Biochemistry of B vitamins.

[31] Garrison (History of Medicine) asserts that it was Bordeu's ambition to confirm and uphold the humoral pathology of Hippocrates.

[32] Hoskins, Endocrinology, p. 15f.

tions are listed Addison's description of the pathology of the suprarenal capsules, Brown-Sequard's of the lack of adrenals, and Schiff's work on the thyroid.

Researches on both the normal and abnormal aspects of the endocrine glands have enriched our knowledge concerning the chemical aspects of organisms. How vast the hormonal type of biological chemistry is appears from the long list of organs known to produce hormones—the pituitary, the thyroid, the parathyroids, the adrenals, the pancreas, the stomach and intestines, and finally the testes and ovaries. As organs with possibly endocrine function Hoskins lists also the pineal and thymus glands, the liver, the heart, and the spleen.[33] Connecting this type of chemistry with all the others known to occur in the organism we can appreciate why some biologists wish to reduce their whole science to the study of chemical reactions. Certainly the list of hormones is a formidable one, the list of their influences more formidable still—an obvious fact when we mention such outstanding hormones as thyroxine, adrenin, cortisone, corticosterone, insulin, theelin, acetylcholine.

b. *Locomotion and Performance.* Among the more fascinating problems of biochemistry is the manner in which energy transformations facilitate locomotion and performance. Muscle chemistry points to the chemical basis for the structural organization of muscles,[34] as well as for all movements.

The role of oxygen in the accumulation and dissipation of lactic acid is highly important, as well as the chemical reaction of breaking down glycogen or glucose by enzymatic catalysis, thus releasing energy and the evolution of heat. Two other types of chemical events in muscle action concern phosphoric acid, iron, and iron-containing substances.

c. *Reproduction.* The chemistry of reproduction, which happens to be one of the most promising biochemical specializations, centers around the search for substances which reproduce themselves. Biologists and chemists believe they have discovered these substances in the nucleoproteins.[35]

---

[33] Endocrinology, p. 18.

[34] Their "morphological" chemistry. Cf., Wilhelmi, Energy transformation in muscle, Howell's Textbook of Physiology, p. 59.

[35] Cf., Davidson, Biochemistry of the Nucleic Acids; Mirsky, Some chemical aspects of the cell nucleus; Beadle, Chemical Genetics.

Biological reproduction becomes the nucleoprotein chemistry of genes. Genes are taken to be not only the unit factors concerned, but also objects reducible to a single complicated chemical molecule. The likenesses and differences of organisms in reproductive succession are attributed to the stability or mutation of these nucleoprotein molecules.

Those who question whether chemistry will make even greater inroads into biology than it has should be impressed by the connections being made between reproductive processes and the dynamics of particles and radiation. It is proposed that gene mutation constitutes chemical changes of molecules resulting from ionization of their bonding electrons. In brief, quantum physicists have gone so far as to interpret gene mutations as quantum jumps.[36]

d. *Hygiene and Chemotherapy.* The biological subdomains of health and disease offer further rich fields for biochemical research. With the modern advances of chemical science the organism's satisfactory and unsatisfactory conditions are correlated with chemical reactions and changes. We are reminded here of the Hippocratic doctrine of the imbalance of the humors. Medical practice throughout the ages points to the fact that the chemical aspects of health and disease are prominent features of biological science. Even before the existence of authentic chemistry, healers worked on the principle that certain things (drugs, potions) could produce differences in the organism. It would be a gross error of scientific logic not to acknowledge the relationship between the progress of healing techniques and the evolution of chemical knowledge. Chemotherapy, for example, though rooted in the everyday contacts of organisms with beneficial and noxious substances, has become an effective technique of combatting poisons, toxins, as well as invading and destroying organisms.

Ehrlich's theories concerning the chemical reactions of cell substance with dye compounds initiated a chemical evolution ending in the recent development of synthetic antibiotics. Since Domagk's synthesis of prontosil in 1935 the development of the "sulpha" and similar drugs has established the importance of chemistry as a weapon against disease.

---

[36] Cf., Weyl, Philosophy of Mathematics and Natural Science, Appendix E; Timoféef-Ressowsky, Zimmer and Delbrück, Ueber die Natur des Genmutation und der Genstruktur.

e. *Chemistry and Biology*. The length of this biochemical sec-
tion indicates in itself how thoroughly chemistry integrates with
biology. What then is the precise relationship? It has been suggested that interest in the chemical constituents and correlations
of biological events has fostered a naturalistic attitude in biology,
even if it has not altogether banished teleology. Undoubtedly
this is true. Because the field of chemistry is a manipulative discipline, organisms and the things with which they interact are
dealt with as concrete things.

Biochemical events, however, occur within the larger biological domain. It is therefore impossible to reduce the entire biological situation to some of its constituents. Such reduction, we have
seen, at once calls for correlated teleological principles to complete the description.

We reject the view that only biochemical investigation keeps
biology within naturalistic bounds. Biological events are self supporting. Biochemistry is related to biology in two ways: (1) it
provides controllable methods for studying biological facts and
(2) since biological events include chemical events, biochemistry
is a biological specialty. In the same sense, physical and mathematical enterprises find a place in biological research.

Pathology. Because scientific workers are so thoroughly imbued with the ideal of regularity, homogeneity, and uniformity
they find it difficult to fit variants into conventional constructions.
So conspicuous are biological variations, however, that they demand representation in descriptive and interpretative systems.
Regularities of difference, as well as of sameness, are the outstanding biological patterns. Pathology is the subdomain of de-
viation and change.

Pathological things and events comprise an expanding phase
of anatomy, physiology, embryology, and ecology. Morphological variants are probably the most obvious. Variations in
shape, size, and general conformation reach the extremes called
teratological monsters.

The functioning of cells, tissues, and organs displays an immense variety of dissimilarities and irregularities. Here the grand
calendar of diseases provides illustrations.

Pathology or extreme biological variation has been aptly referred to as experiments of nature. Nevertheless it is a fact that
the subdomain of pathology grew up in the soil of human and

veterinary medicine. Pathological science, in other words, is based on criteria and values set up by individual and communal interests. This fact, however, does not detract from the objective and naturalistic character of variant situations. The search for curative and preventive means of controlling pathology leads to an analysis of the participating factors.

The distinction between normality and pathology is, of course, a precarious one. Frequently criteria of normality are established on partial or complete ignorance of animal or plant characteristics and variations. For the most part, however, standards of use and convenience are set up. The notion of pathology as nature's experiment really implies a collocation of factors. They may or may not be mediated by intentional human agency, such as administering poison, mutilating an organism or depriving it of some necessity such as food. No room is left for mystical principles or powers.

Pathologies may be described as disharmonies of balance between organisms and environment, as adjustmental insufficiencies and failures. Probably the most striking example is the imbalance between interrelated organisms. The invasion of given organisms by others in parasitic interaction fills the pages of human pathology; this process is general throughout the biological world. In certain instances the reverse takes place: the organism's imbalance and resulting variant life are traceable to the diminution or total disappearance of symbiotic organisms.

Genetics. Geneticists locate the origin of their scientific subdomain somewhere past the middle of the 19th century. Its roots go down to the development of cell theory and the principles of evolution. The scientific stage of genetics, nevertheless, stems from everyday observations concerning likenesses and differences between parents and progeny. Some knowledge of heredity and of the principles of crossings has been available as early as prehistoric, agricultural, and pastoral man.[37]

Among the very earliest germs of genetical knowledge, if not of genetical science, is the successive accumulation of facts about the relationships of organisms. This implies familiarity

---

[37] Cf., Roberts, Plant Hybridization before Mendel; Zirkle, The Knowledge of Heredity before 1900, Gregor Mendel and his precursors, The Beginning of Plant Hybridization; Lush, Genetics and Animal Breeding.

with the interactions between more or less widely varied plants and animals, especially with the possibilities of interbreeding. Writers on the history of genetics give a prominent place to such pre-Mendelian hybridizers as Kölreuter, Gärtner, Knight, Herbert, Goss, Seton, Naudin, Wichura, Dzierzon, etc.[38]

The scientific investigation of heredity begins with Mendel's crossing of organisms and recording the consequences. In fact, the importance of his work lies in the accuracy of his records.

When hypotheses were constructed concerning the mechanisms involved, genetics took on a decidedly more scientific character. Investigations became more numerous, more complex, centering around the discovery of cytological and chemical correlates and components of reproductive processes.

Specific hereditary mechanisms have constantly been sought in the components of cells. At the same time that Mendel published his famous experiments Haeckel asserted in his *Generelle Morphologie* that hereditary events are owing to the nuclear portion of cells.[39] With the development of cytology and experimental embryology by such workers as Weismann, Hertwig, Strasburger, Roux, and others the idea gradually made headway that the nuclear chromosomes, more than other cellular units, were directly responsible for hereditary happenings.

The theory that chromosomes are "carriers of heredity" then expanded on a definitely selective basis. For example, Wilson as far back as 1896[40] rejected Verworn's claim that cytoplasm is essential to inheritance—since without the cytoplasm the nucleus is unable to set up specific forms of synthesis—on the ground that egg cytoplasm is itself a product of nuclear activity.[41] Since that time the notion that chromosomes are the mechanisms of heredity has been considerably refined. In 1903 Sutton proposed that chromosomes are divisible into smaller entities which represent the allelomorphs which may be dominant or recessive.[42] This followed the attempt of McClung to associate a particular in-

---

[38] In addition to references in footnote 36, see Darlington, The early hybridziers and the origins of genetics.

[39] Sturtevant, The Relations of Genes and Chromosomes, p. 101.

[40] The Cell in Development and Inheritance.

[41] Ibid., p. 326f.

[42] The chromosome in heredity, p. 240.

herited character (sex) with a particular chromosome (x).[43] From this point on, the genes have been regarded as the determining agencies for all the characteristics of progeny. The interaction of genes, their domination or recession, their expression and non-expression, their interrelation with environing factors, are presumed to account for all hereditary development.

As usual, the nature of the gene was exaggerated beyond observational limits. Individual genes were regarded as determiners of each distinct biological character. Later the multiple-factor notion was established—namely, many genes contribute to the development of particular characters. Some writers went so far as to assert that every character was the product of all the genes. It has been said that the development of genetics has depended upon separating genes from gene products.[44] There is still a minority group of biologists who regard chromosome mechanisms as holistic and without discrete gene units.[45] More recently the fact that cytoplasm also functions in the reproductive process has led to investigations showing that it is not only chromosome-located genes which are hereditary mechanisms.

Specialized contacts with cells and tissues naturally lead to chemical analysis. Any preoccupation with physiological processes occurring when elements of the nucleus and other parts of cells interact during cell division and chromosome reduction runs squarely into the problem of what chemical reactions participate in the events.

That hereditary processes depend upon the chemical nature and physical state of cellular substances was concluded on three levels: (1) the generalized attitude that chemical processes must be present wherever there are tissues and cell materials; (2) the development of knowledge concerning the specific chemistry of the nucleus—namely, the nucleic acids and the nucleoproteins. The initiation of this development is generally attributed to Miescher who worked in Hoppe-Seyler's Tübingen laboratory about the time Mendel worked at Brünn; (3) the third and unifying level was the realization that nucleoproteins are the bases for

---

[43] Notes on the accessory chromosome; The accessory chromosome—sex determinant?

[44] Darlington, Genes, Plants, and People, p. 62.

[45] Cf., Goldschmidt, On some facts pertinent to the theory of the gene; also Position effect and the theory of the corpuscular gene.

reproduction or self-duplication. As a result, hereditary processes could be investigated as generalized reproductive events, whether localized in the chromosomes of complex organisms or in the simpler domain of the viruses.

Although it is admitted that chemical genetics faces extremely difficult problems, it is securely established as a subdomain of genetics and of physiology.[46] To a great extent chemical genetics is in the elementary stage of (1) analyzing the nuclear and cytoplasmic contents of cells, (2) ascertaining the chemical reactions of genes and chromosomes, and (3) determining their interaction with the contents of nonnuclear elements. For example, biochemists are convinced that ribonucleic acid (RNA) is present in both the nucleus and cytoplasm, while the nucleus or at least the chromosomes contain only desoxyribonucleic acid (DNA). Still, the active development and use of effective techniques, such as chromatography and measurements of ultraviolet absorption,[47] as well as the extension of knowledge concerning nucleic-acid biosynthesis, have produced a general optimism concerning the future.[48]

Students of the logic of science may well characterize genetics as the fateful discipline. Concerned as it is with problems of parent-offspring relationship, there is a continual clamor for causes, determiners, inevitabilities. Though genetics is a sister science, if not a subdomain, of embryology, and hence concerned with the physiological and ecological processes of reproductive physiology, the primary cast of genetic thought is deterministic (product creation) instead of factorial analysis and description.

Doubtless the central construct is heredity. But to what event that construct refers is not at all clear. McClung points out:

> It appears from definitions variously given that heredity is at once a "law," "rule," "force," "material contribution," "act," "relation," "process," "fact," "principle," "link," and "organization."[49]

Though heredity is sometimes taken to be an event or process, for the most part it is regarded as a creative or determining power.

---

[46] Cf., Beadle, Genes and the chemistry of the organism, Chemical Genetics.

[47] Cf., Caspersson, Cell Growth and Cell function; Caspersson and Schultz, Cytochemical Measurements in the Study of the Gene.

[48] Cf., Darlington, Chromosome Chemistry and Gene Action.

[49] The chromosome theory of heredity, p. 613.

This is clear from the separation of factor and character. Instead of considering genetic factors as stages in evolution they are taken as prior causal agents. Even when genetic factors are described as transmitted, in the sense of cellular material translocated from parents to offspring by gametic means, there is still a trace of determination. It is overlooked that genetic processes are nodal points in species or races, as successive sets of individuals are maintained by the reduction of two mature zygotes to gametes which, when united in bisexual reproduction, go through a complex evolutionary process.

Causal and determining views are responsible for the inordinate emphasis upon gametic factors. Howsoever excusable in the early days of genetics, it has long appeared absurd to insist upon genes as the sole determiners of all complex characters. Despite the fact that such mechanisms as presences and absences, gene position, crossings, linkages, quantitative and polygenic influences are resorted to, geneticists still cling to the determination of the whole organism by one or several parts.

The development of genetics parallels the progressive discovery of more and more factors in the continuation and modification of parent-offspring relationships. With the assimilation by geneticists of the facts concerning cytoplasmic contributions to heredity, and recognition of the actual place of chemical substances in chains of physiological processes, the notions of development and evolution should completely replace cause and determination.

Determinative and causal ideas dictate not only that genes, chromosomes, or nuclei are overemphasized as against the rest of the cell at the gametic stage, but also as against the parental organisms, and still more blatantly as against essential environmental factors. Whenever developmental processes are dealt with, as, for example, in studying any chemical reaction or radiational mutation, the interaction of factors cannot be ignored. The view that chromosomal genes alone determine the future characters of successive generations of organisms is more metaphysical than scientific.[50]

---

[50] Consider Darlington's statement that "genetics has demonstrated the unity not merely of biology, but of science itself." Genes, Plants, and People, p. xxi.

Genetic analysis that takes into account relevant field factors dispenses with illegitimate abstractions and prevents the reduction of complex events, such as intelligence and character, to simple qualities similar to skin color or texture. Obviated, too, are internal substances or processes which determine human character and conduct, but which are assumed to be controllable for improvement of the human race.

Ecology. As a technical subdomain of biology ecological investigations have evolved from what has been traditionally called natural history. Ecology deals with the interrelations of organisms and their environment; it is based upon the worker's developing series of contacts with organisms in their native habitats.

Students of biology sympathetic with the view that unit biological events comprise organisms interbehaving with their surroundings under specific conditions may well look upon the ecological subdomain as the typical field of biological investigation. In fact they may agree that morphological and physiological investigations always constitute phases of these larger unit events.

After all, however, it is best to consider every type of biological event as highly relational. This seems to be true even for plant viruses.[51] Certainly, typical ecological facts concern the environmental factors favoring the maintenance of organisms, their numerical increase or decrease, their modifications in morphology and function because of isolation from other environments. Investigations of organism variations owing to a limited type of surrounding lead to constructs concerning evolution and devolution. In another sense, too, ecological investigations constitute refined studies of a taxonomic sort.

Even those who focalize ecological relations as organism-environment events accord a large place to plants and animals as environing factors of still other plants and animals. In consequence a sizable part of ecology is devoted to studies of commensalism, parasitism, and symbiosis.[52] Obviously, too, the ecological subdomain penetrates deep into the areas of hygiene and pathology.

Bioecologists have recently expanded their investigations to include animal behavior. Because organismic adaptation and ani-

---

[51] Cf., Pirie, A biochemical approach to viruses; Kennedy, A biological approach to plant viruses.

[52] Cf., Caullery, Le Parasitisme et la Symbiose.

mal learning are far more complex and flexible than sheer biological maintenance, behavioral ecology emphasizes the complex field aspects of biological events.

C. BIOLOGICAL THEORY CONSTRUCTION

Before considering the laws and principles unique to biology it may be helpful to compare the biological with other scientific systems. Since the physiochemical type is conventionally regarded as the model, we compare (a) data, (b) investigation, and (c) theorizing in biology and physics.

(a) On the side of *data*, a biologist is somewhat more concerned with events than with things. His principles, therefore, pertain to origins, functions, growth, development, individual and group survival, variation, dysfunction, decline, and dissolution. Physicists, on the other hand, stress relative permanence, similarity, repetition, composition. Physical interactions, too, are less dependent on internal processes than on external relations.[53] Pertinent here is a statement by Fermi:

> Perhaps the most central problem in theoretical physics during the last twenty years has been the search for a description of the elementary particles and of their interactions.[54]

On the whole, physical things are regarded as discrete and separable. Each object originates from previously existing independent elements. When one body divides off from another there is simply a division of material. Whatever family relationships exist are in such a case owing to the presence of common elements in the several parts. Not so in biological things: here there is a parent-offspring connection. Clone, species, family, and genus relationships are obvious and compelling. Biological individuality of necessity implies relations with other similarly organized things.

These distinctions, of course, are entirely relative; actually biological science consists in great part of descriptions and analyses of things. Witness the prominent departments of taxonomy, of gross and histological anatomy. Physics, on the other hand, main-

---

[53] Biological reductionists attempt to transform internal biological processes into biochemical events.

[54] *Elementary Particles*, p. 1.

tains a powerful interest in action and reaction. All the dynamic features of physical things are events. In recent times, with the development of radioactivity, kinetic theory of gases, and the energy equivalence of mass, the emphasis is increasingly on actions and transformations.

(b) While biological investigation must follow the pattern set by the structural and behavioral characteristics of organisms there are situations in which biological and physiochemical investigations are identical. Organisms, we have seen, are in part chemical compounds and, in some of their behavior, subject to the same conditions as are physiochemical things. The specificities of biological systems, however, call for certain variations in working hypotheses and manipulations.

In the first place, the biologist cannot overlook the results of organization and adaptation. Even in situations bearing most resemblance to general chemical circumstances, such as the pharmacal, pathological, and infectional, he must take account of individual differences, tolerances, fatigue effects. It is such facts that make for uniqueness of biological investigation, and for difficulties as well.

The approach to biological events is difficult because they are so complexly integrated. Not only do they include isomerisms and side chain shiftings of chemical compounds but ecological complications besides. Contrary to the physiochemical situation, in which events comprise only current factors, biological happenings represent growths and evolutions no longer available. It is these historical factors that complicate the average biological investigation.

(c) Biological *systems* differ the most from physiochemical ones at the point of theory construction. The physiochemist leans heavily toward general and universal laws. Physicists depart unwillingly from the ideal of rational mechanics, of deductive systematics. Biologists, on the other hand, are limited to a narrow domain. Physical laws, it is claimed, cover biological events, but biologists, unlike metaphysicians like Bergson, Whitehead, and others, hardly dare to propose organismic theories of cosmic dimensions.

Biological laws therefore keep closer to specific events, imply less free creation than physiochemical laws which can be erected on the basis of mathematical or other abstract models. In biology, when extrapolation is made it reaches out toward qualitative principles. Even chemical participants are transformed into powers and forces.

Because of the intricate organization of biological events, biology is encumbered with more undesirable protopostulates than the physiochemical sciences. These metaconstructions play their harmful role both in the working hypotheses of specific investigations and in the development of basic laws. Despite the long struggle of biologists to free themselves from vitalistic principles they are still hampered by them. This situation is certainly aggravated by the number of variables to be taken into account. Consider fertilization: the gametes must simultaneously reach maturity; they must come together under special time and place conditions, under optimum chemical and physical circumstances. By comparison with such complexities, the kinetic conditions of gas molecules, including their numerous probabilities, are comparatively simple. Surely the biological situation, in contrast even to quantum mechanics, contains many more factors which are only indirectly observable.

Special Biosystem Problems

System Principles. Since theoretical constructs consist of interrelating events and the records of observing them the biologist faces two general systemic problems: (a) how comprehensive should his explanatory propositions be? and (b) what should be their source?

In one sense the problem how comprehensive theories or explanations should be is quickly solved. When biologists study organism-environment events there is no need to resort to traditional philosophical principles. If they do so, they damage their science. For example, Woodger has listed the noxious theories and explanations which have arisen from phenomenalism.[55] But his adoption of semantic and linguistic philosophy[56] strongly suggests that to fall back to a formalistic philosophy is to discard specific description and explanation. The prime necessity, it seems, is to dispense altogether with traditional philosophical systems.

---

[55] Biological Principles.
[56] Axiomatic Method in Biology, Technique of Theory Construction.

From an interbehavioral standpoint biological systems are not only local with respect to particular problems and data: they are tentative and corrigible. The interbehavioral system builder freely acknowledges blind spots and lacunae. The scientist's ignorance is bound to cut short his descriptions and explanations.

Derived and Imposed Constructs. Biologists who build systems closely geared to events avoid imposing constructs *upon* events. It is a mistake to think that the rule of derivation disallows free construction. Considerable leeway is available for working hypotheses. For specific investigative procedures biological events may be restricted to cells, organisms or parts of organisms. But such refined terms as pure germ plasm, autonomous chemical or cellular genes—items entirely unrelated to properties of organisms—are to be avoided.

Mechanism and Vitalism. Frequently it is easy enough to observe the beginning and end of biological events, but the intervening processes are a challenge. Take the embryological domain: fertilization initiates a colossal number of processes which eventuate in a new individual. The specific steps of this development are difficult to ascertain.

Processes more or less directly open to view are interpreted as mechanical. The term *mechanical* in this connection means simply that the happenings are so readily observable that the investigator is able to construct mechanisms or models of them. It is quite otherwise with obscure processes, in which case those theorists who thoroughly respect the claims of events remain silent. On the other hand, the vitalistic interpreter simply posits general determiners such as entelechies, or he proposes that general ends or teleological principles are in operation.

Epigenesis and Preformation. Most likely neither epigenesis nor preformation is a current theory of embryological development. This does not mean, however, that they do not operate as metasystemic protopostulates. Today the scatulation theory of Haller, according to which the germs of all animals are nested in the ovaries of successive generations, is but a curiosity of biological history. Similarly, the absolutistic extrapolation of Wolff that organisms are completely created in epigenetic processes may be dismissed as metaphysical fantasy. Nevertheless, both dogmas are today accepted as biological theories. Preformationism may be clearly seen in genetic thinking concerning absolute germ plasm and inevitable determination. Epigenesis is recognizable in the theory of absolute environmentalism.

The difficulties with these forms of biological theorizing is not that they do not articulate with events: they depart too far from them. When Wolff observed the rounding of the "germinal disk" and its breaking up into four folds as the rudiments of the nervous, muscular, vascular, and alimentary systems, he had no valid ground for assuming that he was concerned with a detached egg unrelated to other biological things. Even the most advanced embryologists make the same error of overlooking essential relations. The penalty, of course, is unverifiable, even false theory.

To a great extent the solution of the epigenesis-preformation problem reduces to the actuality-potentiality relation. This relation is simply a matter of prior developments serving as necessary preliminary steps to later evolution. In other words, prior conditions constitute potentialities for later developments when certain necessary conditions become adjunct to the former factors. Looking backwards to the parent organisms one observes conditions which are called potentialities when considered from the standpoint of present and future evolution.

Design or Chance. Theory construction in biology reaches its peak in the ever-recurring opposition between those who affirm and those who deny that biological events are strictly amenable to law. Historically the uncertainties, even the indefiniteness, of biological events have been treated either as chance or arbitrary design. Those who reject both design and chance assume that biological events are subject to law because they are orderly and regular.

Teleology, purposiveness, design, and determination are all metasystemic constructions imposed upon events. Those who argue for strict laws oversimplify the facts, even try to reduce them to something else. The teleologists stress the difficult features of biological events and trade upon ignorance of detail.

A signal tribute is paid the power of impositional constructs by the widely held view that neither design nor chance can be disproved. Those who hold this view merely indicate that they still cling either to design or chance philosophy. Cultural beliefs obviously have nothing to do with the objects stimulating those beliefs. The opinions, for instance, that the earth is the center of the universe, that demons control disease, that the brain thinks, are not derived from study of the earth, disease, or the brain. Such beliefs, as well as those of biological chance, purpose, and determinism, are eradicable when we analyze the cultural conditions under which they were built up and assimilated.

Biological and Nonbiological Time. Many badly constructed biological theories stem from prior faulty presuppositions concerning time intervals. For example, there is the theory that biological and nonbiological events are absolutely different because the former are historical. Again, biologists propound metaphysical doctrines of time on the ground that tissue healing and regeneration occur at different rates under different conditions.

These misconstructions concerning the temporal aspects of biological events occur when constructs and events are confused. Time, for physiochemical scientists, enters comparatively little as a constructional ingredient. They consider events as more or less instantaneous; at least not as durative but as momentarily occurring. Development, therefore, is not featured. Even though the physical scientist takes into account such processes as hysteresis and metal fatigue, durational factors are not prominent. Symmetry and balance, as in D'Alembert's principle, also put a premium on immediacy and instantaneity. Furthermore, radioactive processes are dealt with by amount of substance present. The frequent use of the half life of distintegration is suggestive here. Another point to consider is the rapidity and frequency, in consequence the repetitiveness, with which events happen. Laws accordingly tend to minimize details. In physics, therefore, time intervals are brief.

How different in biology! The step-by-step details of physiological happenings cannot be passed over. The many distinctive stages in embryological evolution take place in a definite sequence. Time intervals are of considerable length. What these differences mean is that discontinuities and variabilities automatically enter into biological theory construction. But no profound break separates biological from any other kind of event. Temporal factors are components of *all* constructions.

Cause versus Factor Participation. Some biological theorists, on principle, have been unwilling to subject their data to interpretations of purpose and indeterminacy; they have chosen instead theories descended from traditional causal constructs. This causal idea stems from the older creative-agent construction which ranges from (1) a personalized or nonpersonalized omnipotency, capable of creating something from nothing to (2) the absolutistic power of one thing to bring about a change in something else.

The causal type of construct may be illustrated by a problem of pathology. The biologist isolates an invading organism; then he regards the attacking microorganism as the determining (causal) factor. Historically this has been referred to as the germ theory of disease. Proper causes were assumed to have been discovered as over against demonological interpretations. Improved observations, better techniques of dealing with microscopic organisms, soon indicated that these microorganisms were likewise present when the undesirable pathological condition was lacking. The simple notion of causes thus became unsatisfactory. The final interpretation, then, is that the pathological situation is a sum of factors: the invading organism must be present; the host must be receptive, in the sense of not being immune or not in optimal hygienic condition—in other words, not able to counterbalance the effects of the invading organism. Biology, therefore, operates on the same basis as any other science—interrelationship of field factors.

Opposition between the theories of determining cause and factor participation is excellently illustrated by recent virus research. Students searching for the causes of the costly and baffling afflictions of various plants were munificently rewarded when they turned from physiological conditions to virus information. Previously the question "What are viruses"? was answered in terms either of chemistry (molecules) or biology (organisms). Finally when Stanley in 1935 isolated the virus of tobacco mosaic in crystalline form the causationists felt supported in their view. Not only could the virus itself be studied independently of the diseases it caused,[57] but as Bawden and Pirie recently put it:

> Most work so far has been directed toward obtaining apparently homogeneous preparations with the highest infectivity.[58]

[57] Smith, Plant virus research at Cambridge p. 776.
[58] Viruses, 1950 (ed. M. Delbrück), p. 39.

Apparently, however, an understanding of the chemical characteristics of viruses is not sufficient even for the study of viruses in isolation. They cannot flourish or reproduce apart from living tissues. As factors in pathology we must also consider how viruses spread and reach their host tissue:

> ... the ability to spread or to be actively infective, is the one character that clearly distinguishes viruses from other cell constituents.[59]

What is the relationship of viruses and vectors? Since insects provide the commonest known means of spreading virus,[60] the analysis of pathological situations projects the problem of the ecological relations between insect carrier, plant-virus host, and the virus material itself. As Kennedy points out, insects are not mere vectors; their role in virus translation may be a serviceable adaptation. Also, viruses themselves can hardly be considered as independent particles, since they merge into the metabolism of the plants they infect. Such considerations point to no other possible conclusion than that viruses as particulate and independent causes of disease must give way to the view that they are participants in sets of factors constituting fields larger than any single unit or member. This in no way minimizes or reduces the properties of any participant factor: it merely obligates the observer to discover what part each factor plays in the total situation.

---

[59] Bawden, Plant Viruses and Virus Diseases, p. 321.
[60] Kennedy, A biological approach to plant viruses, p. 890.

EVENTS AND CONSTRUCTS IN PSYCHOLOGY

Psychology and the Logic of Science

THE psychological department of science distinguishes itself not merely by its own difficult problems: it also forces to the front a huge paradox. From the earliest days psychology as the domain of intellectual and rational powers has occupied a central position among the disciplines concerned with the logic of science. Yet none of the sciences, in the same degree as psychology, has had to defend itself against the charge that it was no science at all because not concerned with actual events.

Consider a particular case: a specialist in the logic of science asserts:

> ... psychology has certain relations to all the remaining sciences depending on the fact that all the sciences owe their existence to certain types of mental activity, expecially to the type of activity we have already alluded to as 'intellectual'.[1]

He then declares that psychology, unlike the other sciences, deals not with public facts but with private ones, known only to their unique possessor by a process of introspection.[2] This is the old familiar supposition that psychological events constitute spiritistic processes.

Psychological events are among the most ubiquitous in the entire scientific domain. Moreover, for a century they have been subject to mathematical, mensurational, and experimental treatment. Yet psychologists, along with laymen, persist in the conviction that psychology is concerned with inaccessible subject matter. Tradition has overlaid psychological events with constructs nowise derived from interbehavior with psychological happenings. Psychology therefore is held to be a unique discipline,

---

[1] Woodger, Biological Principles, p. 33.
[2] Ibid., ch. 11.

its subject matter capable of being but indirectly or substitutively dealt with.

But psychology began its career in a completely naturalistic setting. Among the Greeks, in the environment of general biology and Hippocratic medicine (p. 255), it was a study of definite contacts with organisms and stimulus objects. How is it, then, that today psychology is presumed to concern itself with paranatural and extraspatial entities?

The answer: Psychological constructions since the Greeks have originated not in first-hand interactions with events, but in the unique social and political situations dominating European culture after the decline of the Roman empire. These extrascientific circumstances have resulted in splitting the world into extensional things on one side, thought or spirit on the other (p. 62 f.). Extension has been preempted by the natural philosophers (physicists and chemists); the intangible (unreal) spiritual essences were thrown into the lap of theologically inclined philosophers, from whom psychologists derived them. Thus the alleged subject matter of human psychology—namely, the soul and its variants *mental processes*—is unamenable to the sort of observation and experimentation employed in the "natural" sciences. On this basis psychological processes can only be known through physiological manifestations. So runs the *psychic* version of psychology.

From the standpoint of the logic of science psychology has consequently been denied systematic character. *Data* constructs have not been coordinated with *investigational* and *interpretive* constructs—the prime requisite for a coherent system. But because psychological events, after all, comprise the interbehavior of organisms with stimulus objects, psychologists have been able to construct hypotheses, design experiments, and accurately formulate results. Naturally, these products of investigation have badly matched the description of psychological data as intangible processes. Notice, for instance, how psychologists have hesitated to work on such complex events as thinking, reasoning, and remembering. Why? For no other reason than to keep safely within the bounds of crude adjustments—for example, conditioning—and the simplest forms of learning. Even the event of perceiving has been investigated only by selecting trivial instances.

Psychology's Place among the Sciences

Once the culturally based constructs are removed from their blocking position psychology assumes its proper place among the sciences (p. 94 f.). More—it contributes to the solution of problems common to the various disciplines. For instance, we may expect psychology to throw light on the problems of observation and interpretation which have been troubling physicists since the development of quantum and general microphysics. These problems of observability and indeterminancy would never have arisen if tradition had not separated perceiving and knowing from things and from contacts with them.

The paramount question is: How can we tear down the cultural barriers to a scientific psychology? There is but one way: study psychological facts as they actually happen. Doing so we arrive at the following results.

First, psychological events are no less, if no more, available features of nature than the events studied by astronomers, physicists, chemists, and biologists. Only a special license permits psychological data to be disregarded or depreciated. Certainly those who recognize the continuity of natural events can scarcely tolerate a break in the continuity of the sciences. Why, for instance, should we seek laws of chemical constitution, of energy radiation, and neglect the nature and history of psychological behavior? Such a diremption results not only in an overevaluation of physiochemical things and processes, but in a mystically grounded shyness in the face of animal behavior.

Secondly, since science is the work of man, an understanding of psychological processes is indispensable for formulating problems, designing researches, making hypotheses, constructing apparatus, calculating and interpreting data. Scientific work demands sensitivity to event situations, to cultural controls, to beliefs and opinions. The student of human behavior, the psychologist, therefore has a stake in the scientific situation. This is not simply to urge fair shares for all: it is a plea to consider the scientific value of rendering essential service. Surely it is within the province of psychology to evaluate and regulate intellectual attitudes.

How amazing, for example, that competent astronomical and physical scientists indulge in such sentimental reactions to events as to proclaim how mysterious is the universe. To confound ignorance with mystery is to obstruct the path of research. Assuming that the scientific enterprise is not merely the technology of making telephones, planes, and radios, but a means of becoming oriented with respect to events, would it not be advantageous to inhibit scientists from propagating mysticism in the name of idealism? Certainly it is unfortunate that scientists, by. their reputations, maintain historical mysticisms.

Too numerous to mention are the eminent scientists who combine superior knowledge and theories of physics and biology with the most obscurantistic ideas of man and his nature. For instance, those same scientists who would utterly condemn anyone who cannot appreciate the importance of nuclear reactions in accounting for the energy of sun and stars flounder in the morass of "immediate experience," "insight," "unique knowledge." Can we then overestimate the value of scientifically understanding the nature of speech, thought, and the essentials of theory construction?

Thirdly, if it is true that psychology has recently made notable advances it is only reasonable to assume that psychological findings should throw light on important scientific issues. Indeed, from the history of science we learn that astronomical and physical laws have been influenced by psychological considerations. Even if Newton, in his mechanics, did not approach psychological events too closely, in his optics he certainly did. All science teems with views about the nature of "mind," how this "mind" is concerned both in the existence of events and in the formulation of laws concerning them.

What a record of unsavory inventions scientific history displays concerning the capacities of the "mind" and its legislative powers in structuring nature. Consider Kepler's pronouncements concerning the scientist's ability to know only quantities. In our own day witness the scientists' conclusions that the ultimate nature of the universe is mental, that science culminates in theology.[3]

Recently, however, the science of psychology has developed to the point at which we now recognize that no natural event

---

[3] Cf., Whittaker, Eddington's principle in the philosophy of science; also Smart, The Origin of the Earth.

furnishes the basis for such a construct as *mind* which stands over against the concrete things and events of man's environment or which, indeed, creates them. Now, if it is true that such traditional ideas have influenced astronomical and physical sciences it is high time to effect the needed corrections.

In short, we have passed the period when a scientist can assume the right to take his psychology from a purely cultural source. Doing so he resorts to folklore. Innumerable writers, strong proponents of mathematical and statistical principles, of exact logic and effective experimentation, still maintain in their thinking the ancient mythology of two worlds—an inner private and an outer public universe.

Because the dualistic position is so deep seated it prevents a thoroughgoing objective and naturalistic psychological attitude from spreading far, though undeniably an excellent start has been made. The prediction is good that the numerous mentalistic constructs will in the end be superseded by constructs drawn from interbehavior with events.

Most psychological happenings are readily available, at least for superficial contacts. The psychologist has this advantage over the physicist who must work with subtle energies and radiations. The psychologist's problem centers around the proper interpretation of such events as the organism's discriminations and its development of adaptive action with respect to surrounding things and events. We have seen, however, that cultural influences prevent straightforward description and explanation. Priests, physicians, philosophers, as well as psychologists, persistently impose nonscientific constructs upon original happenings. In other words, constructs developed in a theological age still operate in our current experimental period.

Study Pattern for the Logic of Psychological Science

The system problems of psychological science touch upon the very nature of the original data. Unlike systems of physiochemical or biological events the logic of psychological science is radically skewed in the metasystemic direction. Traditional protopostulates must be cleared away before an adequate psychological system can be erected.

The first step is to establish the complete coordination of

psychological events with all other types. Actually, a psychological system differs only *in detail* from biochemical and biological systems. The best way to eradicate the prejudice that a psychological system is intrinsically different from any other is to review the operational and cultural development of psychology.

Next, because the topics *Perception, Language,* and *Reasoning* are of crucial importance in systemological investigation we shall consider (p. 262) these activities for the light they shed on scientific logic in general and on the relations of psychological systems to other types.

Historical Coordination of Culture and Constructs

Greek Biological Psychology. The Aristotelian Corpus comprises the first organized psychological treatise. Whether we consult the *De Anima, Parva Naturalia, De Partibus Animalium,* or *De Generatione Animalium* we find that the Greeks, despite their simplicity and naïveté, were completely free of any spirit-matter constructs. They treated psychological events as interactions between organisms and stimulus objects. *Psyche,* later misconceived and misnamed *spirit* or *soul,* was clearly action or function. Furthermore, Aristotle made no difference in kind between such actions as digestion, locomotion, sensing, perceiving, remembering, or reasoning.

Hellenistic Psychology. Cultural history testifies to the enormous changes which successively took place in the lives of the early transmitters of our civilization. As far as science is concerned, the interest in nature fostered so vigorously by the Greeks was gradually supplanted by an intense concern for man and his destiny. With the expansion of Greek conquest and the breakdown of the Alexandrian empire the general thought of the time took on a humanistic coloring. Moreover, the intermixture of Eastern and Western ways of thinking introduced a salient change in ideas centering around what we cultivate as psychology today.

The Neoplatonists set the stage for the spiritistic view of man. This is a period when human organisms were divided into two aspects: (1) perishable material and (2) immortal spirit. Preparation for such a dichotomy may be traced back to Philo's attempt to reconcile Greek ways of thinking with the Hebrew scriptures. This spiritistic doctrine was elaborated by Plotinus and expanded by the Greek and Latin Church Fathers. The basic technique adopted was to hypostatize words or symbols. "In the beginning was the Word" indicates the operation. They turned away from things and events in favor of dialectic. Argument was based on the assumed need to preserve man amidst his chaotic and hostile circumstances. Think here of Tertullian and his *credo quia absurdum*.

Better to appreciate the change of view at this time notice the emphasis on signs and manifestations. Stress on hidden powers brought to the front the idea of manifestation: that is, various happenings were asserted to be the revelation of invisible forces. One started, of course, from actually observed happenings, then verbally attributed them to the design and intention of some creative force.

From this matrix evolved something unknown in Hellenic times—the intangible and invisible *soul*, believed in especially because it could not be seen. The "soul" became the occult source of all psychological powers and gave rise to the momentous tradition of mind-body which to this day dominates psychological and general scientific thinking.

Scholastic Psychology. In the 13th century this line of thought became incorporated into a technical psychology. Culturally speaking, this was an era of vigorous development, a period of increasing contacts of peoples not only in Western Europe but also in the Near East. Recall the Crusades, their religious and commercial fermentation and the resulting interchange of goods and ideas; the development of various national units, the struggles of emerging states with the papal dynasty for control of temporal power.

Of interest to us is the interaction with Near-Eastern peoples, especially the Arabs and Jews from whom Western European scholars received the works of Greek science. Among Western scholars Albertus Magnus, and especially Thomas Aquinas, remade the Aristotelian psychological doctrine into a form suitable for a different culture from that out of which it originally developed.

To begin with, Aristotle's *psyche*, which, we have indicated consisted of actions or functions of biological organisms, was transformed into a *spiritual entity*. In line with the theological tradition of Hellenistic and later times man as the direct creation of God was endowed with theistic properties. This theological tradition granted man more than immortality: it endowed him with creative powers.

Considered as individual psychological processes these creative powers were declared to be *faculties* of the soul. Though the soul in its sensory activities must cooperate with the body in order to know what occurs outside itself, in performing intellectual activities it is not so restricted. Through its intellectual faculties the soul is able to make sense materials into knowledge, also to anticipate and transcend all facts of experience. Rational powers of soul attest to man's partial identity with God.

Modern Psychology. St. Thomas' spiritistic reformulation of Aristotle's psychology has already maintained itself for seven centuries. The development of science and technology has simply brought about variations of the medieval construction. The following paragraphs point up this constant change which leaves things where they were.

(a) *Descartes.* The ambiguous position of Descartes in modern psychology is well founded. Obviously a descendant of the Scholastics, he still ranks as the first of the moderns. His formula separating mind from matter, thought from extension, has become the leading motif in modern thought.

When Descartes slashed all of nature into two parts he allowed those sciences which at the time could make use of geometric and calculative constructs to free themselves from theological dogma. In short, he acknowledged the importance of an intimacy with technology and the mensurational activities of scientific work. As we have seen (chap. 3), Descartes' formula separating thought from extension became the basis for important experimentation, though, on the other hand, it meant separating measurable or geometric properties from others, such as color, warmth, sound, etc.

For psychological thought in particular, Descartes helped to establish the precedent that the soul with its innate ideas was intimately associated with the brain. As a consequence, spiritual substances could maintain themselves because of their power to exert effects on the brain and in turn their ability to be affected by the brain. The spiritual factor, however, became so powerful that not until a century later did the organic part of the individual attain any prominence in psychological theory.[4]

(b) *Variations in Spirit Doctrine*. An outstanding example of the persistence of spiritistic dogma, despite minor variations, is the difference first mentioned in Chapter 1 between Continental and British writers. On the whole, the Continentals, from Leibniz, Wolff, Kant, Herbart, down to the most recent Gestalt psychologists, emphasize totality, and favor unified and continuous mind. By contrast, the Britishers, from Hobbes through Locke, Berkeley, and Hume, tend toward discontinuous states, mental atoms, flashes of consciousness.

(c) *The Psychological Organism*. In the earliest theological period the soul was stressed as the basis for saving the individual from his worldly difficulties by making him in part a supernatural being. With the evolution of industry and technology the more tangible part of the human organism—the body—took on increasing significance, though the importance of the soul or mind was not thereby minimized. This phase of psychological history is represented by the construct *the psychological organism*.

(1) *Growing Role of Bodily Organism*. Descartes who identified the body with extension, the mind with thought, hypothesized a mutual interaction between mind and body. Leibniz, on the other hand, maintaining that such absolutely different substances could not interact, invented the notion of absolute parallelism, a pre-established harmony. Spinoza regarded the mind and body simply as aspects of a more fundamental substance. From those days to the present, psychologists have in some way made use of these constructs, the end point of which is simply saying: The two ultimately different factors are identical.

Probably the viability of events forced dualistic psychologists for some centuries to give the body an increasingly important place. From Hartley down to the 19th-century physiologists, the organism's bodily parts have assumed growing significance, especially the brain and other portions of the nervous system. In more recent times the glands and muscles have received more and more prominence in descriptions of psychological happenings.

(2) *Behaviorism*. The tenets of modern behaviorism are well known. As a psychological doctrine it is the end point in the

---

[4] Cf., Kantor, Problems of Physiological Psychology.

dualistic development we have just sketched. The psychological organism becomes the *body without mind*. The behaviorists, for instance, simply deny the necessity to deal with any psychic factor. The strict behaviorist attempts to interpret all psychic happenings in terms of the operation of the brain and other nervous structures.[5]

But has the behaviorist disposed of "mind"? Hardly. He simply throws away one half of the traditional mind-body construction and builds his system on the remainder. In no sense does he extricate himself from the dualistic tradition. What is required is to withdraw completely from historical constructions. We need to start over again. *Interbehavioral* psychology, we shall see, makes this attempt.

(d) *Retreat from Spirit*. To the power of scientific institutions we may attribute the tortuous process of eliminating spiritistic constructs and attitudes. Behaviorists, we have just said, do little more than evade psychic issues. Materialism, of which behaviorism may be counted a part, was a similar failure. It was simply a counter movement within the cultural framework of spirit and matter. Ironically, its detailed development served to maintain dualism.

Consider French materialism of the 18th century. Following the Cartesian lead, according to which the human being is a bodily machine coupled to a soul, infrahuman animals merely machines without a soul, materialism stood for spirit dependent on matter. De la Mettrie and others regarded mind as the product of matter. As Cabanis put it, the brain secretes thought as the liver secretes bile. The larger materialistic movement in 19th-century Germany collected masses of facts from biology and chemistry in order to bolster up the doctrine that mind is an epiphenomenon, a shadowy principle hovering over the organism. But as diaphanous as spirit became it still prevailed.

Developmental Stages of Scientific Psychology

Whether the technique to make psychology a science was quantization or experimentation it resulted in an abortive attempt to "naturalize the soul." But this attempt, along with earlier efforts to associate mental with biological or organic proc-

---

[5] Cf., Lashley, The behavioristic interpretation of consciousness.

esses, was all to the good: it fertilized the ground for an authentic scientific psychology. Let us briefly follow through this development.

Kant. As a scientist-philosopher imbued with Newtonian principles, Kant set up a mathematical criterion for natural science:

> Ich behaupte aber, dass in jeder besondern Naturlehre nur so viel eigentliche Wissenschaft angetroffen werden könne, als darin Mathematik anzutreffen ist.[6]

This view lies imbedded, of course, in the Cartesian-Leibnizian matrix wherein spiritistic dogma intermixes with the doctrine that the empirical aspects of all sciences must be underlaid by formal *a priori* principles. Were this true, psychology, even less than chemistry, could be a natural science, since, unlike chemistry (which also lacks a formal *a priori* mathematical foundation) psychology is bereft of manipulatory and experimental possibilities. It is significant that Kant did not question the reality of psychic processes; he took for granted, however, that they had no spatial extension, hence could only be accorded temporal dimension.[7]

Herbart. Kant's view was challenged by his successor in the philosphical chair at Königsberg. Herbart assumed a close connection between scientific constructions—especially mathematical formulae—and the things one describes and explains. Accordingly he asserted that mental facts could be quantized. Making the assumption that mental processes had the property of intensity, he constructed a mechanics—a statics and dynamics of mental states. He undertook to calculate the power of ideas to attract and repel each other. Herbart, however, agreed with Kant that psychology could not be a science if, in addition to calculation, it had to be experimental.

Fechner. Imbued with experimental attitudes derived from his training as a physicist, and with the motivation of the deeply religious mystic, Fechner undertook to prove that Herbart was wrong. Psychic states *could* be experimentally measured. Indeed he found an excellent beginning for such an enterprise in Weber's

---

[6] Metaphysische Anfangsgründe der Naturwissenschaft, Vorrede.

[7] Denn die reine innere Anschauung, in welcher die Seelenerscheinungen construirt werden sollen, ist die Zeit, die nur eine Dimension hat. Op. et loc. cit.

experiments on touch and visual sensitivity. Weber asserted:

> In comparing objects and observing the distinction between them, we perceive not the difference between the objects, but the ratio of this difference to the magnitude of the objects compared.[8]

The assumption is that for a just noticeable difference the ratio of the variation in a stimulus to the original or compared stimulus is constant. This situation may be formulated as $\delta M / M = K$, M indicating the magnitude. Fechner elaborated Weber's result and finally reached his famous formula $S = C \log R$. In so doing he thought he had achieved his aim of indirectly measuring the unmeasurable sensations or spiritual units. How? By the indirect process of measuring their invariable correlates—namely, the stimuli. As for the science of psychology, the Fechner episode appeared to establish the existence and manipulability of sensations and, presumably, other psychic energies (ideas, feelings, etc.).

Psychology an Experimental Science. Although the operations of Weber and Fechner consisted mainly of measuring procedures, they provided a powerful impetus for an experimental tradition. In 1879 Wundt established his Leipzig laboratory which became a center for scientific psychology. To that laboratory flocked many of the future leaders of a new science devoted to the investigation of mental processes. In the early history of experimental psychology the greatest interest was in studies of sensation and perception—in short, knowledge processes. Later the laboratory became hospitable to researches in attention and feeling, to studies on reaction time and association of ideas.

With the multiplication of laboratories the experimental study of mind carried over to other topics. In Külpe's laboratory at Würzburg thought processes were studied and scientific techniques extended to cover "will." Ebbinghaus, at first without academic connection, began the investigation of what was called memory. To the psychologists of this period it became apparent that no phase or action of the soul needed to remain without benefit of ministration by the votaries of experimental methods.

What greater demonstration is needed of the great divergence of theory and practice! Obviously what all these workers actually

---

[8] From Titchener, Experimental Psychology, Vol. 2, pt. 2, p. 172.

did was to observe individuals reacting to particular stimulating objects. In many cases they really succeeded in training their subjects to observe their own reactions. But what the experimentalists *thought* they were doing with their introspective methods and their experimental techniques was to make the "contents of consciousness and the transpatial processes of mind" thoroughly amenable to scientific attack. In spite, then, of experimental and laboratory developments nonobservable factors were postulated. The early experimental tradition in psychology is but another example of the massive power of cultural tradition, even in the face of mathematical and scientific methods.

Psychology a Natural Science

Notwithstanding the heavy load of atavistic cultural impediments which psychology still carries, the quantization and experimental procedures have helped in good measure to undermine those traditions. The addition of mathematical and laboratory institutions to the cultural armory of psychology promises that it will ultimately attain the competence to produce a valid theoretical system. To follow the rules of scientific work outlined in our early chapters means for psychology the study of the interbehavior of organisms with stimulus objects. Above all, it implies that the objects with which an organism interacts are not somehow created by mental powers.

Perception, Language, and Reasoning in Naturalistic Psychology

We come now to the three strategic topics which bring psychology into close relation with most of the other sciences. Whatever improvements we make in understanding observational procedures and the techniques of referring, recording, and interpreting can be brought to bear upon the logical problems of all the sciences. The value of an objective psychology for science as a whole consequently can best be illustrated by considering Perceiving, Language, and Reasoning.

A. PERCEPTION: INTERBEHAVIOR OR CREATIVITY?

Current demands that scientists turn to philosophy as a foundation study, to axiomization, to logic, to semantics and general linguistic analysis, signify nothing new under the intellectual sun. There has never been a time when scientists have been exempt from the common culture of their time, and this includes philosophy and religion, politics and social organization.

What *is* new is the cumulative character of current culture. There are so many sciences, so many workers. Most of the possible changes have been rung on the old metaphysical themes. Dissatisfaction is rife with respect to the restricting bonds which traditional philosophical theories place upon modern scientific discovery. It is widely realized that scientific work cannot be encompassed in the age-old dogma concerning interior mind and external world. How can scientists reconcile scientific law with protocols which record only what goes on in the scientist's mind, whether that is called direct or immediate observation, or sense data?

Logicians of science who ask psychologists about the nature of observation (perception) receive answers not derived from studying individuals observing things and events, but answers which reiterate the sentences framed by Renaissance metaphysicians and epistemologists. When we observe, they are told, we create the things observed. Create from what? From impressions, from immediate sense data. Create how? By imposing upon these "immediate experiences" certain forms or categories of organization. Is there any doubt that present-day theories of perception go back to Kantian epistemology?

A workable logic of observation demands constructs (theory) obtained from the study of observation itself. But this means undermining the influence of our metaphysical culture. The most effective way of getting into this situation is to examine traditional theories of preception. We begin with the influence of Kant.

The problem of scientific logic which Kant faced was to satisfy the demand of science for stable law. According to Newtonian mechanics the universe was subject to rigorous formulation. Newton, of course, worked primarily from the extensional side of the Cartesian dichotomy. Then there was Hume who showed how all knowledge could be reduced to sense impressions which left no room for the essential category of cause. Kant's solution to this paradox became the model of our current perception doctrines. It consisted of subjecting the elementary "sense data" he derived from Berkeley and Hume to the organizing processes of mind.

Unlike Hume, Kant did not believe that the thinking side of the Cartesian dualism could be exclusively reduced to psychic atoms. In other words, he could not renounce his Continental heritage. A place, therefore, must be found for the unified Soul which he called by the traditional name *transcendental unity of apperception*. Things and events for Kant were definitely created though the materials were sense data excited in the mind by external causes. This creativity was the basis of his Copernican Revolution (p. 69), the justification of his formula that sensations without conceptions are blind, conceptions without sensations empty. The external world and all objects of science are synthetically created by the organism's processes of *mind*.

Succeeding generations adapted the Kantian epistemology to their needs by naturalizing it—namely, by connecting the soul with the brain. Helmholtz was influential in making this modification. He lived at a time when the anatomical and physiological divisions of biology had reached a fair degree of development. Though he knew far fewer details concerning the neural organization of organisms than we do, he was certain that the nerves and the brain operated to mediate particular sense qualities. Building upon the ideas of Johannes Müller, he assumed that the particular neural elements constituting the sensory pathway mediated particular sense qualities—colors, taste, etc. Thus after neural impulses reached the brain "immediate experience" came into being.

After all, from the standpoint of the logic of science the naturalization of the soul had been attempted long before Helmholtz's time. Although biology was little developed when Newton composed his *Principia*, he made use of the nervous system to mediate sensations (psychic processes):

> And now we might add something concerning a certain most subtle spirit which pervades and lies hid in all gross bodies; by the force and action of which spirit the particles of bodies attract one another at near distances, and cohere, if contiguous; and electric bodies operate to greater distances, as well repelling as attracting the neighboring corpuscles; and the light is emitted, reflected, refracted, inflected, and heats bodies; and all sensation is excited, and the members of animal

bodies move at the command of the will, namely, by the vibrations of this spirit, mutually propagated along the solid filaments of the nerves, from the outward organs of sense to the brain, and from the brain into the muscles. But these are things that cannot be explained in few words nor are we furnished with that sufficiency of experiments which is required to an accurate determination and demonstration of the laws by which this electric and elastic spirit operates.[9]

Even the extensive development of biological science in the 19th century merely modernized a traditional viewpoint; it did not correct it.

From Helmholtz's day to our own the only variation in this theological way of thinking has concerned the process by which the sense object is organized. Whereas sensationists stressed the additive connection between sensations to form mental objects, Gestalt psychologists have insisted that the object is a unique totality neither compounded nor divisible.

The interbehavioral psychologist is the first to reject completely any theory that the brain or any portion of the nervous system performs creational acts. Perceptual activities are ways in which organisms interbehave with things on the basis of prior contacts. Only because the psychological story has been unnecessarily complicated and distorted does the interbehavioral view seem overly simple. What the brain does in this perceiving process is merely to coordinate the organism; in no sense does it mediate "sensations" by means of neural impulses or transform "sensations" into objects.

B. THE ROLE OF LANGUAGE AND SYMBOLS IN SCIENCE

Man is a talking animal; he interbehaves with things and his fellows by referential performances which become increasingly complicated. Indeed, human organisms develop such intricate behavior that much of it must be done by substitution and vicarious performance. This complex linguistic interbehavior which has developed throughout the evolution of civilization has taken on the varied forms of our conventional languages.

The use of linguistic products as symbols represents a unique stage. Once language acts become fixated in the process of making marks and developing a script these symbols can be used in a

---

[9] Principia Mathematica, General Scholium to Bk. III.

variety of ways for recording what was said, for representing all kinds of events, even for asserting things impossible to happen. This is the level of ordinary interbehavior.

Turning to the scientific evolution of symbols we find statements or sentences taking on a commanding position in formulating hypotheses and propositions, in recording data and constructing laws. From the earliest records of scientific work, sentences and sentence systems have been objects of increasing interest. Perfect illustrations are the evolution of Aristotelian Analytics (Syllogistics) and Euclidean systematics in the flourishing period of Greek science.

In current scientific and logical circles language and symbol problems have reached a high peak. Among scientists witness the intense interest in semantics, symbolic logic, and operationism. While no clear-cut distinctions are made between concepts and terms, between statements and propositions, linguistic and symbolic studies have been definitely incorporated into theoretical science. As for logicians, linguistic materials in the form of sentences have become the exclusive substance of logic, a procedure encouraged by the mistaken assumption that mathematics is a language. Follows then the error that logic is simply the organization of words and symbols in the form of sentences, propositions or equations, without regard to things spoken of or symbolized. How can such a logic be helpful in scientific situations?

It is but a minor failure that the semanticist's admonition to mind one's language, to use words and symbols properly, has been of little service. More serious is the fact that this good admonition is blasted because of improper psychological foundations. Scientific problems are confused and slanted in wrong directions.

Current difficulties with language and symbols can be summed up in two ways. First, words and symbols are unwittingly taken as autonomous things instead of products which individuals produce in particular situations. This leads to the identification of language and symbols. Mathematics, for instance, is not a language for describing events in such a way that descriptions and symbolizations are confounded with the things described or symbolized.

In the second place, current theories are based on dualistic ways of thinking. Language is taken as motor action expressing psychic processes called thoughts. Words and symbols therefore become embodiments of these processes. As a consequence, terms presumed to refer to psychic states are confused with phases of events; for example, "sense data" are confused with qualities of things.

From an interbehavioral standpoint linguistic and symbolic things and events are treated as objectively as any other scientific data. We keep separate (1) the acts of referring to things (language), (2) the processes of symbolizing them, and (3) both these acts from (a) the resulting products and (b) the things which occasion the linguistic or symbolic behavior.[10] So far as technical situations are concerned, the words and symbols in scientific propositions and equations are definite constructions for the express purpose of describing and explaining events. The form and structure of such propositions and equations represent the scientist's adaptations to the original events he investigates.

C. REASONING

Conventional justification for making language the basis if not the essence of logic consists largely in the freedom from spiritistic trammels such a procedure promises. Reasoning and related activities like thinking, imagining, and remembering have historically been regarded as a psychic stronghold. Linguistic theory has really never departed far from its dualistic core. By no means do the majority of logicians proceed on the basis of free and concrete observation.

Nothing, however, stands in the way of investigating reasoning as concrete interbehavior with stimulus objects, interbehavior in all respects as free from psychic essences as reflex action and the purely biological processes of respiration, circulation, and digestion. Take the situation in which an individual constructs a proposition or develops an attitude. He concludes that A was not concerned with some happening because A was out of range at the time. This conclusion may be symbolized by a mark or verbal record.

---

[10] Cf., Kantor, Principles of Psychology, ch. 23 and An Objective Psychology of Grammar.

Specifically, reasoning behavior constitutes inferential action, the construction of an intellectual attitude (belief, proposition) after interbehaving with things in a situation occasioning inferential interbehavior. This intellectual attitude may remain as an abstruse product or it may subsequently be associated with some manipulative or other sort of performative action.[11]

Reasoning interbehavior ranges from informal and personal situations which begin with premises interesting only the original reasoner to formal operations based on standardized starting points. Historical syllogistic systems and the implied sentential systems of modern symbolic logic typify the formal class.

Historically, formal reasoning has been divided into two exclusive types—deductive and inductive. In the latter the conclusion or inferential product is regarded as a general principle. In the deductive type the inferential action is presumed to begin with a principle already established. The deductive type of reasoning having developed under mathematical auspices was presumed to yield absolute and universal certainty; the entire behavioral procedure was believed to be independent of concrete human behavior. Naturally, inductive reasoning was regarded as less precise and valid.

Barriers to a Naturalistic Interpretation of Reasoning

Even those who free themselves from mystical views about the manipulative types of psychological activities confront the following difficulties upon approaching reasoning interbehavior.

(1) Because intellectual activity is usually subtle it appears different from gross manipulative action. However, if we reject inner and outer behavior, the act of inferring that a man is honest is in principle no different from seizing him by the arm.

(2) Since the intimate circumstances of the reacting person are so prominent in a reasoning situation they mask the coordinate operation of stimulating objects. The things reasoned about and the occasions for doing so should never be ignored.

(3) The conventional view that reasoning involves "psychic phenomena" results in confusing products of concrete actions

---

[11] For the distinction between informational and performative behavior see Kantor, The Principles of Psychology, ch. 2; A Survey of the Science of Psychology, ch. 2.

with those actions. Thus the term *reasoning* is used to refer both to an action and to its syllogistic product.

(4) Many inferential situations are complex and remote, thus require chains of substitutes. The task of determining the recessional velocity of nebulae, for instance, requires long chains of inferences. The mistake is then made of confounding actual reasoning behavior with diaphanous mentalisms.

These various circumstances highlight the differences between naturalistic and dualistic interpretations. Any *ad hoc* interpretation imposed upon original events violates all scientific rules.

Reasoning and System Building

Logic has conventionally been defined as the science of valid reasoning. In the first place, it has always been tacitly assumed that inferential processes could be organized by systematically arranging the steps leading from premises to conclusion. On the other hand, inferential processes are obviously effective actions for system building, even though not subject to rigid control.

Not until the development of an objective psychology could logic as system building be properly evaluated or the role of system building and reasoning naturalistically described.[12] Reasoning as interbehavior can now be studied as it occurs under specific auspices.

Impact of Objective Psychology on other Sciences

The naturalistic psychology now available is bound (1) to influence our ideas concerning the range and limits of science and (2) to help us avoid pseudoproblems.

(1) As to range and limits, each of the three basic factors of scientific systems are clarified.

(a) *Thing and event factors.* Since perceptual observation implies coming into contact with things surrounding individuals, there are unlimited opportunities for scientific work and an indefinite number of raw materials, the qualities, behavior properties, and relations of which the scientist proceeds to assess.

Investigative limits, however, are set by size, frequency, distance and refractoriness of things and events. The availability of

---

[12] Cf., Kantor, Psychology and Logic.

data, their resistance to analysis and synthesis may be either temporary or lasting. When scientific investigation is hindered by such difficulties workers simply acknowledge their present ignorance and devise measures to overcome it. Problems such as the age of the earth, the processes intervening between fertilization and maturation, the gradual or saltatory evolution of organisms, the synthesis of protein molecules, the source of cosmic rays, the cure of cancer, the existence of an ether, may wait long before scientific interbehavior makes satisfactory solutions possible.

Meanwhile, the scientist continues to develop hypotheses. Notice, however, that hypotheses set up on the basis of interbehavioral fields are alone acceptable. Verbal-formulae solutions are repudiated. Limitations of knowledge founded on the metaphysics of soul, such as DuBois-Reymond proposed in his famous *Ignorabimus* declaration,[13] are definitely ruled out.

(b) *Operation factors.* Since investigational operations involve modifying one's manipulations, increasing one's approaches to things, and penetrating below the surface, the scientist constantly seeks to develop new instruments and techniques. These can be described as means for facilitating contacts with stimulus objects.

It is a strange circumstance of scientific history that the instrumental improvement of observations has not more often resulted in rejecting the view that events are created when they are observed. Scientists act as if it were possible for microscopes, telescopes, or Geiger counters to create the things seen or counted! Can the 200 inch telescope enlarge the astronomic universe or only facilitate inspection of more of it? Does a microtome prove that tissues exist in slices? A centrifuge that cell contents are separated?

Tradition has its way. Because our knowledge of things is conditioned by our observational facilities we therefore assume that our knowledge makes things. This is a reversion to the view that since sense organs are instruments of observation they are the constructors of things, or that since animals with different sense organs react differently—namely, things appear different to them—this fact reduces what is interacted with to the inter-

---

[13] Ueber die Grenzen des Naturerkennens.

action. Interesting here is Verworn's dictum:

> With our death, with the destruction of the senses and the nervous system, the physical world in its previous form disappears.[14]

We may agree that if the "physical world in its previous form" refers to a world in which a particular organism is living, that world certainly is changed by the organism's death. But this is no more than saying that something has happened—a change has occurred. Unfortunately, Verworn really establishes a psychomonistic form of metaphysics.

An objective psychology thus clarifies the difference between the dependence of knowledge upon investigative operations and the existential relativity of things and events. In addition, it throws light on the misuse of the scientist's errors to support belief in his creative powers. Errors in measurement and experiment strongly indicate that things and events set the criteria for accuracy and sufficiency. Such a mistake as substituting some other event for the one which originally stimulated the problem also emphasizes events. When we replace a protocol of observation by a linguistic record or an equation, by a proposition about something that did not happen at all, we have a creativity which certainly should not be mistaken for scientific investigation.

(c) *Explanatory factors.* An objective psychology definitely influences the scientist's basic assumptions, his theory and explanations. For example, by rejecting autonomous spiritistic entities (a power of reasoning, a well of unconscious impulses) it rules out such absolute distinctions as Whittaker makes between theorems of pure mathematics, inferences from experiment, and postulates of impotence.[15] The human mind from whose structures arise theorems of pure mathematics exists only as a product of an individual's manufacture. Mathematical theorems are derived from the same interbehavioral sources as experimental inference and convictions of impotence. Mathematicians, pure or applied, draw their theorems from the matrix of interbehavior with mathematical and physical things, relations, and events.

Naturally, objective psychology encourages freedom to invent theorems, even speculative propositions. But definite limits

---

[14] General Physiology, p. 36.
[15] Cf., Eddington's principle in the philosophy of science.

are set by contacts with events. Evolutional speculations, for example, drawn from observations of plants and animals, are distinguished from assumptions of special creation. Geometrical constructions are free only if entities and relations of the field are handled without the metaphysical assumption that any system represents the limits and possibilities of the human or cosmic "mind."

Emancipation of science from the tradition of transpatial mind permits a proper place for intellectual hazards and indeterminacies. Hesitations and insecurities are preferable to wrong interpretations based on well established trends and fashions.[16] Physicists who limit themselves to atomic or nuclear events, biologists who scorn taxonomic studies, merely follow the temporary fashion of what is considered worthwhile. They can scarcely assume that their localized studies are equivalent to the whole field.

(2) A naturalistic psychology can eliminate the pseudoproblems engendered by spiritistic epistemologies and ontologies. Both empiricism (positivism) and realism (rationalism) introduce spurious issues, since both are based upon assumptions concerning the intuitive power of the "mind" or the dependence of knowledge on mental states excited from without.

From psychic sources arise, too, all ontologies concentrated in meaningless questions concerning the nature and reality of the external world. Witness the epistemic and ontologic pseudoproblems in this striking quotation from Verworn:

> At first sight bodies appear to us as actual objects outside of our own minds. Any doubt as to the existence of a physical world outside of mind, will appear absurd to one who has not reflected upon it: a body, e.g., a stone, a tree, a man, which we look upon, really exists, no one will deny this; we actually see the body, others see it; and we say it exists. We are right; without a doubt it exists, but it does not exist outside our mind. . . . [17]

Whether one adopts this solipsism or a realism, one assumes the existence of purely fictitious substances engendered in theological tradition. A naturalistic investigation of perceptual or other observational acts could never yield the following:

> When I see a body or perceive it by means of my other senses, in reality I have not a body outside of myself but only a number of sen-

---

[16] Cf., Schrödinger, Science and the Human Temperament.

[17] General Physiology, p. 35f.

sations in my mind. Beyond these I know nothing concerning it and can only form hypotheses.[18]

Verworn's statements constitute a frank expression of a scientific philosophy which other writers attempt verbally to palliate. But in whatever style such ideas are presented they contaminate the logic of science. It is an achievement of naturalistic psychology to be able to extrude them from science.

---

[18] Ibid., p. 36.

CHAPTER

13

ANTHROPIC EVENTS AND CON-STRUCTS: SOCIAL

THE foremost logical problem concerning anthropic events is whether they can be organized into scientific systems (anthropology, history, economics, etc.), comparable to physics, biology, and psychology. Probably most systemologists discriminate against anthropic disciplines on the ground that it is not feasible to subject anthropic data, investigations, and theory constructions to the canons of the traditionally exact sciences.

The primary complaint is that anthropic data are too unique to be generalized. Laws and universal principles according to the traditions of scientific logic require simplicity, interchangeability, repetitiveness. Behind this attitude lie the protopostulates we seek to eliminate—namely, (1) that generality, precision, and stability are based upon rational principles of mind, (2) that anthropic events involve psychic processes, and (3) that mental powers create anthropic products.

Ambiguity in Anthropic Sciences

Few of those who believe that man's proper study is man are really convinced that a scientific knowledge of men, of their interrelations and achievements, is an attainable goal. For the most part, then, the term *human or social science* is employed in an honorific sense.[1] Does any social scientist actually believe that the investigation of human events is on a par, either in quantity or quality of results, with the study of binary stars or atomic structure? Most social scientists are of the opinion that astronomy and physics are the paragon sciences; their methods and results to be approximated if possible. This is an anomalous situation. No one even questions the need for an effective social science. Is there matter more relevant, more useful, more engrossing than

---

[1] Cf., the adverse comparison of the social and medical sciences in Henderson, The Study of Man.

human facts? Is there anything about these events or about the techniques of observing them, to prevent the development of a sound social science?

Once more we face the opposition between tradition and concrete happenings. For it is only convention which relegates the anthropic sciences into caretakers of the ephemeral and vague soul; only cultural tradition which decrees that the nonanthropic disciplines, in contrast, deal with stable, solid, and attainable things. A potent reminder of the gulf supposed to exist between the two is the denomination of the anthropic sciences as *Geisteswissenschaften* as over against *Naturwissenschaften*.

Now there are powerful reasons for rejecting these cultural traditions. In the first place, anthropic events only *in part* comprise psychological factors. Moreover, since psychology is now an authentic member of the natural-science family the same hospitality can be extended to the anthropic disciplines. As we saw in Chapter 12, psychological events have been dementalized: they are in every respect like the events of physics, chemistry, or astronomy. The nonpsychological components of anthropic data comprise biological and geographical events whose naturalistic character has never been questioned.

Can anyone doubt that anthropic facts consist of concrete interactions of organisms with stimulus objects, which, of course, include other organisms, plus the cumulative products of such interbehavior. The observer no more creates anthropic events than he creates physiochemical happenings. Investigators of both anthropic and nonanthropic events simply describe them according to their similarities and differences. The fact that social scientists employ spiritistic terms does not imply that the events they study are spiritistic. All they accomplish is the unhappy identification of their descriptions with the things described, since spiritistic entities exist only by virtue of the words referring to them.

Study Pattern for Anthropic Systems

The particular characteristics of anthropic events oblige us to deal mostly with general problems and principles. Our procedure then differs from that used in handling more rigidly structured systems. For one thing we shall not be able to show in detail how abstract constructs are derived from specific anthropic events.

Since to a great extent our task is to mitigate cultural prejudices, we plan to compare the basic characteristics of anthropic data, investigation, and theory construction with those of the physio-chemical disciplines. From such comparisons we hope to gain a greater insight into the logic of the anthropic field, also to reach a better understanding of *all* scientific systems.

The extensive range of anthropic events permits but a cursory sampling of system problems. For convenience of treatment we divide the field into the subgroups of social and humanistic sciences as follows:

I.	II.
Social Sciences	*Humanistic Sciences*
Economics	Linguistics
Anthropology	Ethics
Sociology	Esthetics
Politics	Theology
Jurisprudence	Philosophy
History	Religion

The social sciences we shall discuss later in this chapter; the humanistic in the next.

Nomos and Physis

From earliest times thinkers have set human (cultural) things over against natural things. To be sure, the basis for this distinction has not always been the same. Thus in the Greek period of our cultural history the criterion was not *Geist* on the one side and *Natur* on the other. The Greeks simply stressed the artificial and intentional traits of cultural things; that is, they distinguished between things and events occurring with and without human agency. For example, language, because it is primarily a human activity, has some base in natural events, but there is much that is arbitrary and artificial about it.

When Socrates, Pyrrho (the Sceptic), Zeno (the Stoic) and Epicurus turned sharply toward the study of morals and politics, they did so only as specialists who preferred certain kinds of studies, not because there were ultimate qualitative grades of data.

This is quite a different situation from that which existed at the time of Vico. This writer, it is said,[2] distinguished himself among the opponents of Descartes in that, unlike others who attacked the great thinker on the ground of his danger to religion, Vico fought Cartesianism because it was inimical to all knowledge not reducible to geometrical deduction. Fairly early in the Cartesian era Vico fervently attacked this philosophy because it attached no value to history (since founded upon human testimony), to observations of nature (when not subject to mathematical interpretation), or to practical wisdom (because based upon an empirical knowledge of human nature).

Today there is no commoner maxim than that the social "sciences"—for example, economics, sociology, and anthropology—are not natural sciences. Students of these departments, accepting the stigma that attaches to all ghostly disciplines, do no more than attempt to show that mathematics—at least statistics—is applicable to their studies. Whether or not the anthropic disciplines are admitted to the family of natural sciences is a matter of basic postulates. Above all, and this is now an old story, it depends upon freeing ourselves from presuppositions concerning occult powers as well as refusing to treat numbers and the procedures of the so-called exact sciences as fetishes.

The historical designation of physics, chemistry, and astronomy as the natural sciences is an instance of symptomatic naming. To contrast natural and cultural science implies a tacit belief in a supernatural or nonnatural domain. But obviously to deal with such a domain we must first linguistically create it.

Whatever human organisms do is localizable in a definite space-time frame of reference. Hence, the behavior of the mythologist, the creator of myths, answers to definite laws of psychology and anthropology. Linguistic creation is just as natural as any collision between molecules in a gas container. Essentially it consists of analogical description. Thus when Prometheus is made to steal fire from the gods and bestow it on man there is an obvious source for the myth. Prometheus was invented to explain how fire came to man. The uniqueness of a myth is the unusual way in which the original base is treated. The psychologist is well equipped to explain the origin and operation of such behavior.

[2] Croce, The Philosophy of Giambattista Vico.

Anthropic and Nonanthropic Sciences Compared

Anthropic and nonanthropic studies are conventionally contrasted on the basis of questionable presuppositions. For example, the belief that any one science is final and complete in contrast with another is groundless. All sciences are both strong and weak; none is an absolute model for any other. We arrange our comparisons along the convenient lines of (A) Data, (B) Investigation, and (C) Interpretation.

A. DATA

One of the basic presuppositions of the conventional logic of science is that the cultural are inferior to the "natural" sciences. But such a view is only possible when one illegitimately evaluates anthropic data. To start with individuals interbehaving with particular materials puts the data worked with in all sciences on an equal basis. But now let us consider the various grounds upon which the superior-inferior presupposition is held.

Simplicity Criterion. "Natural" data are simple, it is asserted, cultural data complex. One might ask how important is simplicity? It has been correctly stated that the simplicity of natural data is really a matter of simplifying complex data—the preferential choice of materials by abstraction and interpretation.[3] Implied in this procedure is the glorification of geometry, which, as Newton says: "From those few principles brought from without it is able to produce so many things."[4] Newton further states:

> For the whole burden of philosophy seems to consist in this: from the phenomena of motions to investigate the forces of nature, and then from these forces to demonstrate the other phenomena.[5]

In Newton's time science itself was simple, and such a striving for simplicity seemed proper. Recall that all the qualities of things were safely stored away in the beholder's mind. Now, with the evolution of electricity, thermodynamics, and other branches besides mechanics, the simplicity of the natural sciences has become dissipated. With respect to the Newtonian achievement of gravi-

---

[3] Cf., Lindsay, The meaning of simplicity in physics; Lindsay and Margenau, Foundations of Physics, p. 18; Bridgman, The Logic of Modern Physics, ch. 4.

[4] Principia, Preface.

[5] Ibid.

tation and the laws of motion, which were the goals of simple Newtonian science, Einstein remarks:

> But how about the rest of physics? Gravitation and the law of motion could not explain everything. What determined the equilibrium of the parts of a solid body? How was light to be explained, how electrical phenomena?[6]

Consider the colossal complexity of an atom; the vast complications of the forces holding the electrons and neutrons together. When Chadwick discovered the neutron in 1932 there were only three elementary units of matter and energy—neutrons, electrons, and protons. By 1951 numerous additions, including the neutrino, various kinds of mesons (positive, negative, neutral π, positive and negative μ and τ), raised the total number to 19.[7]

On the other hand, many cultural things and events are extremely simple. So, as we have indicated, if we base our analysis on specific items the simplex-complex differentiation evaporates.

Absolute-Relative Criterion. Even those scientists opposed to absolute space and time still accept the absolute-relative dichotomy as a criterion for separating "natural" from cultural data. But notice this procedure flouts the accepted view that science abjures all absolutes. Even relativity must be considered as relative rather than absolute. Things and events as data of science always consist of a number of qualities or properties. At least these data pose problems as to their nature. No absolute-relative dichotomy sets off one science from another.

Quantity-Quality Criterion. "Natural" sciences, it is alleged, are quantitative; cultural sciences, qualitative—again an unsuitable criterion. Quantization in physics and chemistry is made easy, after all, only by a suitable selection among events. This facility, however, does not hold for many physiochemical data. Consider the physicist's inability to quantize particle motions in thermodynamics, where events are so elusive as to leave one with probabilities. Then there are those instances of extremely difficult mensuration and quantization leading to indeterminism doctrines.

By contrast, the immense number and variation of cultural data provide occasions for every kind of quantization. Statistical

---

[6] Out of My Later Years, p. 22.

[7] Cf., Stranathan, The "Particles" of Modern Physics; Fermi, Elementary Particles; Marshak, The multiplicity of particles.

and probability techniques were employed, as a matter of fact, to solve anthropic problems even before they were put to use in nonanthropic situations. Such facts completely break down the alleged barriers between the natural and the anthropic.

Predictability Criterion. Scientific theorists who feel frustrated because of the evaporation of absolutes in science seize upon prediction as a substitute. By all means, prediction is an important criterion of scientific competency when repetitive events are studied. But predictability or unpredictability cannot be taken as exclusive evidence for the existence of events nor as a basis for differentiating between anthropic and nonanthropic sciences.

In the first place, predictability is not a single property: it is a function of a large number of factors, a feature of total scientific enterprises, and therefore depends on the type of problem pursued. Prediction becomes, then, an intimate process of both anthropic and nonanthropic situations. Just how easily anthropic events are predicted may be demonstrated by the fact that simple psychological tests, judiciously chosen, may be employed to predict future complex behavior.

Controllability Criterion. It is commonly believed that because the scientist cannot control anthropic events they belong to a different order. To be sure, it is not only difficult, but also impossible, to carry out some sorts of manipulation of human individuals and groups. There is no difference, however, in the principle of limitation as between anthropic and nonanthropic events. In both cases limits are set by social and economic circumstances, by technically backward procedures. From time to time, alas, we see how dictators and minority powers have removed many of the humanistic and axiological obstacles to the radical treatment of human beings.

For the most part, restrictions on anthropic control are based on the erroneous notion concerning the privacy and inaccessibility of man's "inner essence." The dogma that one person cannot even observe what goes on in another person's "mind" still haunts the house of anthropic theories.

B. INVESTIGATION

Research methods and techniques, we have seen, reach enormous extremes. Still, no matter how vastly investigation differs in anthropic and nonanthropic researches, there are still greater extremes in the *research*, say, within the physiochemical department. What more striking variation than that between photographing distant nebulae with a 200 inch telescope and spinning electrons or protons by means of a cyclotron or betatron? And compare both of these with the calculative and systemizing procedures employed in relativity and quantum mechanical investigations.

Invoking the golden rule of science that the methods and procedures of investigation should be those best adapted to the data and problems, we find that considerable similarity may exist between anthropic and nonanthropic research. On the other hand, we are not surprised when anthropic situations present problems which call for entirely different hypotheses, apparatus, and procedures from those required in nonanthropic situations. The conclusion is inescapable that research conditions cannot serve as strict criteria to identify and differentiate science classes, even if in one class we have a preponderance and frequency of experimentation and in another a lack of it.

C. INTERPRETATION

If there are no jarring differences between data and investigation in anthropic and nonanthropic systems, we should expect the same to be true for the interpretative feature. Still, as we mentioned at the beginning of the chapter, the attitude is solidly established that because anthropic sciences allow for too free an exercise of presuppositional behavior they do not permit stable and rigorous laws. The underlying assumption apparently is that only the kind of laws prevalent in the physiochemical domain are laws, and since anthropic laws are different they are *ipso facto* not laws. We choose however, to look upon laws as statements of order, of regularity, and interrelation of event factors or total fields. Anthropic laws, therefore, possess as much stability and rigor as are required by anthropic events.[8]

Once more, if it were not for the dichotomy of thought and extension no barrier would have been erected in the first place between anthropic and nonanthropic sciences. Are we then, one

---

[8] Cf., Lesser, Research procedure and laws of culture.

might ask, minimizing the differences between sciences? No: we are simply rejecting the notion that the traditional differentiation between natural and social sciences points to an absolute difference in events.

Anthropic Sciences Defined

Even the comparatively large list of anthropic subdepartments set up at the beginning of the chapter offers but a limited sample of the whole field. The task of uniquely specifying the characteristics of anthropic events is still before us—a task we hope to carry out in part when we survey the various anthropic subdomains.

Also, in defining anthropic science we face the question how to relate anthropic events to nonanthropic ones. This is an extremely important issue, since both types of events are intricately interwoven. For example, anthropologists find it necessary to divide their domain into biological and cultural phases, on the ground that man is an animal and thus must be studied in his anatomical, physiological, and ecological aspects. Up to a point of course, the study of man the animal can be entrusted to the biologist. Note, however, that the biology of the human animal, as well as of his domesticated cousins, is greatly conditioned and altered by cultural circumstances. Therefore, it is feasible, though arbitrary, to regard anthropic sciences as concerned primarily with man in his role of creator and conserver of culture.

But we cannot stop here: cultural data are also closely integrated with psychological data. Think of the psychological factors in social, legal, moral, and esthetic behavior. It is quite impossible consequently to separate anthropic from psychological science.

We need not, however, be overimpressed by these definitional difficulties. Nothing prevents our treating anthropic events as elements in complex structures, as the central nuclei of a field in whose surroundings biological, psychological, and other factors are localized. When we study, for instance, the invention and evolution of such cultural things as tools, buildings, laws, garments, decorative and art objects we must take into consideration (1) the biological characteristics of the human animals who participate in this work and (2) the chemical and geological-geographic conditions of the group's environment.

We begin our examination of the specific anthropic sciences with the social series. Here we are concerned with the systemic problems which arise when one stresses groups and the societal aspects of human behavior and its products, as compared with the humanistic series which emphasize the individuals who perform the actions. There are, of course, no absolute differences between the two.

Economics

Data. Economic science stands among the favored members of the anthropic division. Its original data are among the most apparent and available. Economic events involve the handling of the organic and inorganic materials of man's environment necessary to satisfy his organic needs; they also include the palpable facts of goods distribution among group members and the interchange of goods among groups.

We may justifiably speculate that the constructs of current economic science had their germinal origins in an early period of civilization. Economic thinking must have begun when individuals first found themselves in groups sufficiently populated to give rise to problems of controlling things necessary for maintaining life.

The very fact that economic events are so readily available has made it difficult to isolate and select the characteristic features of the economic field. As a result, economics has been variously defined as the science of wealth and welfare, of economic behavior and processes, of organized business enterprise, of the conditions of individuals or of larger groups, social, political, and international.

What one selects as economic data naturally depends upon social and cultural circumstances. Whether economics is a science altogether or an art, whether concerned with processes and requirements of the state (the wealth of nations) or of individuals in a given group (society or economic status), whether it deals with work and welfare or the abstruse structure of economic institutions, depends upon the inquirer's cultural background. This same factor operates in determining if economics as a science is empirical and inductive or formalistic and deductive.

Possibly even more important influences are the scientific

institutions which shape the pattern of scientific work. If economics as a formal science dates only from the 19th century[9] we can easily trace the views of economists concerning economic principles and laws to the influence of the ideas established in the natural sciences. By this means economists carried over from physics ideas of univeral laws, invariable causes and effects, the power of quantities, and so on.

We learn a lot about scientific foundations if we watch economists attempting to isolate their refined data. Originally, economic science, as distinguished from economic art, centered around the constructs of wealth and value. In 1811 Boileau formulated the economic problem as the increase, distribution, and consumption of wealth. Ten years later James Mill added the process of wealth interchange.[10] Somewhat more analytic constructs have included utility, supply and demand, and value.

Investigation. Economic investigation is thoroughly continuous with economic practice. The earliest economic manipulations consisted of producing, exchanging, and accumulating goods, and controlling services.[11] If these early studies lack the detachment of the physiochemical and biological sciences, they make up for it by showing better the integration of constructs with original happenings. Whatever hypotheses are formulated and tested belong to the practical situations of national policy and social manipulation.

When economics began to make use of statistics concerning production, cost, transportation, and dispersal of agricultural and industrial products it took a distinct leap toward the goal of formal science. This development coincides, of course, with increase of population, expansion of local and foreign trade, and the evolution of technology and industry.

Basically, economic investigation consists of actuarial analysis. The data worked upon are represented in reports and other documents setting forth the facts of economic transactions. No less important are the analogical natural-science procedures of studying (1) the operations of men at work (time and rate studies),

---

[9] Seligman, The discipline of economics, *Encyclopaedia of the Social Sciences*, Vol. 5, p. 345.

[10] Seligman, op. cit., p. 346.

[11] Cf., Childe, Man Makes Himself.

(2) the chemical and physical events involved in agriculture and industry, and (3) the analyses of cost accounting methods.

Interpretation. More than other anthropic disciplines economics has been dominated by the dogma that it should develop universal laws. This erroneous notion was supported by the belief in absolute principles of human nature. The early founders of Classical Economics not only localized the basic economic principles in human behavior but also made them center on springs of action. All of man's activities were presumed to be governed by his search for personal advantage, by his seeking pleasure and avoiding pain. These and other similar principles were derived from the fixed "laws" of human nature as established by traditional "moral science."

When, however, economic theorists became increasingly interested in (1) the way persons interbehave with natural resources and (2) industrial processes, the absolutistic and universalistic "laws" were turned in the direction of products and their consumption. Laws of supply and demand became expanded to effect a complete coverage for economic data. Utility as a grand category emerged.

Doubtless, because economics is concerned with quantities— amount of (1) income, (2) necessary or actual consumption, (3) work, (4) available resources—it can be most closely related to the so-called natural sciences. The statics and dynamics of economics are common topics of discussion. The thriving movement to transform the discipline into econometrics[12] is the consummation of prolonged attempts to turn economics into a mathematical or statistical discipline.

From the first application of mathematics to economics by Giovanni Ceva, a mathematician and hydraulic engineer, in 1711 there have been numerous related or isolated movements in this direction. Prominent figures here include Beccaria, Lloyd, Isnard, Cournot, Walras, Pareto, Dupuit, Gossen, Jevons, Marshall.[13]

Among the unsatisfactory consequences of the mechanics initiating econometrics and mathematical economics are the simplification of events and the substitution of powers for factors

---

[12] Cf., Davis, Theory of Econometrics; Tintner, Econometrics.

[13] Cf., Morgenstern, Mathematical Economics, in *Encyclopaedia of the Social Sciences*, Vol. 5, pp. 364–368.

in an interrelated field. Methodologically speaking it is an advantage, as Marshall indicates, to employ mathematical aids to illuminate:

> ... some small part of the great economic movement rather than representing its endless complexities.[14]

A distinction must be made, however, between a pragmatic simplification and the substitution of abstractions for concrete events. It is a pertinent question whether economics, or any social science, can afford the luxury of mechanics—that is, setting aside, even denying, the existence of concrete properties. An example is treating supply and demand as the physicist treats gravitation, without the consideration of arbitrary cultural and political controls.

More cogent even than the simplification procedure is the use of mathematical symbols and equations to substitute for events altogether. This introduces explanatory constructs in the form of statistical trends which take on a mystical character. To assume that algebraic and analytic curves represent trends in the form of controlling forces makes economics metaphysical, not mathematical.

Anthropology

Data. The crude data of anthropology comprise (1) the behavior of the members forming unique types of groups (primitive), (2) the things and conditions constituting the group's environs, and (3) the products of behavior employed to further the group's adaptations.

Behavior as anthropological data is differentiable into (1) contacts with the pristine environment, including other group members, and (2) interbehavior with the cultural products and practices of the group. Such behavior may be either the activities of individuals operating dependently and independently[15] or the large-scale activities of a definitely group type.

Among the things interesting to the anthropologist are the various impedimenta of the group's civilization—for example,

---

[14] Pigou, Memorials of Alfred Marshall, London, 1925, p. 313; see also Stigler, The Mathematical Method in Economics.

[15] The assumption here is that independent behavior, too, is conditioned by the group auspices under which it is performed.

cooking utensils, tools and instruments used in hunting, fishing and food production, musical instruments, articles of decoration and adornment, implements of war, clothing, etc. Included, too, are the innumerable concerted actions called ceremonies, customs, group habits, and linguistic systems.

Even the simplest ethnic group possesses so varied an array of objects and actions that enumeration is impossible. We can merely indicate a series of categories suggesting the scope of anthropological data. Every human group possesses in some form the following cultural departments: economics, social organization, science, religion, law, language, technology (invention), craftsmanship, play, and art. It is the general distribution of these various types of data among all ethnic groups that justifies the phrase "unity of man."

Investigation. Obviously, investigational techniques in anthropology must be exclusively of the field variety. Less effective is the method of getting information from an informant, either imported for the purpose or accidentally discovered.

The basic problem of anthropological investigation is to describe things and events on their own merits and with a minimal influence of hampering presuppositions. Presuppositions are of two general sorts—systemic and methodic.

We have already referred to the systemic presupposition that anthropic events are inferior, hence not rigid enough to belong to science. This kind of protopostulate also leads to improper selection of data—stress of things rather than group practices.

Methodic presuppositions constitute interfering attitudes engendered by one's own membership in a certain group. Everyone knows how fatal it is to assume that cultural differences are abnormal deviations, that practices varying .from one's own are inferior. But the persistent use of such terms as savage, barbarian, and civilized[16] suggests that this knowledge is easier to possess than to put into practice.

Both types of presupposition encourage false analogies. Striking examples are describing (1) simple group ceremonials as if they were highly evolved religious practices, (2) myths and legends in terms suitable only for the sophisticated products of European theologians, (3) linguistic behavior as textual products based on

[16] Cf., Childe, Social Evolution.

Latin and Greek paradigms, and finally (4) primitive interpersonal relations as instances of action based on one's own moral code. Favoring an egocentric attitude is the fact that the cultural environment and biological characteristics of the group the anthropologist studies diverge widely, as a rule, from those of his own.

Interpretation. It is characteristic of anthropologists to make use of certain kinds of facts as explanatory principles. In many instances some factor of an ethnic complex is expanded to explain the total. A familiar example is to explain the comparatively primitive and simple civilization of non-Europeans and non-Asians by the construct *primitive mentality*. The procedure is simple. One observes differences between so-called civilized and primitive peoples, and then concludes that these differences are to be attributed to a difference in mentality. Such is the history of Lévy-Bruhl's construct of prelogical mentality.[17]

Aside from other objections—for example, explaining a whole by a part—objective psychology nullifies, as we have seen, the concept of mentality as an entity or force independent of the total cultural complex and able to exert an effect upon it. Psychological events are themselves not only thoroughly embedded in anthropological situations but also shaped by them.

Similar explanatory use is made of other disciplines—for example, geography. Eskimo culture is explained on the basis of geographical location and ensuing environmental effects. History, too, has been employed as an explanatory principle. Some writers assume a unilinear evolution of cultures, such that different groups owe their variations to different points on the historical evolutionary scale.

Race or biological make-up as an explanatory principle has been adequately criticized. This type of interpretation is partially historical, in the sense that an evolution criterion is employed. Even a casual examination indicates the inadequacy of any single explanatory principle.

Sociology

Data. The fact that we have both a science of anthropology and sociology signifies the many-sidedness of human events. Con-

---

[17] Cf., Lévy-Bruhl, How Natives Think; Primitive Mentality.

sidering that anthropologists as a matter of principle cannot neglect the investigation of complex current groups, or that sociologists can ill afford to bypass origins, we find it difficult to set up rigid boundaries between these two disciplines. This is in no sense a serious problem; we need but indicate the practical differences between anthropology and sociology. The latter on the whole concerns itself with contemporary societies, with the larger and more complicated groups originally occupying European territory. Anthropology, on the other hand, influenced by evolution theory, has kept closer to simpler and distant groups.

It is probably not too far fetched a comparison to say that while anthropology, ethnology, or culturology, to use synonyms, is more concerned with people, sociology deals more with the organization, changes, and efficiency of societies. Even if anthropology excludes the biological structure and function of individuals there is still an emphasis on persons, their behavior and products. Sociology, by contrast, is statistical where behavior is concerned, and abstractively descriptive when things (weapons, tools) and events (affairs) are treated.[18]

The crude data of sociology consist of individual societies or communities localized in specific environments. The emphasis must be placed upon a group of people, both its gross organization and the interoperation of its component persons. Because societies are so complex and specialized, sociological data may be separated from economic, technological, political, and intellectual facts. The size, stratification, stability, and irregularity (pathology) of groups are typical sociological materials. These features are all interrelated—the character of a group depends upon its size, while stratification is a function of the intellectual, occupational, and economic aspects of the component units (individuals, families) of a particular society. Shifts in strata, through the development and conflict of subgroups, lead to pathological events such as revolutions and internecine strife.

In the refinement of sociological data such variables as social forces are constructed. As in modern physics such a term as *force* really has no objectionable connotation. Social forces refer

---

[18] History to a great extent constitutes a third type of study of people and groups—describing and explaining ancient or modern societies like the Japanese, Chinese, etc.

to mechanisms or factors in a set of variants—for example, environment, catastrophe, military clash, excessive immigration, population increase, ratio of population to resources; add to these the activities of individuals and groups which influence and change a societal system or some of its features.

Indeed, in the origin, maintenance, and modification of a social system it is impossible to overestimate the power of individuals, acting alone or in concert. We need but mention the clashes between various strata. Organized individuals constitute pressure or power groups. Through their activities, through the exigencies of economic, political, and military conditions, numbers of individuals become integrated and operate by making their communal voice heard, their force felt. The formulation of such societal variables may be rather abstractive, but they inevitably refer back to numerous concrete actions of individuals.

Investigation. Sociological investigation lacks nothing in the way of available concrete events. But it is a different story when one considers the *recording* of investigative results. Various presuppositions serve as checks; also those who are apprehensive of the outcome for established interests interfere.

On the whole, the character of sociological events determines that research is observational, either directly by planned inquiry into the circumstances of towns or other local communities[19] or indirectly by means of documents and records—census reports, questionnaire results, etc. A modicum of experimental manipulation, however, is possible with respect to some particular feature of a society, such as a military organization, church or school group. Such vast reorganizations of communities and nations as recently carried out by the Germans, Italians, Russians, and Chinese, to mention but a few political units, are not to be excluded from experimental study simply because some practical interest, instead of free inquiry, motivated those who carried on the work.

Interpretation. The availability of sociological data warrants an interpretative capstone good enough to provide a proper scientific system. But such a system has not yet evolved, chiefly because sociologists impose philosophical and analogical constructs upon

---

[19] Examples of such studies are Lynd, Middletown, Middletown in Transition; Dollard, Caste and Class in a Southern Town.

their data. Because of these ill-fitting impositions the interpretations and explanations of sociological events are characteristically absolute and universal, in striking contrast with the palpable and contingent properties of the events themselves. Sociological theorists thus aim to simplify the complexities of societal happenings, to fixate their shifting and changing aspects.

Most sociological theory resembles philosophical evaluation more than scientific analysis. Sociologists are so fond of abstract propositions that concrete events escape through the meshes of formal laws and verbal principles. Such terms as statics and dynamics are employed though they hardly apply to the elaborate interbehavior of individuals in a group. In extenuation it may be said that sociologists believe their search for uniformity and order accords with the procedures of natural science. Quite properly, they assume a continuity in social and physiochemical events. It is inexcusable, however, to borrow constructions deleterious to the events studied.

The opposite extreme occurs when psychic interpretations are used to separate sociological materials from those of the exact sciences. Through the influence of philosophical dualism the fact that sociological events concern individuals, and hence include psychological factors, leads sociologists to fall back on psychistic principles. The presumed fixity of physiochemical principles is thus dissipated. The entire construction of the *Geisteswissenschaften* is subject to the criticism that even authentic psychology is not a basic discipline for sociology; sociological events are in the same sense basic to psychological events.

Less objectionable probably than gross philosophic interpretations are various attempts to explain total sociological situations in terms of single or a few participating factors.

A number of writers have made up lists of interpretative principles taken from sociological complexes. Examples are those of Wundt[20] and Hankins.[21] Wundt lists four explanatory principles: (a) biological, (b) cultural, (c) conflict, and (d) imitation. Hankins' series is much longer, including the following main types of determinism: (a) geographical, (b) biological, (c) psychological,

---

[20] Logik der Geisteswissenschaften, pp. 464–485.
[21] Sociology, in Barnes (ed.), The History and Prospects of the Social Sciences, ch. 6.

(d) cultural, and (e) a set of social reform principles. Such principles conceal, and even replace, constructs which really cover the events studied. There is no reason why sociological situations cannot be described with such fullness and relevancy as lead to valid interpretation. This means setting up descriptive propositions in place of conventional abstractions. Some of these propositions meriting the appelation *laws* may well serve as bases for prediction and experimental manipulation.

Political Science

Data. As ill advised as it may be for students of political science to emphasize things rather than behavior, this does reflect a commendable scientific trend. Because they describe concrete situations they stress instruments and apparatus. Such political scientists deviate from William Penn's view concerning the relations of men and governments:

> Governments, like clocks, go from the motion men give them; and as governments are made and moved by men, so by them they are ruined too. Wherefore, governments rather depend upon men than men upon governments.[22]

A well constructed system should accord proper places to all factors in complex political situations. Whether we are concerned with a unit of large magnitude such as a state, nation or a subunit of either, or with a relatively minor organization of persons, as in a club, trade union or college faculty, the behavior performed looms up prominently. No less conspicuous is the apparatus by means of which authority, power, and sovereignty are maintained. Think of the importance of such instruments as charters, constitutions, bills of various sorts (rights, obligations), and informal (unwritten) codes. There is likewise the effective application of powers resident in theories, traditions, even maxims, which are presumed to embody or point to truth, reality, and propriety in matters of interpersonal regulation or governance. In refining political data it is proper to sift out for study all sorts of potencies and rights, legitimate or not, which operate in the interrelations of persons within a political unit or among groups in international systems.

---

[22] Rogers, Politics, in *Encyclopaedia of the Social Sciences*, Vol. 12, p. 225.

Scientific criteria for political events are met also by various norms or sanctions. These are rightly regarded as sources of political action. Norms as tools for political interbehavior spring from the needs of persons and groups, but are sometimes regarded as more or less absolute directives. The actual operation of norms shows that they are entirely disconnected from their reputed source in human or nonhuman nature or in some occult matrix.

Investigation. National and international organizations provide abundant data for political investigation. True enough, this study is primarily observational instead of experimental, but the measure of control present gives the situation a potentially experimental aspect. As a matter of fact, from a scientific standpoint, the orientation of political systems on a grand scale like the League of Nations or United Nations involves most of the features of a scientific experiment. All that is lacking is the indispensable advantage of free inquiry, a condition which sorely limits investigation and consequent results. After all, the manipulators are many, their local interests conflicting.

Despite the possibility of studying political events directly the method actually used is still overwhelmingly of the indirect documentary sort. As in so many other instances we return to Aristotle for an example. Recall his pioneering work in bringing together the constitutions of a hundred and fifty city states. Documentary studies inevitably tend to emphasize the more static aspects of anthropic events. And so Aristotle's work, as well as that of his successors, is limited to activities of the relatively large political unit (city, state, nation, etc.). All the viable factors of individual interrelationships are ignored.

Interpretation. Interpretations in political science are rarely based upon the behavioral events observed. Questionable ideals of rigidity and universality of description vie with the concrete details of competition, strife, organized power and influence. All too frequently political events are explained on the ground of transcendent factors, such as divine and natural rights. It is difficult to conceal the mechanisms operating here: intellectual and practical interests are so closely integrated that political theories merely support the powers and activities of particular rulers and leaders, to the end of justifying certain existing conditions and encouraging others.

Political scientists tend to occupy themselves with problems of norms. This means they entertain presuppositions concerning the aim and quality of political actions. For example, political science is contrasted with natural sciences on the ground that the latter are interested in what exists, whereas in the political domain there is an element of desirability or *ought*. To dispel this view it should be sufficient to observe that even the natural sciences, being closely involved with technological interests, are tied up with specifications arbitrarily set up. On the other hand, in political affairs it is the crassest error not to be able to separate the existential from the desirable.

Now that the psychic is eliminated as an anthropic property we are assured that any asserted norm does not refer to some mythical ought or necessity. When considered as criteria or instruments of power exerted by individuals, norms are data. They may also be taken as statistical enumerations of instances of exercised authority. There is no occasion to make norms nonexistential. All normative factors are functional relationships, modes of adjustment, between individuals or state units.

Jurisprudence

Data. The data of legal science are fairly divided between things and actions. The legal aspect of anthropic situations is found in the behavior of individuals acting singly or in concert according to rules. These rules comprise social and political institutions, embodied in statutes and other formal or informal codes. Codes specify limits of conformity and nonconformity; in specific communal situations they are looked upon as rights and obligations. Because of the prominence of formal codes and legal statutes incorporated in law books and records of decisions, the science of jurisprudence seems to be concerned mostly with things.

This point is stressed further when we consider the instruments for making and enforcing laws. While such instruments naturally evolve from legal behavior, once produced they stand out starkly in their *thing* status. Recall how cluttered legal situations are with legislative machinery; police functions and paraphernalia; courts with their personnel; buildings and administering operations; and, finally, the elaborate apparatus of prisons designed to enforce legal rules.

Investigation. Probably the chief characteristic of scientific law study is the necessary emphasis upon collateral anthropic departments. One cannot study jurisprudence without studying history, on the one hand, and economic and sociological disciplines, on the other. Methodologically speaking, therefore, we expect no variations in procedure from anthropic disciplines.

For the most part, of course, the technique is field observation. Legal investigation covers such data as distribution of property, status, and privilege: observe the civil and criminal sanctions which result in modifying the economic and social status of individuals.

Since human societies are historically continuous, laws and customs carry over in modified form from age to age. It is no small part, therefore, of legal investigations to determine the effects of legal instruments in previously existing societies. In many cases this historical information is applied to current conditions, though such application is contested on the ground of too wide a variation in specific situations.

Granting that legal events constitute behavior by code, we are forewarned against limiting them to large-scale activities ruled by enactments of municipal, state, and federal political units. Prescribed modes of action include behavior within social, industrial, and professional groups as well—an important fact for the problem of experimentation in legal science.

For small groups, optimum conditions exist for rigid and precise experiments. In such situations it is possible to set up and validate a spectrum of hypotheses. But experiments of a sort are not excluded even from the most highly organized political units. Examples are various national alcohol prohibitions or free-divorce experiments.

Interpretation. Despite the prominence of legal things and events and the ease of contacting them, legal theories partake more of philosophical than scientific propositions. Legal students tend to assume that the study of law is more a matter of determining what *ought* to be than of discovering what exists. The error that two different things are involved here is based on the traditional principle that norms are not as objective as other things (p. 324 f.). It is overlooked that *every* legal situation includes the question of what ought to be. When a judge must decide who incurs the penalty, who pays and who receives the damages, the situation does not include an interior subjective process.

The interpretation of values as unreal or subjective harks back to mentalistic psychology. Ends, purposes, ideals, values are divorced from the behavior and concrete situations in which they occur. Actually, however, the comparison of behavior possibilities and the preferential performance of certain acts on the basis of specified conditions constitute the genuine bases of statutes, precedents, codes, and other behavioral guides. Any theory of legal criteria based on spurious ultimate foundations—theistic injunctions, cosmic principles—can easily be recognized as a purely verbal construction.[23]

History

Data. Of all anthropic events the facts of history have been most favorably looked upon as candidates for inclusion in the scientific domain. This is easily explained. To begin with, historians have stressed large-scale happenings, the interbehavior of states, nations, alliances—happenings that stand out for all to see. In the rise and decline of groups, in the conflicts within and between them, observers find abundant identifiable materials which in number and replication offer opportunities for analyses, comparisons, and evaluations.

As early as the 5th century B.C., the contrasting manner in which Herodotus and Thucydides treated historical events was keenly noted. Of the former it is narrated how delightfully he transmuted historical facts into the products of literary creation. But as to how the facts actually happened, the safe guide was Thucydides. Of him it is said that he was a scientist endeavoring at all times to handle historical happenings with the same fidelity and precision which motivated the Hippocratic School of Physicians and the other natural scientists of ancient Greece.[24]

History as the study of change is concerned with the most fundamental characteristics of all events. Hence there is a his-

---

[23] For a comprehensive coverage of legal theories and relevant literature, see Pound, Jurisprudence, in Encyclopaedia of the Social Sciences, Vol. 8, pp. 477–492: Sayre, (ed.) Interpretation of Modern Legal Philosophies; Stone, Province and Function of Law.

[24] See, for example, Bury, Thucydides; Cochrane, Thucydides and the Science of History.

toric aspect to all sciences. This is obviously the case with such biological branches as genetics and embryology; it is becoming increasingly evident in the astronomical (novae, cosmic expansion), chemical (radioactivity), and electrical (energy-level shifting) subdomains of the physiochemical sciences. One might even go farther back to the time when history was the study of the general nature of all objects and their conditions.[25]

Objections to numbering historical facts among scientific data are based on the mistaken notion that history pertains exclusively to events in principle *different* from physiochemical ones. We have already sufficiently considered this error.

Again, writers on the problems of historical science trip over time questions. They assume that a historical fact, because of its pastness, must be nonexistent. Admittedly, historical continuity comprises many completed and currently nonexistent events. It is forgotten, however, that if it is true, for example, that history is partially past politics, it is equally true that politics is present history.

Authentic historical data consist of ongoing events inextricably articulated with many others. Facts of human history, like geological fossils, may be extracted from their spatiotemporal setting in a complex event field and treated like an isolated stone. At the least, authentic past events must be considered as specific instances in which a continuous process has slowed down or ceased. For example, to treat facts about the Sumerians or the Babylonians as isolated, is to abjure contact with large-scale situations. As historians, however, we should not forget that the activities of those people and the products they produced still continue. That a circle has 360 degrees, an hour 60 minutes, a day 24 hours, are facts signifying that our life is continuous with that of the Mesopotamians. This justifies the statement that we are the inheritors of, not only Greeks and Romans, but of many other peoples as well.

It is obvious, too, that, since time is an integral feature of all events, and therefore that every observation both in the natural and historical sciences involves a past and a present, all events can only be observed as partially past. Again we suggest that the scientific student of history is led astray by the distorted picture of

---

[25] Cf., Cohen, The Meaning of Human History, p. 8.

historical data which arises when social and political events are made the sole models. Every event, social, psychological, biological, physical, has its historical or continuative aspect.

Investigation. Even the hazards of selection and analysis in historical study—considerably multiplied when only results of behavior and late phases of a complex succession are available for direct observation—we regard merely as variants in scientific work. It might be argued that, since details of individual events are sought more in historical than in physiochemical situations, historical research is more difficult, presuppositions more obtrusive; but these are relative conditions only.

If there is a unique characteristic of historical research it is the substitutive procedure. Direct observation of past events being impossible resort must be had to the inferential process, the study of evidences. Now the range of historical evidences is large and increasing. At once one thinks of the great variety of documents, annals, records of military and commercial exploits, archives preserved by the participants in national conflict and cooperation, personal diaries, and so on. Likewise of unique importance are the objects which the archaeologist recovers from the sites of past group life. The difficulty of using things (tablets, household objects, monuments, art works, sherds) as evidences for complicated behavior is really only a routine one. Nor is it a serious matter that scholars separate history from prehistory. The continuity of historical events extends beyond conventional historical limits, both backward and forward.

Interpretation. Even those who accept historical events as comparable in objectivity to physiochemical ones hesitate to admit that there are laws and explanations of history. Setting aside such misinterpretations of human events as involve mystic forces of direction and interference is but the first step toward naturalistic explanation. What is required in addition is freedom from wrong ideas concerning the scientist's constructions. But such freedom is made difficult by the fluidity of human facts. After all, historical events are constantly changing; there are no permanent discrete elements. It has been easy, then, to deny history the security and authority of laws.

True enough, when laws are taken as propositions concerning events unique enough to be thrown into simple statistical distributions, they are out of place in historical situations. But why adopt such an inept construction? As we have repeatedly stressed, laws must be derived and formulated from events observed, not imposed upon them. This eliminates metaphysical statements about ultimate and abstract origins, growths and decays, as well as rules of action in one situation being taken over from another. Legitimate laws of social events are statements of similarity, regularity, and order which relate phases of ongoing events or those which have terminated at some past time.[26]

Descriptions elaborate enough to be law constructions consist of propositions interrelating factors in an event complex. Historians, in describing the events they study, make excellent use, as a rule, of a variety of participating factors: (1) geographic location, including climate and topography, (2) societal location, national neighborhood, (3) natural resources, (4) institutional heritages, (5) biological factors, structural and physiological types, population growth, and (6) numerous intrinsically historical facts of the interrelationships of successive and simultaneous groups. Even the briefest of lists suggests numerous possibilities for naturalistic explanations of historical anthropic events, thus avoiding (1) enlarging any one of them to the magnitude of a single and powerful causal agency or (2) abstracting some of them into universal powers or forces.

---

[26] Cf., Lesser, Research procedure and laws of culture.

14

ANTHROPIC EVENTS AND CONSTRUCTS: HUMANISTIC

A S WE have remarked (p. 283), the humanistic class of disciplines emphasizes individual activities relatively more than the groups in which the individuals live. Although such events as linguistic, ethical, esthetic, theological, philosophical, and religious interbehavior exist only under the strictest group influences, they may still be effectively described as individuo-cultural happenings. Scientific systems of the humanistic variety should take this into account.

Linguistics

Data. Linguistic materials constitute so vast a body of data as to engage the labors of many different kinds of specialists. The main types of linguistic studies we have enumerated elsewhere.[1] Here we shall concern ourselves with a summary treatment of the two sharp divisions of linguistic data—performances and the resulting products. The former include acts of speaking, gesturing, and writing. The product or thing aspect naturally inclines one toward such historical problems as development and change in linguistic forms.

Emphasizing the individual aspect does not mean we minimize societal auspices. We acknowledge the plausibility of the frequently made observation that linguistic behavior originated in the interpersonal circumstances of community existence. Keeping in touch, however, with the fact that language consists of individual activities helps considerably in understanding linguistic events.

By following through the roles of individuals we also get closer to linguistic products. When linguistic behavior is vocal instead of manual or mimetic, sounds are the products. When these sounds

---

[1] Principles of Psychology, Vol. 2; An Objective Psychology of Grammar, ch. 2.

are recorded or symbolized they provide an impressive amount of thing data. The evolution of writing signifies a tremendous accumulation of linguistic products; their preservation has resulted in an extensive variety of literary, ritualistic, annalistic, and mnemic records.

Investigation. In a unique way linguistic research carries within itself the conditions of its historic development. Scientific interest in language first developed with respect to its palpable and fixated aspects—namely, texts, inscriptions, documents. Linguistic things as fairly static materials were first in the field. Not until the 19th century was there any paramount interest in the historical origins and relationships of languages. Inquiry into developmental phases, into the intimate derivations of one language from another, thrust into relief the more dynamic aspects of linguistic events. The behavioral aspects of language have only recently been cultivated. In this type of research, sounds and their production are stressed, thus providing a basis for interrelating languages according to sound similarities and changes.

Current linguistic science is frequently divided into linguistics proper (language activity) and philology (problems of structure and other thing aspects).

Linguistics tends toward the description of sound production, the organization of sound patterns in a single language or in a series. In the latter case the study is comparative; it employs techniques for analyzing likenesses and differences in speech systems. Linguistics also includes the problem of origins. Did language behavior originate as a faculty of human organisms? Has it had one or many evolutions? Linguistic investigation also carries the student across study boundaries: hence the investigations of biological factors involved in language performance.

Philology centers on the structural variations and changes in words. The general name for such investigation is *grammar*. Besides this morphological aspect, grammarians are also interested in combinations of words as found in different language systems. Again, they investigate semantic or meaning relationships.

The textual branch of philology departs farthest from the strictly linguistic aspect, since philologists study their material with little regard to its function. They are interested rather in the correction, clarification, and interpretation of texts. Obviously these studies cross lines with sociological and historical undertakings.

One of the most prominent recent developments in linguistic research is the elaborate investigation of symbols. The view has developed that on the basis of symbols and symbol systems even mathematics is a language. Symbolic logic (p. 266) with its putative relations with mathematical principles is an outgrowth of general linguistics.

Interpretation. Doubtless because linguistic events are so close to personal behavior they are interpreted primarily on a psychological basis. Unfortunately, linguists cling to some nonscientific version of psychology and consequently explain language as the expression of mental processes.[2] This procedure is fruitless in itself, but when employed in connection with the uniformities and divergencies of specific linguistic facts it becomes ridiculous. Even when describing correspondence between linguistic behavior or linguistic structure and other cultural events, linguists conclude that the *genius*, the *mentality*, the *soul* of a people have been manifested.[3]

Partially to avoid the above interpretation, partially to stress the viable materials of language products, linguists presumably assume they are dealing exclusively with things having independent properties of existence and interrelation. Indifferent units (morphemes) are analyzed out as textual materials, then presumed to be synthesized into traditional syllables, words (morphology), and sentences (syntax).[4]

By adhering more rigidly to actual language things and events we secure another and more appropriate type of interpretation. Speech and conversation, for instance, are described and explained as active *interbehavior* of individuals with their stimulus objects. Textual and other materials, on the other hand, are handled as *things*, with full regard to their origin as products of behavior.[5]

Ethics (Axiology)

Data. The data of ethical science are perhaps the easiest to describe in brief. Axiological behavior consists of actions per-

---

[2] Cf., for example, Wundt, Die Sprache.
[3] Cf., for example, Vossler, The Spirit of Language in Civilization.
[4] Cf., Bloomfield, Language.
[5] Cf., Kantor, An Objective Psychology of Grammar.

formed with respect to some relevant norm. *Ought* I or *should* I do this or not?

A characteristic of ethical data is their extreme abundance. Every human group teems with occasions for regulating one's conduct according to many varieties of norms. The more complex the group the more numerous the ethical situations. Yet no prejudice among anthropic students is more fundamental than that there can be no science of ethics. The primary argument is: Norms are not natural entities as are geological transformations or planetary motions. Even the eminent Poincaré opposed a scientific ethics on the ground that there could be no behavioral injunctions similar to the laws of nature.[6] In view of the fact that no one really denies the existence of ethical situations, it is only a nonscientific bias which prevents us from accepting them as materials for study and evaluation.[7]

At this point we face a language problem. Ethical norms are indeed not natural things as are mountains or lakes. They are not the less natural, however, for being humanistic behavior products. Theories and hypotheses concerning moral principles constitute constructs which originate as descriptions of ways of acting and later serve as established criteria of conduct. As such they play a decisive role in ethical situations. Such constructed data operate as adages, maxims, injunctions, or large casuistic systems sponsored by various groups. The many scientific systems of research regulation (chap. 2), the philosophical rules for rightly conducting reason, and all professional codes, are really axiological objects.

Investigation. Because ethical events are so diffused throughout cultural situations they are investigated by sociologists, anthropologists, and also by students of philosophy and law. Ethical science still appears to be in a primitive taxonomic stage. Normative behavior has not even been separated from personally projected constructions (propositions) concerning permissible or useful action, nor have different types of norms (mores, ideals) occurring on various individual and group levels been separated and described.

Interpretation. When events are meagerly studied scientific in-

---

[6] *Dernières Pensées*, ch. 8.

[7] Frequently scholars reject ethical norms on the ground that they are absolutes—for example, assertions concerning the will of God. This motive is laudable but unnecessary.

terpretation occurs only as promise not performance. The developmental trend of ethical systems, however, can be detected, since axiological data cross the borders of various sciences. To illustrate: Problems of normative behavior are brought to bear on the cultivation of the physiochemical sciences when the question is raised to what point atomic-energy research should be encouraged unless the results are employed for civil and industrial ends. It is also possible to foresee the development of interpretative rules, their validity being derived from the fact that they stem from an examination of behavior performed under specified auspices.

Esthetics

Data. Interbehavior with beautiful things marks off the esthetic from other humanistic domains. Such interbehavior can be subdivided into (1) production of esthetic objects in whole or in part and (2) their appreciation and enjoyment.

The problem of beauty at once looms up. Invariably esthetic objects are overlaid with a patina of cultural presupposition. For example, esthetic properties have traditionally been reduced to mental qualities: (a) grouped together with all other properties of things or (b) added to the physical characteristics of objects—for instance, beauty is taken as the capacity possessed by objects to impart pleasant feelings.[8] Despite such preconstruction the fact remains that there is a unique esthetic field. Beautiful objects and actions exist as autonomous features of every culture; moreover, they are interrelated with most other cultural components.

Esthetic objects comprise both natural things and the products of artistic behavior. Esthetic actions include appreciative behavior as well as creative. Many times the prominence and importance of a certain esthetic object tend to overshadow the act of creating it. In other words, works of art are more imposing than the work of making them. Similarly, objects of natural beauty may obscure the corresponding responses of appreciating them. Also, beautiful objects of nature pale by comparison with immediately available and palpable works of art—even for students of esthetics.

The intense cultivation of esthetic things and events has given rise to specialized interests and consequently to numerous investigative branches. In each of these subdomains—the historical, so-

---

[8] Ducasse, The esthetic object.

ciological, philosophical study of art—attempts are made to refine esthetic data. Probably the extreme of refinement extends to the iconographical. The iconographer analyzes esthetic objects and relates them to sociological, historical, and anthropological situations.

Investigation. Esthetic investigations have hardly progressed beyond the most embryonic scientific stage, because students of esthetics do not keep to authentic interbehavioral data. In consequence, conventional philosophical or literary investigation has set the pattern. A definite desideratum is to investigate the single individual's development of esthetic interbehavior, with or without strict influence of societal and group conditions.

Effective esthetic investigation stresses (1) the origin and development of esthetic fields—that is, behavior with respect to beautiful objects—and (2) the development of techniques for producing esthetic effects. We can trace out the evolution of these forms of response in the lifetime of individuals and on the basis of their particular social and historical auspices. Hence, taste and the criteria for esthetic activities can be investigated as definite events.

The art historian cooperates in this study by investigating past esthetic events, as in the case of Spanish, French, and African early drawings. For the most part, however, he selects and treats art objects within the interval of historical man. His earliest data, therefore, coincide with the materials of human history.

Interpretation. Since no available body of scientific results has issued from esthetic investigation, the interpretative problem is characteristically speculative. Estheticians debate whether esthetic things possess objective existence, instead of formulating propositions about their order and stability. Esthetic data continue to be regarded as so subtle, elusive, and impalpable as to belong to some nonobjective domain—the "mind." Alas, this view continues the tradition that all nonextensional qualities subsist in the realm of "experience."

Despite the presence of so many hard facts, such as natural objects of beauty and works of art, the current esthetic scene affords scanty material even for a partial scientific system. This unnecessary situation strongly points to the devastating imbalance of cultural imposition and factual observation.

Theology

Data. No one who sympathizes with the view that the sciences arise from contacts with events will refuse to include theology in a survey of the logic of science. Certainly there are definite data, investigations, and interpretations to serve as materials for the organization of scientific systems.

Theological events, of course, are thoroughly humanistic, consisting as they do of interbehavior with things remote from natural events. Theological things—creative forces or personalities—are constructed and fostered in particular social situations, resulting in a wide variety of doctrines—deism, mono- or polytheism, immanent and transcendent theism, unitarian or trinitarian theism, universalistic or tribalistic theism, and so on. To a certain extent deities are constructed analogically to account for the existence of natural events. For the most part, however, theological things serve to provide status and comfort for the reacting persons.

Theological behavior consists of believing and arguing concerning the existence and nature of supreme beings and powers. Historically the most outstanding argument centers about the revealed basis for theological belief or the absence of such revelation. As study material this behavior is embodied in linguistic objects. Once theological entities are proposed and accepted they achieve an independent existence as transcribed doctrines. A typical illustration is the classical ontological argument: "Since God is a universal Being, he must be absolutely real." Similar arguments involve the attribution of perfection. The most perfect being can only be thought of as the most surely existent.

Theological events approach nonanthropic nature most closely at the point where theistic interpretations are imposed upon physiochemical, biological, and psychological happenings. Theological explanations concerning the origin and nature of things and events are constructed on the basis of forces and powers derived from human behavior as a model. Deities and their activities are endowed with human, purposive, manipulative, and reflective properties. On the other hand, there is the negative theology which prohibits any definite description.

Investigation. Investigation obviously is historical and cultural. Students are forced to follow the theologian's constant shift in technique and viewpoint. Each change in cultural circumstances results in a modified view. Throughout all the variation, however, there is a fundamental continuity. Present day theistic beliefs can be traced back to classical origins in which constructions about gods were entirely different, as the plural reference form readily indicates.

A prominent type of theological investigation is the comparative study of god constructs among different societies. Gods are immanent, transcendent, personal, impersonal, primarily omnipotent, primarily omniscient, and so on.

The logician of science refines theological material by comparing various theological constructions. He differentiates, for instance, between natural and revealed theology; he takes note of those pragmatic and functional theologians who, establishing their interest in God on the basis of need, declare that man requires something to believe in, something to give oneself to, to lose oneself in. For them a fundamental human problem is the question: What must one do to be saved?[9]

Interpretation. Since theological interpretation concerns essentially behavioral data, interpretation and investigation fuse. Both consist of interrelating linguistically fostered and embodied assertions with variations in the social, political, and economic conditions of the theologian's group. Theological interpretation, of course, is aided by separating religious from ritualistic cult behavior. Religious study is a broader field than the theological, which is actually a minute subdivision of the field of religion. Perhaps the most characteristic relation between the two is that theology seeks to formulate arguments for theistic types of religion. Ritualistic cult behavior may or may not be connected with theological events. Ceremonies and group dances, for example, may simply correspond to processionals, banquets, and symposiums—activities quite remote from theological behavior and systems.

Philosophy

Data. Systematics in the philosophical domain consists primarily of structuring the processes whereby intellectual workers build up orientating attitudes. Reflective and speculative behavior involves judging and evaluating events; also carefully analyzing

---

[9] Calhoun, Theology as a Humanity.

evidence accepted on the basis of critically chosen presuppositions.[10] Philosophers operate within specific intellectual environments, adopt general principles, and then formulate propositions
which constitute their philosophical systems. Thus have arisen
"philosophies," "logics," "grammars," of any subject whatsoever:
politics, banking, science, morals, and so on. As a rule, philosophical data comprise formulated reactions toward anthropic and
nonanthropic objects and happenings. The trend is toward large-
scale structures consisting of many generalized and universalized
evaluations. Thus arise the grand systems—*Scientia Scientiarum*
or *Scientia Universalis.*

Philosophical behavior has a long history. The numerous system products cover every variety of interest, every type of structure. Consequently, the suggestion is understandable that philosophy resolves itself into the *history* of philosophy. This view is
reinforced by the assumption that philosophy, the one-time universal science, has become superfluous through the evolution of
the special sciences. On the other hand, philosophizing enterprises
are irrepressible; there is no abatement on the part of specialized
scientists to broaden the interrelations of their data and laws.
Philosophizing is thus a well established cultural institution.

The logician of science accepts as data the work of philosophers
and their products, whether historical or current. And he does not
discriminate against any viewpoint. Thus he includes systems
close to scientific events, as well as those concerned with supernatural problems like God, Freedom, and Immortality.

Investigation. Philosophical behavior can be effectively studied
by means of surviving and current treatises. Since these products
are precisely dated they reflect the conditions under which they
developed, especially when they refer to predecessors and com-
petitors. There is an advantage, however, in studying current
philosophies since they are more directly observable. Such behavioral influences as public acceptance, prestige, and freedom from
bondage to conventional institutions can be determined with considerable facility.

An extensive portion of philosophical science is taxonomic. The
student faces the problems of classifying and interrelating philo-

---

[10] See the brief discussion of the relation of science and philosophy in the
following chapter.

sophical systems, small or large. Another department is devoted to the study of origins, a double sort of investigation. On one side is the derivation of one system from another, owing to small changes in human circumstances. Such were the slight variations in the systems of the many Romantic philosophers (Fichte, Schelling, Hegel, Fries, etc.). On the other side is the relatively novel development of a philosophical system under the influence of large-scale changes in cultural events. An example is the revolutionary shift from the natural systems of the ancients to the supernatural and theistic systems of the Church Fathers and Scholastics (p. 62).

Interpretation. Since philosophical behavior is primarily intellectual, interpretation naturally centers around the philosopher's postulational background. Whatever his motivation, whether it is wonder—that is, intellectual curiosity following release from practical occupations—or the attempt to satisfy some prosaic need, the selection (or construction) of premises is always prominent.

Philosophical systems may be evaluated on the basis of numerous criteria. Observing the philosopher's sensitivity to prevailing social, political, and economic conditions, we find it easy to determine if a system is an escape philosophy, an attempt to achieve an intellectual freedom from and superiority over things and events. Other systems constitute contemplative reactions to conditions as they are actually known and understood. Philosophical systems may be judged valid or invalid on systematic ground. Do the constructors carefully set forth their premises and then build their superstructure? Systems, accordingly, can be appraised as positively or negatively good, helpful, and so on. Similarly, by analyzing the auspices under which the system is built, we interpret it as mildly or extremely speculative, or as based on tested and confirmed knowledge.

Of course, as the logician of science weighs and measures the presuppositions of the philosophical system before him he would do well to examine his *own* presuppositions. This is the problem of self examination or retroflexion, illuminated by Wundt's assertion that whereas logic (Methodenlehre) is capable of investigating all other sciences, it cannot itself be investigated.[11] His basic presupposition is that logic as philosophy is a finalistic discipline,

---

[11] Logik, Vol. 3, pp. 664ff.

because one cannot go beyond the intrinsic activity of mind. Though Wundt reiterates that methodology as the logic or philosophy of science rests upon the specialized disciplines, he cannot, because of his metaphysical notions of mind, escape transcendent principles. Thus he himself is building a system on the basis of contacts with definite materials (philosophy and its products) and with traditions (philosophical principles) engendered in particular civilizational circumstances. Once this principle is realized it serves as a check on the philosopher's finalizing and absolutizing procedures.

To adhere strictly to the fact that logical systems are products of interbehavior is to reject the attitude that philosophical systems are confined to cognitive materials. They may be constructed within the esthetic, industrial, economic, or any other event field.

Religion

Data. The domain of religion, like that of theology, is so complex as to permit wide choice in selecting essential data. At the very least one must differentiate between public and private events. Among the former we place all varieties of concerted ritualistic ceremonies, cult practices, processions, and other officially instituted behavior. We assume that a science of religion is concerned primarily with unique personal performances with respect to religious objects. The interbehavior may be described as a specialized type of awe, obeisance, worship, admiration or reverence.

The stimulus objects corresponding to such responses may be scenic grandeur, immensity of things, unattainable desires, or simply constructs such as institutional deities. Since religious behavior may or may not involve a deity it cannot be defined as an act of constructing descriptions about deities or arguments concerning their existence. Significant here is James' objection to the description of God as an *Inevitable Inference*:

> Would martyrs have sung in the flames for a mere inference, however inevitable it might be?[12]

Because religious behavior comprises responses to personal stimulation it comes closer to the interests of psychologists than to those of anthropologists. Anthropologists in their discussions, how-

---

[12] The Varieties of Religious Experience, p. 502.

ever, have appropriately stressed stimulus objects. Generally they hold that religious responses are made to a supernatural kind of object.[13] Occasionally the variant *superhuman* is employed.[14] Actually those religious stimulus objects consist of strange, possibly harmful, things and events. Again, because students of religion are invariably influenced by their own religious cultures they assume a universal dichotomy of "experience" or man's environment into the sacred and profane.[15] In other words, they project contrasting terms to indicate these differences of stimulus objects among primitive cultural groups.[16]

Unfortunately, even students of religion who equate the sacred with the hostile, the strange, the unavailable, still identify the religious domain with some sort of spiritism. This view has a cultural origin in the fact that psychology was once all too hospitable to notions of transpatial existence. It was against such a background that Tylor minimally defined religion as the "belief in spiritual things."[17]

Although religious behavior covers a complex range, the notion is prevalent that it constitutes some sort of feeling—a feeling described as a thrill, exaltation, exhilaration, in the presence of some supreme power or deity.[18] The intention is to distinguish authentic religious reactions from beliefs and ceremonial behavior.

Investigation. In a domain so crudely defined as a science of religion the discussion of investigation pertains more to requirements dictated by scientific canons than to actual work accomplished. On the whole, then, the science of religion consists more of problems than of achievements; an unnecessary situation, however, since there are authentic events to be treated.

For the scientist of religion there are definite taxonomic and statistical jobs to determine: (a) the nature and variety of religious behavior, (b) the number of persons concerned, the frequency of religious reactions, and (c) to compare the religious behavior of variously situated individuals—scientists, artists, in-

---

[13] Goldenweiser, History, Psychology, and Culture; Wallis, Religion in Primitive Society; Radin, Primitive Religion.

[14] Bertholet, Religion, in *Encyclopaedia of the Social Sciences.*

[15] Durkheim, The Elementary Forms of the Religious Life.

[16] Wallis, op. cit., chs. 1 & 2.

[17] Primitive Culture, Vol. 1, p. 424.

[18] Radin, Primitive Religion, p. 4; Goldenweiser, History, Psychology, and Culture, pp. 377–384.

dustrialists, men, women, and so on. An important problem is what kind of objects carry religious stimulus functions and what sorts of economic, social, war-and-peace circumstances play a part in religious situations. Implied also are periods of waxing and waning of religious behavior.

Again, religious investigations may emphasize individual or social interbehavior—in other words, person-centered activities or those influenced by groupings of individuals.[19] For instance, an individual may not share his reaction of dependence, awe, or hopelessness with others. Or contrariwise his response of helplessness in the face of uncontrollable happenings may well be the result of a group's communicated teachings.

Interpretation. Where so little precise investigation has been achieved available accurate interpretation is sparse. As a matter of fact, the most characteristic feature of religious discussion is the inability to evaluate religious behavior without adorning the original events with characteristics derived from one's own religious culture. When Whitehead, for example, wishes to compare religion and science he makes use of the definition: "Religion is the reaction of human nature to its search for God."[20] Again, he declares: "Religion is the vision of some hopeless quest."[21] The result is to telescope data and interpretation. For one thing, the religious is so confounded with the theological situation that the interpreter's own theological views are injected into the religious events he studies.

Most scientific interpretations of religious events therefore comprise violations of scientific canons, especially the assumption of the nature and existence of some entity or power which human nature demands. That religious behavior is not universal is entirely overlooked; more, that when it does occur the stimulus objects may be widely different in character; finally, that it is only *certain* individuals who are influenced by their cultural circumstances to interbehave with deities. There is also a failure to differentiate between the adoration or worship of a deity and the verbal assertion that there *is* one.

---

[19] For a distinction between individual and social psychological behavior see Kantor, An Outline of Social Psychology.

[20] Whitehead, Science and the Modern World, p. 274.

[21] Ibid., p. 275.

V

SCIENCE AND CIVILIZATION

15

SCIENCE AND THE LOGIC OF CULTURE

The Systemic Significance of Science

SCIENTIFIC enterprises constitute one of the loftiest peaks of man's development. As processes of orientation to technical, hygienic, and agricultural circumstances the sciences have proved superb.

Still we may ask: What is the systemic significance of science? What do the techniques and results of focalized investigations contribute to a general cultural system? Do they facilitate the development of personal attitudes and social institutions essential to a comprehensive cultural orientation of an individual, scientist or layman? To what degree have scientific methods and results raised the general level of civilization?

Fundamentally this is a problem of the interrelationship of the various sciences and their coordination with other cultural components. Such admittedly effective procedures and results as science includes should be compatible with the principles and practices of (a) social organization, (b) art creation and appreciation, (c) philosophic reflection and (d) religious and ethical evaluation. Compatibility implies the practical employment of scientific methods to solve humanistic problems as well as those categorized as natural. Certainly social conventions should not operate as criteria of scientific validity and achievement.

As long as there is no thoroughgoing assimilation of the sciences with the other cultural components there is no comprehensive cultural system. Conversely, as long as we do not have a coherent cultural system scientific work is limited to nonanthropic situations—namely those concerned with nonhuman events in which immediate applications are most readily achieved. Furthermore, under such circumstances the argument prevails that science can only determine the results to be obtained by research but not the value of those results. Evaluations and their criteria, in other words, are regarded as outside the scientific horizon. Most damaging of all: even the most capable scientists under such circumstances are unable to further the general advancement of civilization.

Those who are disturbed by this state of affairs naturally speculate about the underlying conditions. In the first place they find that the chief merits of science—its specificity and precision—promote extreme specialization and thereby prevent the scientist from becoming oriented to many other civilizational components. The expert in mathematical analysis, the precise measurer of light velocity cannot apply his techniques in art or economics.

We have also called attention to the powerful competition of interests, the pressure of economic and religious groups which aim to preserve the *status quo*, to prevent the results of scientific work from clashing with traditional practices and ways of thinking. Science becomes a weapon in the hands of one set of persons in conflict with another. Books like those by Draper,[1] White,[2] and Murray,[3] recount the struggles centering about scientific discoveries.

But what chiefly prevents scientists from accelerating civilizational progress is the domination of our culture by dualistic traditions, which, as we have reiterated, encourage the imposition of conventional values upon events. Consider the views of Schrödinger. First he asserts:

> ... all specialized research has real value only in the context of the integrated totality of knowledge.[4]

Then it turns out that a cultural system is dominated by metaphysical problems; in fact, science for him is:

> ... an integrating part of our endeavor to answer the one great philosophical question which embraces all others, the one that Plotinus expressed by his brief: τινες δε ἡμεῖς; who are we? And more than that: I consider this not only one of the tasks, but *the* task of science, the only one that really counts.[5]

Were Schrödinger not so influenced by folkloristic puzzles as to

---

[1] Conflict between Religion and Science.
[2] Warfare of Science and Theology.
[3] Science and Scientists of the 19th Century.
[4] Science and Humanism, p. 7.
[5] Ibid., p. 51.

believe "the observing mind is not a physical system: it cannot interact with any physical system" (ibid., p. 53), he would place more value on the findings of (a) comparative biology concerning the evolution of man; (b) anatomy, physiology, biochemistry, experimental medicine—sciences which have uncovered innumerable facts about man's form and function; (c) sociology and anthropology, both with well stocked treasuries of data concerning social organization and evolution, as well as personal interactions, and, finally, (d) objective psychology, which has made valuable discoveries concerning man's behavioral evolution.

We now consider some of the relationships between science and other civilizational fields, pointing out in what ways the various components fail to become satisfactorily integrated into a cultural system.

Science and Philosophy

Contrary to conventional belief, science has never been separated from philosophy. But the relationship is in no sense one of coordination. Whereas scientific investigation has moved on from one great conquest to another, and is successful precisely because workers interbehave with concrete things and events, the historical philosophy to which scientists still cling is at complete odds with their methods and findings. Metaphysical attitudes, we have seen again and again, are so powerful as to prompt eminent scientists like Planck, Einstein, Born, Eddington, Jeans, Compton, Millikan to raise questions about reality and the validity of knowledge. Strange that an interbehavioral science such as physics can be associated with a philosophical system built upon phantasies as a foundation.

Scientific Philosophy and Philosophic Science

A scientifically analyzed philosophy (chap. 14) and an authentic philosophy of science not only can be completely integrated: they can supplement each other in every intellectual context. A philosophy dealing with concrete happenings affords a larger orientation to natural events than is available in any specialized scientific enterprise. For example, a philosophical system is not confined to the findings of physics, psychology or one of the social sciences; it takes all of them into account, as well as the mutual influences of technology, social organization, and other cultural factors. Philosophical orientation is coordination of knowledge; the philosopher is a moderator, a critic.

By comparison, scientific enterprise is more restricted. But this does not mean it is not an advantage to the scientist if he knows something of philosophy. Both the scientist freed from speculations about historical theocosmology and the philosopher who concerns himself with the things and events involved in scientific investigation reject the two following theorems as the cardinal principles of the whole structure of physical science:

1. There is a real outer world which exists independently of our act of knowing.
2. The real outer world is not directly knowable.[6]

Science and Religion

Many scientists insist that there is neither possibility nor hope of science ever being reconciled with religion. Others take the opposite position. Generally, when religion is opposed to science it is defined as a creed established and fostered by a church. When, on the other hand, religion is taken as a type of personal belief or practice, it is easily argued that it does not conflict with science, and that a mystic or poet may also be an effective manipulator of a microscope, cyclotron or telescope, just as he may also be a good bridge or billiard player.

From a systemological standpoint, however, it is unfortunate that the above argument fosters the assumption that religious behavior is something different from personal sentiments—in fact, a method of knowing and reasoning which competes with that of scientific research.

Probably one of the greatest obstacles to a satisfactory cultural system is that it is required to be absolute and all-inclusive. The scientist needs religion, it is alleged, because science has definite limits. In consequence he must resort to religion to escape from the insecurities of scientific work. Only recently Einstein has written:

> ... the scientific method can teach us nothing else beyond how facts are related to, and conditioned by, each other. ... Yet it is equally clear

---

[6] Planck, Where is Science Going?, p. 82; see also Dingle, The Significance of Science.

that knowledge of what *is* does not open the door directly to what *should be.*[7]

Those who yearn for an absolutistic and universalistic system cannot rest short of "ultimate and fundamental ends." For a "complete" man Einstein believes there can be no legitimate conflict between religion and science; the two are required to complement each other:

> Science without religion is lame, religion without science is blind.[8]

Naturally, scientists differ with respect to the kind of religion they try to coordinate with science. Einstein explicitly disavows a personal god, whose fiats supervene upon events, such as Jevons accepts:

> From the preceding reviews of the value of our scientific knowledge, I draw one distinct conclusion, that we cannot disprove the possibility of Divine interference in the course of nature.[9]

The "reviews" to which Jevons refers, of course, do indicate that scientific inferences must always be of a hypothetical and provisional nature, that knowledge is never absolute.

Scientists attempt to harmonize science and religion on the ground that traditionally scientists have been imbued with religious doctrines. To go no further back than our own experimental era we may cite Copernicus, Kepler, and Newton.[10] Newton's tutor, Isaac Barrow, wanting to devote himself to theology, resigned his tenure of the Lucasian chair in Newton's favor. Today, Planck argues for the legitimacy of conjoining religion and science because the great scientists of the past did so:

> The most immediate proof of the compatibility of religion and natural science, even under the most thorough critical scrutiny, is the historic fact that the very greatest natural scientists of all times—men such as Kepler, Newton, Leibniz—were permeated by a most profound religious attitude.[11]

Evidence has recently come to light that Newton was much

---

[7] Science and Religion, pp. 21, 22.
[8] Ibid., p. 26.
[9] The Principles of Science, p. 766.
[10] Cf., Mach, Science of Mechanics, pp. 446ff.
[11] Scientific Autobiography and Other Papers, p. 186.

more interested in theology than in science or practical affairs.[12] Andrade estimated that he left upwards of a million three hundred thousand words in manuscript on theology.[13] It is significant also that the biographer of Huygens, a contemporary and scientific opponent of Newton, can write:

> He alone among the men of science of his day found the temper of scientific enquiry alien to orthodox religious faith.[14]

Mach, however, points out that Galileo and Newton, as well as Huygens, did not contaminate their science with theology.

> Newton never, despite his profound religiosity, mingled theology with the questions of science.[15]

In a sense this is true. But even if Newton did strive to keep his science separate from his religion, the integration of scientific and religious ideas in the end had its effect on Newtonian science. In a more subtle way than Newton's defenders realize, his science is permeated with the supernatural. For that reason the author of the Théodicée could criticize Newton for requiring his deity to meddle constantly with his cosmic machine.[16] It was hardly an accident that Newton perpetuated the nonscientific belief that colors and sounds have no existence other than as psychic substances. Such ideas are deeply stratified in a dualistic culture.

When scientists interfuse their findings with ideas of universality, ultimate reality, and creative causality, there is but one conclusion: they permit their religious beliefs to dominate their scientific thinking. When Planck asserts that science brings us only to the threshold of the ego,[17] that in this realm of moral and esthetic problems there is a demand for principles different from science, he is definitely assuming there are other ways of solving problems besides scientific methods—namely, only by using his nonscientific facilities can man answer such questions as: What is

---

[12] Keynes, Newton the Man.

[13] Andrade, Newton, p. 21. See also McClachlan, Sir Isaac Newton, Theological Manuscripts.

[14] Bell, Christian Huygens and the Development of Science in the Seventeenth Century, p. 8.

[15] Science of Mechanics, p. 457. Cf., also Strong, Newton and God.

[16] Cf., Brewster, Memoirs of the Life, Writings, and Discoveries of Sir Isaac Newton, Vol. 2, p. 285.

[17] Where is Science Going?, p. 167.

the good life? What is the significance of suffering? What is the chief end of man? What ought men to do?

Evidently those who consider science less efficacious than religion with respect to human problems believe that religion is a source of knowledge. They assume, for example, that responses of fear, awe, insecurity, and dependence mirror an entity which stimulates these reactions, just as a measurement is assumed to correspond to the thing measured. But even when religious attitudes are as effectively distinguished from scientific ones as Einstein indicates in the following, it is still evident that spiritistic institutions facilitate the injection of metaphysical convictions into scientific situations:

> To make clear these fundamental ends and valuations, and to set them fast in the emotional life of the individual, seems to me precisely the most important function which religion has to perform in the social life of man. And if one asks whence derives the authority of such fundamental ends, since they cannot be stated and justified merely by reason, one can only answer: they exist in a healthy society as powerful traditions, which act upon the conduct and aspirations and judgments of the individuals; they are there, that is, as something living, without its being necessary to find justification for their existence. They come into being not through demonstration but through revelation, through the medium of powerful personalities. One must not attempt to justify them, but rather to sense their nature simply and clearly.[18]

Numerous scientists write as though the only relation between science and religion is the subordination of the former to the latter. For them science is only to be pursued in the interest of religion. Ultimately they believe that only religious and theological conclusions follow from the successes of science, which they endow with a sacramental quality. Whittaker puts it:

> In the laws of nature, known and unknown, we recognize a system of truth, which has been revealed to us by the study of nature, but which is unlike material nature in its purely intellectual and universal character, and which, if the conclusions we have reached are correct, is timeless, in contrast to the transitory universe of matter. Material has made manifest to our understanding realities greater than itself, realities which point to a God who is not bound up with the world, who is transcendent and subject to no limitation.[19]

---

[18] Science and Religion, pp. 22–23.

[19] Eddington's principle in the philosophy of science, p. 60.

A unique argument for strictly coordinating science and religion is that one equally as much as the other frees man from dogmatism and superstition. Says Planck:

> Religion and natural science are fighting a joint battle in an incessant, never relaxing crusade against scepticism and against dogmatism, against disbelief and against superstition, and the rallying cry in this crusade has always been, and always will be: "On to God."[20]

When so many major prophets of science[21] rush out of their laboratories and observatories to devalue scientific events and methods in favor of "higher things" and intuitive powers the great need for a coherent cultural system stands out.

Science and Technology

Despite the obvious concordance of science and technology they are often set into opposition. To a great extent this is owing to professional and institutional competition. The scientist who claims that he has revolutionized the cultural scene (p. 48f.) is countered by the technician who argues that both as direct operator upon man's environment and as purveyor of scientific tools he, in his engineering role, deserves the greater credit. We do not propose to adjudicate these claims; we merely consider them against the background of cultural circumstances.

We have described science and indicated its mode of operation; let us do the same for technology. By the term *technician* or *engineer* we refer to a skilled worker whose task is to modify, even transform, some feature of man's environment. To carry on his work he develops extensive apparatus for manipulating things; he constructs instruments for measuring his achievements. Environmental transformations are illustrated by the work of the engineer who drains marshes, thereby developing hygienic conditions favoring habitation; who cuts canals making possible the migration of people and the movement of goods. As a toolmaker the technologist develops the means of architectural construction and the apparatus of industry and commerce.

---

[20] Scientific Autobiography and Other Papers, p. 187.

[21] It is not only the votaries of the so-called exact sciences who attempt to intermingle science with religion, but also biologists, though the latter more discreetly talk of values and philosophy—for example, Driesch, Herrick, Lillie, and many others.

But it would be unreasonable to assume that the technologist cannot profit by his fellow worker who specializes in the development of *principles*. Technological practice at certain points really depends upon pure science. "What builder of steam boilers," demands Le Chatelier, "could do without the laws of water tension vapor investigated by Regnault?"[22]

The term *pure* merely points to a contact with things and events different from manipulation. For example, designing a machine is relatively remote from and preliminary to succeeding construction; it simply suggests what can be done. A second characteristic of so-called pure behavior is that it is differently motivated. More often than not the pure scientist is disinterested in applicable results. Striking examples are the performances and products of pure mathematicians. We have mentioned (pp. 25, 132) the scientist's resort to techniques which mathematicians have developed in complete detachment from any immediate application. This process of applying pure-science products is nowise an infrequent occurrence.

Pure science, however, is not outside the domain of manipulation and transformative interbehavior. At most this purity is a matter of subtle action, a preoccupation with abstract relations. In general, the connection between science and technology, even when most distinct, is one of cooperation, of borrowing techniques and products and adapting them to new and different situations.

This distinction between science and technology is clearly a function of the increasing complication of culture. As late as the 17th and 18th centuries, when scientists were lens grinders and toolmakers, the same person was both technologist and scientist. Scientists who required instrumental aids to increase their capacity for interbehaving with things had to produce them themselves. Recall the artisanship of Galileo, Newton, von Guericke, Gilbert, Halley, Boyle, Hooke, Leeuwenhoek, and others.

Then came extreme specialization. Expertness implied separation of functions. The scientist could hardly make progress without the toolmaker's cooperation. Think of the help Crookes received from his glassblower, the similar service rendered Plücker by Geissler.

---

[22] Bouglé, The Evolution of Values, p. 207.

In the 20th century we may safely assert that science and technology have fused. Consider in how many scientific departments the complexity of apparatus involves engineering problems! To what extent a physicist must become an engineer to construct a 200 inch lens, plus all the fittings for its housing and care! Consider, too, the fusion of scientific and engineering functions in the development of machines like cyclotrons and betatrons.

In the biological and psychological domains one can scarcely overestimate the technologist's contribution. He has developed the vacuum tube and all the complex electronic apparatus without which the physiologist, the geneticist, the embryologist, the psychologist could not proceed in their investigations. Indeed, the marriage of science and technology is responsible for the effective development of each.

Science and Values

Problems of value stimulate more disharmony between scientific and social attitudes than any of the previous relationships we have been considering. When modern science in its infancy as natural philosophy took its first steps in the direction of independent inquiry, it conflicted very little with age-old social institutions. It could even help the heavens declare the glory of God. But gradually as science matured through increased contacts with events, through the development and use of apparatus, and by turning away from speculative reason toward technological proficiency it achieved an autonomy of thought and evaluation that threatened established wisdom and certainty. The more science permeated the entire range of events, and the more it attained success in the biological and anthropic domains, the more rapidly it lost its inferiority in the face of ultimate Reason and Reality. Slowly, but surely, science crowded out first causes, extranatural powers and forces—in other words, challenged the unexamined acceptance of ancient values.

Now, since values had traditionally been interpreted as higher and more significant than scientific things and events, the devotees of "values" felt acutely the danger of substituting natural for divine law. The more science verified its constructions, the more it demonstrated the workings of nature, the less room for eternal values. The issue of *being* versus *significance* sharpened. Science, it was argued, could deal only with existence, with observed things; their underlying meaning it could never fathom.

The value issue arises from setting totalities and absolutes over against concrete activities. Science is placed outside the domains of religion and philosophy, the disciplines of Absolute Reality. We have seen how Einstein sets up an insuperable barrier between what *is* and what *should be*. Values are thus erroneously taken out of the field of concrete problems, thrown into a personally constructed region of superexistence and transcendent significance. Arguments for superpersonal values grow out of constructs concerning the mental as contrasted with the material. The value issue is summed up in the following:

> But it must not be forgotten that . . . it was religion, and not science, which first inspired men to try to unify all their experiences, and that it is religion still which alone seems to justify all experiences—the corporeal and the mental, the inward and the outward, the ideas of value and the facts of existence, the events of time and their significance for eternity.[23]

Unless we interpret values as ultimate and eternal entities it is clear that scientists are continually concerned with them. More: one of the most important features of scientific work is to assess values. What are values but characteristics of things, especially their interrelations? Are not scientific equations records of values ascertained and formulated? All scientific determinations of the strength of materials, of the fitness and adaptability of things, are interbehaviors with values. Essential scientific questions are: What are the values of cobalt or chromium for strength? Of aluminum and magnesium for strength and weight conjointly? What is the value of these chemicals for disease control and eradication? Of such and such a form of social organization for specified political, economic, or social purposes? Nothing is more eligible for inclusion in scientific situations than problems concerning the *value* of certain *means* to achieve given *ends*. Ah, but the mystic declares: these are not the *real* values! The scientist, however, can easily demonstrate that transcendent values are simply verbal creations engendered by the pressures of difficult and constrained existence. The appreciation that such values are

---

[23] Oman, The Sphere of Religion, p. 299.

developed in order to escape intolerable human conditions helps greatly to separate events from constructs, science from folklore, and thereby to achieve a more harmonious integration of all cultural components.

The Interbehavioral Basis of Cultural Systems

Our brief examination of the relation of science to philosophy, religion, technology, and axiology reinforces the point that all discoordination is owing directly to the dichotomy of matter and spirit—a dichotomy which, on the one hand, prompts the denigration of practical and technological pursuits and the glorification of abstract science, and, on the other, limits science to crass events with a singular impotence to cope with "spiritual realities."

This disharmony evaporates when we consider the fact that civilization is nothing more or less than a complicated web of interbehavior. Once it is granted that all phases of culture—art, philosophy, law and social organization, religion, technology and science—constitute specific evolutions of human behavior, the way is cleared to an integrated cultural system; and the logic of science is readily harmonized with the logic of the other cultural departments. On this basis science can definitely help to accelerate the progress of civilization.

Since interbehavior occurs in a spatiotemporal frame of reference is it not fatuous to impose transcendent properties upon man and his surroundings? Both practical and theoretical behavior takes place in a continuous interbehavioral field in which all capacities and knowledge evolve. Neither modern philosophy nor science allows for the derivation of knowledge, judgment or inference from any other source than contacts with things, thus leaving no vacuum to be filled with mystic entities and powers.

With the extrusion of historical dualism the barrier is removed between what *is* and what *should be*. "Timeless" systems are not pitted against "transitory" systems. Scientific knowledge is harmonized with practical affairs; for knowledge, desire, sentiment, belief, and every kind of manipulation are all coordinate forms of interbehavior. Scientific methodology thus becomes applicable to religious, moral or political problems without resorting to uncontrolled trial and error, folklore, and superstition—on the ground that such problems require higher powers than science commands.

At the same time, on an interbehavioral basis, social ends and ideals are not lifted out of their place in the cultural complex and into a transcendent domain. The civilizational system remains an intact unit in which we can differentiate between practical adjustments to objects and events and the creative production of art objects, poetry, legends, and the speculative systems of metaphysics and theology. On all counts the interbehavioral principle precludes dualizing a person by the false assumption that he acts *naturally* on the one hand, *mystically* and *intuitively* on the other.

BIBLIOGRAPHY

Adams, F. (trans.) The Genuine Works of Hippocrates. Baltimore, Williams & Wilkins, 1939.

Adrian, E. D. The Physical Background of Perception. Oxford, Clarendon Press, 1947.

Alexander, J. Life, Its Nature and Origin. N. Y., Reinhold, 1948.

Allee, W, C., Park, O., Emerson, A. E., Park, T., and Schmidt, K. P. Principles of Animal Ecology. Philadelphia & London, Saunders, 1949.

Anderson, C. D. The elementary particles of physics. *Amer. Scientist*, 1949, 37, 193–201.

——Revised table of elementary particles of matter. *Amer. Scientist*, 1951, 39, 260–261.

Andrade, E. N. da C. Newton. In *The Royal Society, Newton Tercentenary Celebrations*. Cambridge, Cambridge U. Press, 1947.

Aristotle. De Generatione et Corruptione. Oxford, Clarendon Press, 1922.

Aston, F. W. Mass Spectra and Isotopes. London, Arnold, (1933) 1948.

Bacon, F. See Ellis and Spedding; also Robertson.

Barnes, H. E. (ed.) The History and Prospects of the Social Sciences. N. Y., Knopf, 1925.

Bawden, F. C. Plant Viruses and Virus Diseases. Waltham, Mass., Chronica Botanica Co., (3rd rev. ed.) 1950.

Bayliss, W. M. The Nature of Enzyme Action. London, Longmans, (5th ed.) 1925.

Beadle, G. W. Chemical Genetics. In L. C. Dunn (ed.) *Genetics in the 20th Century*, Chap. 11. N. Y., Macmillan, 1951.

—— Genes and the chemistry of the organism. *Amer. Scientist*, 1946, 34, 31–53.

Bell, A. E. Christian Huygens and the Development of Science in the Seventeenth Century. London, Arnold, 1947.

Bell, E. T. Development of Mathematics. N. Y., McGraw-Hill, 1940.

—— Men of Mathematics. N. Y., Simon & Schuster, 1937.

Berkeley, E. C. Giant Brains or Machines that Think. N. Y., Wiley, 1949.

—— Symbolic logic and large-scale calculating machines. *Science*, 1950, 112, 395–399.

Bernard, C. An Introduction to the Study of Experimental Medicine. (H. C. Green trans.) N. Y., Schuman, (1927) 1949.

—— Principes de Médecine expérimentale. Paris, Presses Universitaires de France, 1947.

Bernoulli, D. Hydrodynamica, sive de viribus et motibus fluidorum commentarii. Argentorati. Dulseckeri, 1738.

Bertalanffy, L. von. Problems of Life: An Evaluation of Modern Biological Thought. London, Watts, 1952.

Bertholet, A. Religion. In *Encyclopaedia of the Social Sciences*, Vol. 13. N. Y., Macmillan, 1931.

Beveridge, W. I. B. The Art of Scientific Investigation. London, Heinemann, 1951.

Bloomfield, L. Language. N. Y., Holt, 1933.

Blum, H. F. Time's Arrow and Evolution. Princeton, Princeton U. Press, 1951.

Bohr, N. Causality and complementarity. *Phil. of Science*, 1937, 4, 289–298.

Born, M. Natural Philosophy of Cause and Chance. Oxford, Clarendon Press, 1949.

—— The Restless Universe. London & Glasgow, Blackie & Son, 1935.

—— Experiment and Theory in Physics. Cambridge, Cambridge U. Press, 1943.

Bouglé, C. The Evolution of Values. (H. S. Sellars trans.) N. Y., Holt, 1926.

Bouma, P. J. Physical Aspects of Color. Eindhoven, Philips Industries Technical and Scientific Literature Dept., 1948.

Boyle, R. Of the Mechanical Origins of Heat and Cold. In P. Shaw (ed.) *The Philosophical Works of the Hon. Robert Boyle Esq.*, Vol. 3. London, W. &. J. Innys, and R. Manby, etc., 1738.

—— The Sceptical Chymist. London, Dent., 1911.

Brewster, D. Memoirs of the Life, Writings, and Discoveries of Sir Isaac Newton. Edinburgh, Murray, 1855, 2 vols.

Bridgman, P. W. Logic of Modern Physics. N. Y., Macmillan, 1927.

—— The Nature of Physical Theory. Princeton, Princeton U. Press, 1936.

Brown, R. A. Brief Account of Microscopical Observations made in the months of June, July, and August, 1827, on the Particles contained in the Pollen of Plants; and on the General Existence of Active Molecules in Organic and Inorganic Bodies. *Miscellaneous Botanical Works of Robert Brown Esq.*, Vol. 1, 1866. London, Publ. for the Royal Society by R. Hardwick, 1866–68.

Burtt, E. A. The Metaphysical Foundations of Modern Physical Science: An Historical and Critical Essay. London, Kegan Paul, (rev. ed.) 1932.

—— Method and metaphysics in the science of Sir Isaac Newton. *Phil. of Science*, 1943, 10, 57–66.

Bury, J. B. Thucydides. In *The Ancient Greek Historians*. London, Macmillan, 1909.

Butterfield, H. The Origins of Modern Science, 1300–1800. London, Bell, 1949.

Cajori, F. A History of Physics in its Elementary Branches. N. Y., Macmillan, (rev. ed.) 1929.

Calhoun, R. L. Theology as a Humanity. In T. H. Green (ed.) *The Meaning of the Humanities*. Princeton, Princeton U. Press, 1938.

Campbell, L. and Garnett, W. Life of James Clerk Maxwell. London, Macmillan, 1882.

Campbell, N. R. The Principles of Electricity. London, Jack, 1912.

—— Physics: The Elements. Cambridge, Cambridge U. Press, 1920.

Caspersson, T. Cell Growth and Cell Function. N. Y., Norton, 1950.

Caspersson, T. and Schultz, J. Cytochemical Measurements in the Study of the Gene. In L. C. Dunn (ed.) *Genetics in the 20th Century*, Chap. 9. N. Y., Macmillan, 1951.

Caullery, M. Le Parasitisme et la Symbiose. Paris, Doin, (2nd ed.) 1950.

Cavendish, H. Observations on Mr. Hutchin's experiments for determining the degrees of cold at which quicksilver freezes. *Phil. Trans., Royal Society of London*, 73, 303.

Child, C. M. Individuality in Organisms. Chicago, U. of Chicago Press, 1915.

Childe, V. G. Man Makes Himself. N. Y., Mentor, 1951.

—— Social Evolution. London, Watts, 1951.

Cochrane, C. N. Thucydides and the Science of History. London, Oxford U. Press, H. Milford, 1929.

Cohen, M. R. The Meaning of Human History. LaSalle, Ill., Open Court, 1947.

—— Reason and Nature. N. Y., Harcourt-Brace, 1931.

Condon, E. U. Is there a science of instrumentation? *Science*, 1949, 110, 339–342.

Cooley, C. H. Social Organization. N. Y., Scribner, 1909.

Craik, K. J. W. The Nature of Explanation. Cambridge, Cambridge U. Press, 1943.

Croce, B. The Philosophy of Giambattista Vico. (R. C. Collingwood trans.) N. Y., Macmillan, 1913.

Crowther, J. G. The Social Relations of Science. N. Y., Macmillan, 1941.

Dampier, W. C. From Aristotle to Galileo. In J. Needham and W. Pagel (eds.) *Background to Modern Science*. Cambridge, Cambridge U. Press, 1940.

Darlington, C. D. Chromosome Chemistry and Gene Action. In Darlington and Mather. *Genes, Plants, and People*. London, Allen & Unwin, 1950.

—— The Conflict of Science and Society (Conway Memorial Lecture, 1948). London, Watts, 1948.

—— The early hybridizers and the origins of genetics. In Darlington and Mather, *Genes, Plants, and People*.

Darlington, C. D. and Mather, K. Genes, Plants, and People. London, Allen & Unwin, 1950.

Davidson, J. W. Biochemistry of the Nucleic Acids. London, Wiley, 1950.

Davis, H. T. The Theory of Econometrics. Bloomington, Indiana, Principia Press, 1941.

Davy, H. An Essay on Heat, Light, and the Combinations of Light. In T. Beddoes (ed.) *Contributions to Physical and Medical Knowledge, Principally from the West of England*.

Delbrück, M. (ed.) Viruses, 1950. Pasadena, Div. of Biology, California Institute of Technology, 1950.

Descartes, R. See Haldane and Ross.

Diels, H. Die Fragmente der Vorsokratiker. Berlin, Weidmannsche Verlagsbuchhandlung (6th ed.): Vol. 1, 1951; Vols. 2–3, 1952.

Dingle, H. (ed.) A Century of Science, 1851–1951. London, Hutchinson, 1951.

—— The Significance of Science. Chap. 20. In *A Century of Science*.

Dingler, H. Das Experiment, sein Wesen und seine Geschichte. Munich, Reinhardt, 1928.

Dirac, P. A. M. Quantized singularities in the electrochemical field. *Proceedings, Royal Society of London*, 1931, 133A, 60–72.

Dobzhansky, T. Mendelian Populations and their Evolution. In L. C. Dunn (ed.) *Genetics in the 20th Century*, Chap. 25. N. Y., Macmillan, 1951.

Dollard, J. Caste and Class in a Southern Town. New Haven, Yale U. Press, 1937.

Draper, J. W. The History of the Conflict between Religion and Science. N. Y·
Appleton, 1875.

Dubois-Reymond, E. Ueber die Grenzen des Naturerkennens. Leipzig, Veit,
1882.

Dubos, R. S. Louis Pasteur, Free Lance of Science. Boston, Little, Brown, 1950.

Ducasse, C. J. The esthetic object. *J. of Phil.*, 1938, 35, 322–331.

Duncan, J. C. Astronomy, A Textbook. N. Y., Harper, (4th ed.) 1946.

Durkheim, E. The Elementary Forms of the Religious Life. N. Y., Macmillan,
1915.

Eddington, A. S. The Nature of the Physical World. Cambridge, Cambridge U.
Press, 1928.

—— The Philosophy of Physical Science. N. Y., Macmillan, 1939.

Einstein, A. Geometrie und Erfahrung: Erweiterte Fassung des Festvortrages
gehalten an der Preussischen Akademie. Berlin, Springer, 1921.

—— Maxwell's Influence on the Development of the Conception of Physical
Reality. In *James Clerk Maxwell, A Commemoration Volume*, 1831–1931.
N. Y., Macmillan, 1931.

—— Preface. In Planck, M., *Where is Science Going?*. London, Allen & Unwin,
1933.

—— Considerations concerning the fundaments of theoretical physics. *Science*,
1940, 91, 487–492.

—— Investigations on the Theory of the Brownian Movement. (R. Fürth ed.,
A. D. Cowper trans.) London, Methuen, 1926.

—— Out of My Later Years. N. Y., Philosophical Library, 1950.

—— Science and Religion. In *Out of My Later Years*. N. Y., Philosophical
Library, 1950.

Einstein, A. and Infeld, L. The Evolution of Physics. N. Y., Simon and Schuster,
1938.

Ellis, R. L. and Spedding, J. The Philosophical Works of Bacon. (J. M. Robertson ed.) London, Routledge, 1905.

Elsasser, W. M. Quantum mechanics, amplifying processes and living matter.
Phil. of Science, 1951, 18, 300–326.

Encyclopaedia of the Social Sciences. (E. R. A. Seligman ed.) N. Y., Macmillan,
1931.

Farrington, B. Greek Science, Its Meaning for Us. Hammondsworth, Penguin
Books, Vol. I, 1944; Vol. 2, 1949.

Feigl, H. The mind-body problem in the development of logical empiricism.
Rev. Internationale de Philosophie, 1950, 40, 64–83, 95–102.

Fermi, E. Elementary Particles. New Haven, Yale U. Press, 1951.

Findlay, A. A Hundred Years of Chemistry. London, Duckworth, (2nd ed.)
1948.

Finlay-Freundlich, E. Cosmology. In *International Encyclopaedia of Unified
Science*. Chicago, U. of Chicago Press, 1951.

Frank, P. Einstein, His Life and Times. N. Y., Knopf, 1947.

Fulton, J. F. Selected Readings in the History of Physiology. Springfield, Ill.,
Thomas, 1950.

Galileo, G. Le opere di Galileo Galilei. Edizione Nazionale, sotto gli auspicii di

Sua Maestà il re d'Italia. Favaro, A. (ed.) Firenze, Tip. di G. Barbéra, 1890–1909, 20 vols.

—— Il Saggiatore. In *Le Opere di Galileo Galilei*, Vol. 6.

Gamow, G. Biography of the Earth. N. Y., Mentor, 1948.

—— The Birth and Death of the Sun: Stellar Evolution and Subatomic Energy. N. Y., Viking Press, 1940.

Garrison, F. H. An Introduction to the History of Medicine. Philadelphia, Saunders, (2nd ed.) 1917.

George, W. H. The Scientist in Action. London, Williams & Norgate, 1936.

Goldenweiser, A. History, Psychology, and Culture. N. Y., Knopf, 1933.

Goldschmidt, R. On some facts pertinent to the theory of the gene. In *Science in the University*. Berkeley, U. of California Press, 1944.

—— Position effect and the theory of the corpuscular gene. *Experientia*, 1946, 2, 1–40.

Grebenik, E. Mathematical Sociology. Review of N. Rashevsky, Mathematical Biology of Social Behavior. *Nature*, 1952, 170, 3–4.

Grimsehl, E. A. A Textbook of Physics. (L. A. Woodward ed.) London & Glasgow, Blackie, 1932–1935, 5 vols.

Haldane, E. S. and Ross, G. R. T. (ed.) The Philosophical Works of Descartes. Cambridge, Cambridge U. Press, 1911.

Hardy, G. H. The theory of numbers. *Science*, 1922, 56, 401–405.

—— A Mathematician's Apology. Cambridge, Cambridge U. Press, 1940.

Harvey, W. An Anatomical Disquisition on the Motion of the Heart and Blood in Animals. (Everyman ed.) London, Dent, 1907.

Heidel, W. A. Hippocratic Medicine, its Spirit and Method. N. Y., Columbia U. Press, 1941.

Helmholtz, H. Treatise on Physiological Optics. (J. P. C. Southall ed.) Rochester, Optical Soc. Amer., 1924–1925, 3 vols.

—— Vorträge und Reden, Braunschweig, Vieweg, 1903, 2 vols.

Henderson, L. J. The Study of Man. *Science*, 1941, 94, 1–10.

Herschel, Sir J. F. W. A Preliminary Discourse on the Study of Natural Philosophy. London, Longman, Rees, Orme, Brown, Green, and John Taylor, 1830.

Hertz, H. Electric Waves, Being Researches on the Propagation of Electric Action with Finite Velocity through Space. (D. E. Jones trans.) London, Macmillan, 1893.

Heyl, P. R. The Fundamental Concepts of Physics in the Light of Modern Discovery. Baltimore, Williams & Wilkins, 1926.

Hippocrates, The Genuine Works of. (F. Adams trans.) Baltimore, Williams & Wilkins, 1939.

Hobbes, T. Elements of Philosophy. In W. Molesworth, *The English Works of Thomas Hobbes*. London, Bohn, 1839.

Hooke, R. Lectures de Potentia Restitutiva. London, Martyn, 1678.

Hoskins, R. G. Endocrinology: The Glands and Their Functions. N. Y., Norton, 1941.

Howell's Textbook of Physiology. (J. E. Fulton ed.) Philadelphia, Saunders, (15th ed.) 1946.

Hubble, E. The Observational Approach to Cosmology. N. Y., Oxford U. Press, 1937.

—— The problem of the expanding universe. *Amer. Scientist*, 1942, 30, 99–115.

—— The Realm of the Nebulae. New Haven, Yale U. Press, 1936.

Huxley, L. Life and Letters of Thomas Henry Huxley. N. Y., Appleton, 1902, 2 vols.

Huygens, C. Traité de la Lumière. Paris, Gauthier-Villars, 1920.

James, W. The Varieties of Religious Experience: A Study in Human Nature. N. Y., Longmans, (1902) 1928.

—— Principles of Psychology. N. Y., Holt, 1890, 2 Vols.

Jeans, J. Clerk Maxwell's Method. In *James Clerk Maxwell: A Commemoration Volume, 1831–1931*. N. Y., Macmillan, 1931.

—— The Mysterious Universe. N. Y., Macmillan, 1930.

—— The new world-picture of modern physics. *Nature*, 1934, 134, 355–365.

Jevons, W. S. The Principles of Science. London, Macmillan, (1874) 1924.

Jordan, P. Physics of the 20th Century. N. Y., Philosophical Library, 1944.

—— Die Physik und das Geheimnis des organischen Lebens. Braunschweig, Viewig, (6th ed.) 1948.

Jourdain, P. E. B. The Nature of Mathematics. London, Jack, 1912.

Kant, I. Metaphysische Anfangsgründe der Naturwissenschaft, Vorrede. In Vol. 4 of Kant's *Sämmtliche Werke*. Leipzig, Voss, 1867–68.

Kantor, J. R. An Objective Psychology of Grammar. Bloomington, Ind., Indiana U., 1936.

—— An Outline of Social Psychology. Chicago, Follett, 1929.

—— Goethe's Place in Modern Science. In *Goethe Bicentennial Studies*, Indiana U. Publications, Humanistic Series, No. 22, Indiana U., Bloomington, Indiana, 1950, pp. 61–82.

—— Principles of Psychology. N. Y., Knopf, Vol. 1, 1924; Vol. 2, 1926.

—— Problems of Physiological Psychology. Bloomington, Ind., Principia Press, 1947.

—— Psychology and Logic. Bloomington, Ind., Principia Press, Vol. 1, 1945; Vol. 2, 1950.

—— A Survey of the Science of Psychology. Bloomington, Ind., Principia Press, 1933.

Kaufmann, F. Methodology of the Social Sciences. N. Y., Oxford U. Press, 1944.

Kennedy, J. S. A biological approach to plant viruses. *Nature*, 1951, 168, 890–894.

Keynes, J. M. Newton the Man. In *the Royal Society, Newton Tercentenary Celebrations*. Cambridge, Cambridge U. Press, 1947.

Kitto, H. D. F. The Greeks. Hammondsworth, Penguin Books, 1951.

Köhler, W. Dynamics in Psychology. N. Y., Liveright, 1947.

Krogh, A. The progress of physiology. *Science*, 1929, 70, 200–204.

Lapicque, L. L'Orientation actuelle de la Physiologie. In J. Perrin, P. Langevin, G. Urbain, et al., *L'Orientation actuelle des Sciences*. Paris, Alcan, n.d.

Laplace, T. S. A Philosophical Essay on Probabilities. (S. W. Truscott & E. L. Emory trans.) N. Y., Dover, 1951.

Lashley, K. S. The behavioristic interpretation of consciousness. *Psych. Review*, 1923, 30, 237–272, 329–353.

Lavoisier, A. Traité élémentaire de Chimie. Pāris, Cuchet, (2nd ed.) 1793, 2 vols.

Lavoisier, A. and Laplace, T. S. Mémoire sur la chaleur. In *Mémoires de l'Academie des Sciences*. Année 1780, pp. 355–408.

Lenzen, V. F. The Nature of Physical Theory: Study in Theory of Knowledge. N. Y., Wiley, 1931.

Lesser, A. Research procedure and laws of culture. *Phil. of Science*, 1939, 6, 345–355.

Lévy-Bruhl, L. How Natives Think. (Lilian Clare trans.) London, Allen & Unwin, 1926.

—— Primitive Mentality. (Lilian Clare trans.) N. Y., Macmillan, 1923.

Lewis, G. N. The Anatomy of Science. New Haven, Yale U. Press, 1926.

Lindsay, R. B. The meaning of simplicity in physics. *Phil. of Science*, 1937, 4, 151–167.

Lindsay, R. B. and Margenau, H. Foundations of Physics. N. Y., Wiley, 1936.

Locke, J. Elements of Natural Philosophy. In *The Works of John Locke Esq.* London, S. Birt, D. Brown, T. Longmans, etc., 1751, 3, 710–723.

Lodge, O. Pioneers of Science. London, Macmillan, (1893) 1919.

Loeb, J. The Organism as a Whole, from a Physiochemical Viewpoint. N. Y. & London, Putnam, 1916.

Loeb, L. B. Fundamentals of Electricity and Magnetism. N. Y., Wiley, 1947.

Lucretius. Of the Nature of Things. (W. E. Leonard trans.) (Everyman ed.) London, Dent, 1921.

Lush, J. L. Genetics and Animal Breeding. In L. C. Dunn (ed.) *Genetics in the 20th Century*, Chap. 22. N. Y., Macmillan, 1951.

Lynd, R. and Lynd, H. N. Middletown: A Study in Contemporary American Culture. N. Y., Harcourt-Brace, 1929.

—— Middletown in Transition: A Study in Cultural Conflict. N. Y., Harcourt-Brace, 1937.

McClung, C. E. The accessory chromosome—sex determinant? *Biol. Bull.*, 1902, 3, 43–84.

—— Notes on the accessory chromosome. *Anat. Anz.*, 1901, 20, 220, 226.

—— The chromosome theory of heredity. In E. V. Cowdry (ed.) *General Cytology*. Chicago, U. of Chicago Press, 1924.

McKie, D. Antoine Lavoisier: The Father of Modern Chemistry. London, Gollancz, 1935.

McLachlan, H. Sir Isaac Newton, Theological Manuscripts. Liverpool, University Press, 1950.

Mach, E. Die Principien der Warmelehre. Leipzig, Barth, 1896.

—— The Principles of Physical Optics. (J. S. Anderson & A. F. A. Young trans.) London, Methuen, 1926.

—— The Science of Mechanics. (T. J. McCormack trans.) Chicago, Open Court, 1907.

Macurdy, G. H. Review of Sir W. Ridgeway's The Early Age of Greece, Vol. 2. *American Journal of Archaeology*, 1933, 37, 178.

Magie, W. F. A Source Book in Physics. N. Y., McGraw-Hill, 1935.

Magnus, R. Goethe als Naturforscher. Leipzig, Barth, 1906.

Margenau, H. The Nature of Physical Reality. N. Y., McGraw-Hill, 1950.

Marshak, R. E. The multiplicity of particles. *Scientific Amer.*, 1952, 186, 22–27.

Marx, R. S. A 13th century theory of heat as a form of motion. *Isis*, 1934, 22, 19–20.

Maxwell, J. C. A Treatise on Electricity and Magnetism. Oxford, Clarendon Press, (1873) 1881, 2 vols.

James Clerk Maxwell: A Commemoration Volume, 1831–1931. N. Y., Macmillan, 1931.

Michelson, A. A. Light Waves and Their Uses. Chicago, U. of Chicago Press, 1903.

Mill, J. S. A System of Logic, Ratiocinative and Inductive. London, Parker, 1862.

Millikan, R. A. Science and society. *Science*, 1923, 58, 293–298.

Milne, E. A. Relativity, Gravitation, and World-Structure. Oxford, Oxford U. Press, 1935.

—— Kinematic Relativity. Oxford, Oxford U. Press, 1948.

Mirsky, H. E. Some chemical aspects of the cell nucleus. In L. C. Dunn (ed.) *Genetics in the 20th Century*, Chap. 8. N. Y., Macmillan, 1951.

Moore, C. N. Mathematics and science. *Science*, 1935, 81, 27–32.

Morgenstern, O. Mathematical Economics. In *Encyclopaedia of the Social Sciences*, Vol. 5, N. Y., Macmillan, 1931.

Munitz, M. K. Scientific method in cosmology. *Phil. of Science*, 1952, 19, 108–130.

Murray, R. H. Science and Scientists of the 19th Century. London, Macmillan, 1925.

Needham, J. and Pagel, W. (eds.) Background to Modern Science. Cambridge, Cambridge U. Press, 1940.

Neugebauer, O. The Exact Sciences in Antiquity. Princeton, Princeton U. Press, 1952.

Newton, I. Opticks, or a Treatise on the Reflections, Refractions, Inflections, and Colours of Light. London, Innys, (4th ed. cor.) 1730.

—— Sir Isaac Newton's Mathematical Principles of Natural Philosophy and His System of the World; revised by F. Cajori. (A. Motte trans.) Berkeley, U. of California Press, 1946.

Nordenskiold, E. The History of Biology: A Survey. (L. B. Eyre trans.) N. Y., Knopf, 1932.

Oman, J. W. The Sphere of Religion. In *Science, Religion, and Reality*. (J. Needham ed.) N. Y., Macmillan, 1925.

Oparin, A. I. The Origin of Life. N. Y., Macmillan, 1938.

Oppenheimer, K. Fermente und ihre Wirkungen. Leipzig, Thieme, 1924–1929, 4 vols.

Ostwald, W. Lehrbuch der allgemeinen Chemie. Leipzig, Engelmann, (2nd ed.) 1903.

Pannekoek, A. The Origin of Astronomy. *Monthly Notices Roy. Astro. Soc.*, 1951, 111, n. 4.

Partington, J. R. A Short History of Chemistry. London, Macmillan, (2nd ed.) 1951.

Partition Chromatography. *Biochemical Society Symposia* No. 2. Cambridge, Cambridge U. Press, 1949.

Perrin, J. Nouvelles propriétés des rayons cathodiques. *Comptes Rendues*, 1895, 121, 1130–1134.

—— Les Atomes. Paris, Alcan, 1913.

Perrin, J., Langevin, P., Urbain, G., et al. L'orientation actuelle des sciences. Paris, Alcan, n.d.

Pieper, G. F. Instrumentation for radioactivity. *Science*, 1950, 112, 377–381.

Pierce, J. R. Microwaves. *Scientific Amer.*, 1952, 187, 43–51.

Pigou, A. C. Memorials of Alfred Marshall. London, Macmillan, 1925.

Pirie, N. W. A biochemical approach to viruses. *Nature*, 1950, 166, 495–496.

Planck, M. Where is Science Going?. London, Allen & Unwin, 1933.

—— Scientific Autobiography and Other Papers. N. Y., Philosophical Library, 1949.

Plato. Ion. In Oxford edition of *Complete Works of Plato*. (B. Jowett trans.) Oxford, Clarendon Press, (3rd ed., rev. & cor.) 1892.

Pledge, H. T. Science Since 1500, A Short History of Mathematics, Physics, Chemistry, Biology. London, His Majesty's Stationery Office, 1947.

Poincaré, H. Dernières Pensées. Paris, Flammarion, 1913.

—— The Foundations of Science. N. Y., Science Press, 1921.

Pound, R. Jurisprudence. In *Encyclopaedia of the Social Sciences*, Vol. 8, N. Y., Macmillan, 1931.

Priestley, J. A History and Present State of Electricity, with Original Experiments. London, Printed for J. Dodsley, 1767.

Pupin, M. I. Law, description, and hypothesis in the electrical science. *Science*, 1925, 62, 17–22.

Radin, P. Primitive Religion. N. Y., Viking, 1937.

Rapoport, A. and Landau, H. G. Mathematical biology. *Science*, 1951, 114, 3.

Reymond, H. Science in Greco-Roman Antiquity. London, Methuen, 1927.

Richter, H. E. Zur Darwin'schen Lehre. *Schmidt's Jahrbücher der Gesammten Medicin*, 1865, 126, 243–249.

Ritter, W. E. The Unity of the Organism; or The Organismal Conception of Life. Boston, Badger, 1919, 2 vols.

Roberts, H. F. Plant Hybridization before Mendel. Princeton, Princeton U. Press, 1929.

Robertson, J. M. (ed.) The Philosophical Works of Francis Bacon. London, Routledge, 1905.

Rogers, L. Politics. In *Encyclopaedia of the Social Sciences*, Vol. 12, N. Y., Macmillan, 1931.

The Royal Society, Newton Tercentenary Celebrations. Cambridge, Cambridge U. Press, 1947.

Rumford, B. An inquiry concerning the source of the heat which is excited by friction. *Phil. Trans., Royal Society of London*, 1798, 18, 278–287.

—— An inquiry concerning the weight ascribed to heat. *Phil. Trans., Royal Society of London*, 1799, 18, 496–504.

Russell, E. S. The Directiveness of Organic Activities. Cambridge, Cambridge U. Press, 1945.

Rutherford, E. The electrical structure of matter. *Science*, 1923, 58, 209–221.

Saccheri, G. Euclides ab omni naevo vindicatus. Chicago, Open Court, 1920.

Sayre, P. (ed.) Interpretation of Modern Legal Philosophies: Essays in Honor of Roscoe Pound, N. Y., Oxford U. Press, 1947.

Schillp, P. A. (ed.) Albert Einstein: Philosopher-Scientist. Evanston, The Library of Living Philosophers, 1949.

Schlesinger, F. Astronomy. In L. L. Woodruff (ed.) *The Development of the Sciences*. New Haven, Yale U. Press, 1923.

Schrödinger, E. Science and the Human Temperament. (J. Murphy and W. H. Johnston trans.) N. Y., Norton, 1935.

—— Science and Humanism: Physics in our Time. Cambridge, Cambridge U. Press, 1951.

Seligman, E. R. A. The Discipline of Economics. In *Encyclopaedia of the Social Sciences*, Vol. 5, N. Y., Macmillan, 1931.

Sherrington, Sir C. Goethe on Nature and on Science. Cambridge, Cambridge U. Press, (1942) 1949.

Smart, W. M. The Origin of the Earth. Cambridge, Cambridge U. Press, 1951.

Smith, K. M. Plant virus research at Cambridge. *Nature*, 1948, 161, 776–777.

Soddy, F. The Story of Atomic Energy. London, Nova Atlantis, 1949.

Stevens, S. S. (ed.) Handbook of Experimental Psychology. N. Y., Wiley, 1951.

Stigler, G. J. The Mathematical Method in Economics. In *Five Lectures on Economic Problems*. London, Longmans, 1949.

Still, A. Soul of Lodestone. N. Y., Murray Hill Books, Inc., 1946.

Stone, J. Province and Function of Law. Sydney, Associated Gen'l Publs. Ltd., 1946.

Stranathan, J. D. The "Particles" of Modern Physics. Philadelphia, Blakiston, 1942.

Strong, E. W. Procedures and Metaphysics: A Study in the Philosophy of Mathematical-Physical Science in the Sixteenth and Seventeenth Centuries. Berkeley, U. of California Press, 1936.

—— Newton and God. *J. Hist. Ideas*, 1952, 13, 147–167.

Sturtevant, A. H. The Relations of Genes and Chromosomes. In L. C. Dunn (ed.) *Genetics in the 20th Century*, Chap. 6. N. Y., Macmillan, 1951.

Sullivan, J. W. N. Gallio, or the Tyranny of Science. N. Y., Dutton, 1927.

—— The Limitations of Science. N. Y., Viking, 1933; N. Y., New American Library, 1949.

Sutton, W. S. The chromosome in heredity. *Biol. Bull.*, 1903, 4, 231–251.

Taylor, F. S. Alchemical illustrations. *Nature*, 1952, 170, 12–13.

Taylor, L. W. Physics: The Pioneer Science. Boston, Houghton, Mifflin, 1941.

Thompson, S. P. The Life of William Thomson, Baron Kelvin of Largs. London, Macmillan, 1910, 2 vols.

—— (trans.) Peter Peregrine's Epistle to Sygerus of Foucaucourt Concerning the Magnet. London, Oxford, 1902.

Thomson, J. J. Cathode rays. *Philosophical Magazine*, 1897, 44, 293–316.

—— Recollections and Reflections. N. Y., Macmillan, 1937.

Thomson, W. (Lord Kelvin) Popular Lectures and Addresses. London, Macmillan, 1889, 3 vols.

Thorndike, L. A. A History of Magic and Experimental Science During the First Thirteen Centuries of our Era. N. Y., Macmillan, 1923, 2 vols.

—— A History of Magic and Experimental Science During the Fourteenth and Fifteenth Centuries. N. Y., Columbia U. Press, 1934, 2 vols.

Timoféef-Ressowsky, N. W., Zimmer, K. G., and Delbrück, M. Ueber die Natur des Genmutation und der Genstruktur, Nachr, Ges. Wiss. Göttingen, Math. Phys. Kl. Fachgr. VI. 1, 1935, 189–245.

Tintner, G. Econometrics. N. Y., Wiley, 1952.

Titchener, E. B. Experimental Psychology. N. Y., Macmillan, 1905.

Troland, L. T. Biological enigmas and the theory of enzyme action. *American Naturalist*, 1917, 51, 321–350.

Tylor, E. B. Primitive Culture, Researches into the Development of Mythology, Philosophy, Religion, Language, Art and Custom. N. Y., Brentano, 1924.

—— Anthropology: An Introduction to the Study of Man and Civilization. N. Y., Appleton, 1906.

Urey, H. The Planets, Their Origin and Development. New Haven, Yale U. Press, 1952.

Vernadsky, W. I. The biosphere and the noosphere. *Amer. Scientist*, 1945, 33, 1–12.

Verworn, M. General Physiology. (F. S. Lee trans. & ed.) London, Macmillan, 1899.

Vossler, K. The Spirit of Language in Civilization. N. Y., Harcourt-Brace, 1932.

Wallis, W. D. Religion in Primitive Society. N. Y., Crofts, 1939.

Weyl, H. Philosophy of Mathematics and Natural Science. Princeton, Princeton U. Press, (rev. & augm.) 1949.

Wheeler, L. P. Josiah Willard Gibbs: The History of a Great Mind. New Haven, Yale U. Press, 1951.

Whewell, W. History of the Inductive Sciences, from the Earliest to the Present Time. London, Parker, (3rd ed.) 1857, 3 vols.

White, A. D. Warfare of Science and Theology in Christendom. N. Y., Appleton, 1896.

Whitehead, A. N. Science and the Modern World. N. Y., Macmillan, 1925.

Whittaker, E. Eddington's principle in the philosophy of science. *Amer. Scientist*, 1952, 40, 45–60.

Wiener, N. Cybernetics, or Control and Communication in the Animal and the Machine. N. Y., Wiley, 1948.

Wildhack, W. A. Instrumentation in perspective. *Science*, 1950, 112, 515–519.

Williams, R. J., Eakin, R. E., Beerstecher, E. Jr., Shive, W. The Biochemistry of B Vitamins. N. Y., Reinhold, 1950.

Wilhelmi, A. E. Energy Transformation in Muscle. In Howell's *Physiology*, Chap. 3, 1946.

Willstätter, R. Problems of modern enzyme chemistry. *Chemical Review*, 1933, 13, 501–512.

Wilson, E. B. Statistical inference. *Science*, 1926, 63, 289–296.

—— The statistical significance of experimental data. *Science*, 1923, 58, 93–100.

Wilson, Edmund, B. The Cell in Development and Heredity. N. Y., Macmillan, (2nd ed.) 1900.

Wood, E. H. Special instrumentation problems encountered in physiological research concerning the heart and circulation in man. *Science*, 1950, 112, 707–715.

Wood, R. W. The N-Rays. *Nature*, 1904, 70, 530–531.

Woodger, J. H. Axiomatic Method in Biology. Cambridge, Cambridge U. Press, 1937.

—— Biological Principles, N. Y., Harcourt-Brace, 1929.

—— The Technique of Theory Construction. In *International Encyclopaedia of Unified Science*, Vol. 2, no. 5. Chicago, U. of Chicago Press, 1939.

Wundt, W. Logik der Geisteswissenschaften. In *Logik*, Vol. 3, Stuttgart, Enke, 1893–95.

—— Die Sprache. Vols. I and II of *Völkerpsychologie, eine Untersuchung der Entwicklungsgesetze von Sprache, Mythus, und Sitte.* Leipzig, Engelmann, 1904.

Wycoff, R. W. G. Visualizing macromolecules and viruses. *Amer. Scientist*, 1951, 39, 561–576.

—— Electron Microscope: Technique and Applications. N. Y., Interscience, 1949.

Zechmeister, L. and Cholnoky, L. Principles and Practice of Chromatography. N. Y., Wiley, 1941.

Zirkle, C. The Beginnings of Plant Hybridization. Philadelphia, U. of Pennsylvania Press, 1935.

—— Gregor Mendel and his precursors. *Isis*, 1951, 42, 97–104.

—— The knowledge of heredity before 1900. In L. C. Dunn (ed.) *Genetics in the 20th Century*, Chap. 3, N. Y., Macmillan, 1951.

NAME INDEX

Abderhalden (1877–1950), 231.
Adams (1796–1861), 88n.
Addison (1793–1860), 233.
Adrian (1899–), 10n., 12n.
Albertus Magnus (1193?–1280), 102, 256.
Alexander (1876–), 220n., 230n.
Allee (1885–), 222n.
Al-Sufi (10th C.), 162.
Amontons (1663–1705), 173.
Ampére (1775–1836), 15, 185, 204.
Anaxagoras (c. 488–428 B.C.), 60, 167.
Anaximander (611–547 B.C.), 60.
Anaximines (c. 560–500 B.C.), 60, 166, 169.
Andrade (1887–), 320.
Aquinas (1225–27–1274), 256.
Arago (1786–1853), 185, 204.
Archimedes (287–212 B.C.), 88, 101, 159.
Argelander (1799–1875), 162.
Aristarchus (c. 310–230 B.C.), 78.
Aristotle (384–322 B.C.), 48, 55, 61, 94, 101, 166ff., 194, 202, 255ff., 293
Arrhenius (1859–1927), 171, 220.
Aston (1877–1945), 112n., 113.
Babbage (1792–1871), 127.
Bacon, F. (1561–1626), 64f., 67, 115n., 173.
Bacon, R. (1214–1294), 102, 212.
Barnes (1889–), 291n.
Barrow (1630–1677), 319.
Bawden (1908–), 248f.
Bayer (1572–1625), 163f.
Bayliss (1860–1924), 230n., 232.
Beadle (1903–), 233n., 239n.
Beccaria (1738–1794), 285.
Becher (1635–1682), 170.
Becquerel (1852–1909), 186.
Bell (1883–), 7n., 133, 139n., 320n.
Beltrami (1835–1900), 80.
Bennet, A. (1750–1799), 183.
Bergson (1859–1941), 219, 243.
Berkeley, E. C. (1909–), 20n.
Berkeley, G. (1585–1753), 53, 68, 71, 258, 264.

Bernard (1813–1878), 8, 120n., 129, 229.
Bernoulli, D. (1700–1782), 115n., 161, 174, 208.
Bernoulli, J. (1667–1748), 161.
Bertallanfy (1901–), 214n.
Berthelot (1827–1907), 112.
Berthold (1803–1861), 232.
Bertholet, 311n.
Berzelius (1779–1848), 82, 84f., 112, 171, 229.
Bessemer (1813–1895), 8.
Beveridge (1908–), 8, 37n., 109.
Black (1728–1799), 8, 169, 174.
Blondlot (1849–1930), 15.
Bloomfield (1887–1949), 302n.
Blum (1899–), 220.
Bohr (1885–), 57, 152n., 206.
Boileau, 284.
Boltzmann (1844–1906), 176, 180.
Bolyai (1802–1860), 73, 80.
Bordeu (1722–1776), 232n.
Born (1882–), 52n., 57, 100, 132, 317.
Bouglé (1870–1940), 323n.
Bouguer (1698–1758), 78n.
Bouma (–1947), 200n.
Boyle (1627–1691), 35, 82, 117, 160, 169, 173, 323.
Brahé, Tycho (1546–1601), 20, 78, 118n., 162.
Brewster (1781–1868), 320n.
Bridgman (1882–), 29f., 74n., 136n., 278n.
de Broglie (1892–), 135.
Brown (1773–1858), 177ff.
Brown-Sequard (1817–1894), 233.
Bruno (1548–1600), 7, 23.
Büchner (1860–1917), 85, 229.
Bunge (1844–1920), 231.
Bunsen (1811–1899), 83.
Burtt (1892–), 64n., 141n.
Bury (1861–1927), 296n.
Butterfield (1900–), 99n., 113n., 118n.
Cabanis (1757–1808), 259.

SUBJECT INDEX

Absolute reality, and the value issue, 325.

Absolutes vs. concrete activities, 325.

Acoustics (see Sound), as a science, 207ff.

Abstract science, dualistic glorification of, 326.

Abstraction and elaboration in scientific evolution, 76f.

Air, importance of, in chemical evolution, 166, 169f.

Alchemical manipulations, and the science of chemistry, 81, 168.

Algorithms, as calculating tools, 123.

Amateurs in science, 7f.

Analytic geometry, as scientific technique, 123f., 132.

Anatomy, and medical science, 87; in biological investigation, 222f.

Apparatus, scientific, 18ff.; overemphasis of, 105.

Appearance and reality, invalid scientific institutions, 54f.

"Appearances" vs. things, 17.

Applied mathematics, and measurement, 128, 133, 142f.

Anthropic science, one of four scientific divisions, 90, 157; evolution of, 95f.; improper discrimination against, 274f., 278; vs. natural science, 278ff.; basic nature of, 282f.

Anthropic systems, vs. physiochemical systems, 275ff.

Anthropology, a division of social sciences, 286ff.; systemic presuppositions in, 287f.

Arithmetic, and measurement, 142f.

Astronomy, raw-material stage of, 77f., 162; technological evolution necessary for, 78; physiochemical principles applied in, 164f.

Astrophysics, importance of color for, 198.

Atomic physics (see Quantum mechanics).

Atomic theory, development of, 74, 85f., 170f., 188, 206.

Axiology (see Values).

Averages, 74, 89, 188f.

Basic interactions as biological events: metabolism, 215; biological continuity, 217; responsive interactions, 217.

Beauty, as quality of objects, 304.

Behavior, as aspect of culture, 45; as anthropological data, 286; theological, 306; philosophical, 308; religious, 310f.

Behaviorism, the end point in dualistic development, 258f.; retains historical constructions, 259.

Biochemistry, early career of, 84; a succession of chemical conquests, 226ff.

Bioecology, essentially interbehavioral, 241.

Biological epigenesis and preformation, 245.

Biological events, integrated with interactions, 226ff., 235.

Biological investigation, concerned with interbehavior vs. things and elements, 220ff.

Biological theory construction compared with physiochemical, 242ff.

Biological units, as cells, organisms or *organism-environment field*, 214f.

Biological science, stages of, 93f.

Biology, institutional competition in, 56; employment of statistics in, 129; ready availability of events in, 213; metaphysical constructs in, 213f.; concept of matter as life in, 213f.; an interactional domain, 215f.; field interpretation of, 215, 225, 241; integration of chemistry with, 235; cause in, 240; ecology as interactional subdomain of, 241; comparison of theorizing in physics and, 242ff.; design, teleology or chance in theory of, 246.

Brain, falsely regarded as link between rest of body and mind, 11;

348

Light, physics of, 92, 191; early constructs of, 190; Galileo's experiment with, 191; speculation concerning speed of, 191ff.; particle or wave nature of, 193f.; waves of, identified with electromagnetic waves, 194.

Linguistic theory, dualistic core of, 267.

Linguistics, a division of humanistic sciences, 300ff., interpreted on basis of nonscientific psychology, 302.

"Living" matter vs. interacting organisms, 313f.

Lodestone (see Magnet), 201ff.

Logic, the science of systems, 26f.; Kant's problem of scientific, 263; symbolic, 266; conventionally defined, 269.

Logic of science, a critical discipline, 26; integrates the scientific enterprise, 26f.; vs. original investigation, 36; formal and comparative, 36f.; sensitizes the worker to investigative results, 37; and historical philosophy, 38ff.

Logician, the, as a scientific worker, 26; vs. the original investigator, 36; interested in event relations, 36f.; introduces system, 37.

Machine, the, in science, 19f.

Magnet, discovery of, 201f.; theories concerning, 204ff.

Magnetism, interrelated with electricity, 185, 204f.; first theoretic constructs of, 201ff.; connected with atomic properties, 206.

Magnitude, as mensurational product, 147f.; never absolute, 148.

Manipulation, measurement as, 16; not exclusive type of contact with things, 100; a salient scientific procedure, 103f.; depends upon hypotheses, 108; goes hand in hand with interpretation, 114.

Materialism, French 18th century, 259; German 19th century, 259.

Mathematical deduction, a constructional organization of propositions, 131, 138.

Mathematical formulae, 133; as instruments, 20; and reality, 135.

Mathematics, postulational theory of, transformed science, 73; a science of relations, 120, 123, 136; relationship to other sciences, 121, 125ff.; and the quantitative, 121f.; number as a department of, 122; symbolic branch of, 123f.; as systemization, 124; operational character of, 124f.; functional relationship between investigation and, 126; not criterion for natural science, 126; an aid to science, 126f.; in theory construction, 130; and problem of scientific certainty, 131; aids sciences, 132f.; interbehavioral approach to, 135f.; deduction in, vs. scientific prediction, 138; recent developments in logic of, 138; regarded as a language, 139, 266, 302; theorems of, derived from interbehavioral matrix, 271.

"Matter" vs. "mind," 189f.; vs. spirit, produces discoordination within cultural systems, 326f.

Measurement, and instrument development, 19, 149f.; a form of instrumental observation, 15f.; science not reducible to, 128, 140; developed before experimentation, 141; valid and invalid theories of, 141ff.; applied-mathematics theory of, 142; based on numbers, 143; interbehavioral approach toward, 144; concrete and abstract, 147; sometimes fuses with experiment, 150; metrological levels of, 150f.; objectivity problem in, 152; shifts causality position, 152; turns scientist to metaphysics, 152f.

Mechanical aid, not to be substituted for ideas, 129.

Mechanical world view, 161.

Mechanics, interbehavioral evolution of, 159ff.

Mechanism vs. vitalism, in biological theory, 103f., 245.

Medical science, practical origin of, 86; practice and theory in, depends upon technological factors, 87; modern criterion of, 88.

Values, and existence, 55; abstract type of, 62; assumed to be outside science, 315f.; issue of *being* vs. *significance*, 324; stimulate disharmony between scientific and social attitudes, 324; nature of, 325.

Variables, as factors abstracted from data, 31.

Visibility and the science of light, 190f.

Vitalism, in chemistry, 84; in biology, 103f., 245.

Vitamin chemistry, 230ff.

Wave theory of light, 193f.

Waves vs. particles, 188.